Epiphanized

Integrating Theory of Constraints, Lean and Six Sigma (TLS)

Epiphanized

Integrating Theory of Constraints, Lean and Six Sigma (TLS)

Bob Sproull
Bruce Nelson

Additional copies can be obtained from your local bookstore or the publisher:

The North River Press
Publishing Corporation
P.O. Box 567
Great Barrington, MA 01230
(800) 486.2665 or (413) 528.0034

www.northriverpress.com

ISBN: 978-088427-205-2

Printed in the United States of America

Dedication

One of the true joys of growing older is the mark you leave behind in this world. And while many might think that this book is my mark, it truly isn't. My mark that I'm leaving is being a loving Grampa to my five beautiful and wonderful grandchildren. To Jack, the oldest who is so very inquisitive and just melts my heart....to Ally, the second oldest, and oldest Granddaughter, who is so full of life and love and always has a smile on her face . . . to Evan, our third oldest who is so laid back, yet so happy all of the time . . . to Emma, who is so very pretty and will for sure be our tallest . . . and last, but not least, to Madison, our youngest who has such amazing focus, I dedicate this book to all of you. You all fill Grampa's heart with joy.

Bob Sproull

To my wife Patty, daughter Lindsey Nicole, and son Derek for their encouragement, support and most of all patience. Also, to Johannes and Lucy Amelie Shafer the newest members of the family. Lucy is my new Granddaughter who has filled me with the spirit of being young again. These people are all an inseparable part of my life and the reason for my existence.

Bruce Nelson

We also want to dedicate this book to the memory of our common friend, Eli Goldratt who taught us all the Theory of Constraints. His relentless pursuit of educating the world will be sadly missed. Finally, a special dedication to Bob Fox for his unselfish willingness to share with, and mentor, the world in pursuit of the common cause.

Bob & Bruce

Contents

Foreword

Epiphanized is a very important book for any organization sincerely interested in doing more with the same, or even less resources. Doing so is the essence of increasing productivity. Too much view increasing productivity as squeezing more out of an oppressed workforce. Nothing could be further from the truth. There is a clear, long term connection between increased productivity and an overall increase in both the standard of living and the amount of wealth in our world. Those who argue that too many of these benefits are now going to the rich at the expense of the working class, simply ignore history. The gap between these groups has risen and fallen unevenly over time. In the eras of dictators, royalty and peons the gap was enormous. It shrunk dramatically during the reign of the Vanderbilt's, Rockefeller's and other tycoons. Despite today's economic problems the gap has continued to shrink. The connection between the standard of living of the average person and increasing productivity is etched in stone. As productivity increases, people live better, have more freedoms, live longer and have more fulfilling lives. To me that sounds like progress.

So what is so special about this book? It's about understanding and integrating the Theory of Constraints (TOC), Lean and Six Sigma approaches to improving organizations. If there were ever a negative description for improving productivity, then the Theory of Constraints wins the award. Despite its negative sounding name maybe we shouldn't reject it outright, but look deeper. There is compelling evidence that TOC has resulted in hugely greater, but largely ignored, benefits than the more widely known and popularized approaches such as Lean and Six Sigma. How can such a discrepancy exist between reality and popular perception?

I don't intend to dwell on the reasons for this perception gap. My interest is in understanding and explaining why we haven't yet capitalized on an enormously powerful way of improving productivity, improving overall living standards and the wealth of companies and countries.

The simple answer is that TOC focuses on improving "systems," while almost all other improvement techniques of the past century have focused on improving "pieces" of systems. Improving a piece of a system, as we have learned the hard way, does not necessarily improve the overall system.

The Theory of Constraints was introduced to the world by Eli Goldratt's classic book *The Goal*—reportedly the bestselling business book of all time. Despite being written as a novel about an American manager trying to simultaneously save his plant, career and marriage readers in dozens of different cultures and countries have claimed that it described their world.

As with many successes, misperceptions are created. Most readers of *The Goal* think it is about bottlenecks and manufacturing and that if you break bottlenecks the manufacturing operation is improved. In fact, TOC is about improving all types of organizations by recognizing that a single, sometimes moving, constraint always exists and significantly limits the performance of the organization. Consequently improvement efforts should focus on identifying, or more correctly selecting this point (a Control Point), increasing its Throughput and synchronizing all other activities accordingly.

Since *The Goal* was first published in 1983 a host of applications of basic TOC principles have been developed and tested resulting in systems that have improved the performance of many organizations. Some of the more prominent ones are:

- Drum-Buffer-Rope (DBR) for managing the flow of work in repetitive type operations.
- Throughput Accounting (TA) to provide better overall management of organizations.
- A Replenishment Model for simultaneously reducing inventories and improving availability of products in a supply chain.
- Critical Chain Project Management (CCPM) to better manage project oriented activities.
- Thinking Processes (TP) to identify core problems (what to

change), develop breakthrough solutions (what to change to) and successfully implement them (how to create change).

- Strategy and Tactic trees to develop breakthrough marketing strategies and integrate them with internal operations to assure success.
- Throughput Operating Systems to more sharply focus and synchronize actions to enable organizations to produce more with less while simultaneously improving organization morale.

These applications have both greatly benefitted many organizations while simultaneously confusing people about what TOC is. This book ties together a number of these applications in a coherent and clever fashion. It is written as a novel to enable the reader to discover the underlying thought processes behind several of these TOC applications. The story is supplemented by appendices on these applications that allow the interested reader to delve into greater detail.

The real value of this book is twofold. It provides the first comprehensive picture of what TOC is all about and does so in an eminently readable fashion. Secondly the appendices provide much needed detail for those who which to be understand and capitalize on these applications.

This book provides a much needed comprehensive view on how TOC can be used to help organizations greatly increase productivity and with it wealth and our standard of living. It also provides important insights in how to effectively integrate the TOC, Lean and Six Sigma approaches to produce even greater results.

Bob Fox
Founding member of The Goldratt Institute,
The TOC Center, Inc. and Viable Vision LLC

Preface

How many times have you started reading a book, and you weren't sure of what the author was actually writing about? You read their words, but since the subject is new to you, you want to be sure you've grasped the intent. So what do you do when you're faced with this situation? Do you put down your book and go to a familiar search engine and try to find information about the subject in question on the internet? Or maybe you go to your own personal library of books and try to find out more on the subject? Whatever you end up doing, it is troublesome or maybe even upsetting because it takes time away from your reading and causes an obvious break in the flow of information or the story line. We also have experienced this situation, so when we decided to write this book, we considered this scenario and how we might be able to neutralize it or reduce the effects of the interference. What if we were able to write a story and have the reference material contained within the same narrative? We thought so too so we have added appendixes to make it easier. Using appendixes at the end of the book certainly won't totally alleviate the problem of having to search for reference material, but it may save some of your valuable time and preserve the flow of new information.

Our book is written primarily in a novel format that tells a business story, weaving in an assortment of well-known and not-so-well-known tools and techniques. Some of these tools and techniques may be new to some of you, depending upon your experience and frame of reference. The book is primarily focused on an improvement methodology known as the "Theory of Constraints (TOC)." In writing this book, it is our hope that we will have demonstrated to the reader that TOC, by itself, is not the only improvement methodology to drive significant bottom line improvement. In fact, the best results can be achieved by the integration of TOC with two other popular methodologies known as "Lean" and "Six Sigma." If done correctly, using all three methods should result in significant financial returns. So as we tell our story, we use several appendixes to provide more detail and rigor on the subjects presented.

As an example, one of the subjects presented in our book is the TOC Replenishment Model. In the business novel portion of our book, we demonstrate how this concept was used to eliminate stock-outs of parts while significantly reducing the dollar value of the parts inventory. In the appendix for this subject, we provide additional detail on how this model can be implemented and used within your own organization.

This book is the story of Joe Pecci, a newly hired manager of the Office of Continuous Improvement (CI) for Barton Enterprises, a multimillion dollar company that produces fuel tanks for the aviation and defense industries. When Joe walks into this new organization he finds the situation to be in chaos with some significant issues that need attention. There are serious problems with on-time delivery performance and no clearly defined path to improve it. Joe befriends Sam Henderson, Barton's VP of Operations, and together they discover and forge the future path to prosperity. They accomplish this effort with the help of a very talented bartender named Connor Jackson. This is the narrative of a very rapid and successful organizational transformation. It portrays an innovative approach to rapid and sustained growth and profitability using some uncommon, and yet exceptional, improvement tools and methods. It's a success story with a triumphant ending.

The primary theme throughout this book has been to unify and enhance improvement tools and methods. This is a sort of grand unification that combines improvement methods and tools to create a new level of usefulness. Emerging situations and problems can quickly expose the need to gain access to new and different problem-solving tools. This same spirit of unification has also been manifested within the methodologies themselves. Sometimes tools within methods have been combined to create new tools for solving problems. Systems and people are just not as linear as we would like them to be, and neither is life. Things happen and things change, sometimes at an exponential rate.

We believe that in writing this book we have laid out a pioneering pathway for significant gains in profitability and market share for any company employing the methodology presented here. We are both convinced that the integration of the Theory of Constraints with Lean and Six Sigma, known as TLS, is the wave of the future. We also believe that explaining it through the eyes of Joe Pecci, in a business novel format will add relevance to its usefulness and power. The concepts, tools and principles presented in this book may be counter intuitive to many, but if the principles are followed, the results are sure to come. If your company has been struggling with a Lean or Six Sigma implementation and you're not happy with the bottom line improvement you're getting, the integrated TLS methodology can give you the improvement you are seeking.

As you read this story, please pay particular attention to the subtleties that are presented within the body of the book. You'll see that taking the time to recognize and truly engage the subject matter experts within your company in your improvement efforts will lead you to new levels of profitability—if you'll just let them actively participate in your company's success. This is a lesson that is confirmed several times during the development of this story. We believe that your company is poised for greatness, and if you will use the lessons presented in our book, it will happen.

Bob and Bruce

Chapter 1
Joe's First Day

"I sure am glad I'm finished with my 'check in' through Human Resources so I can finally get to work and meet the people I'll be working with," thought Joe. "I've been anticipating this new job for the last month, and I hope it goes better than my first half-day.

"I mean when I checked in this morning through Human Resources," he thought to himself, "I never imagined I would have spent most of my time just sitting and waiting to fill out my next batch of paperwork or waiting thirty minutes to have my photo taken for my badge. I certainly hope that there is a lot less waste and better flow in their manufacturing area than there is in this transactional area."

Joe Pecci (pronounced PeeCee) had been hired as the new Manager of the Office of Continuous Improvement (CI) at Barton Enterprises. Joe brought a wealth of experience to Barton Enterprises and, as he would soon learn, he'd need to dig deep into his experience and know-how to help turn Barton into something better than it was.

Barton Enterprises, located in Waterford, Mississippi, was a multimillion dollar producer of flexible fuel tanks for the aviation industry and had actually fared pretty well in this dreadful economy, at least compared to many other companies. Of course any industry that was directly connected with the U. S. Department of Defense had a leg up on industries that weren't. We all know how easily money got appropriated and distributed from the federal government, and Barton received their fare share of stimulus dollars. Barton had been around for about fifty years, and just by driving through their manufacturing complex Joe noticed that the buildings appeared old and somewhat dilapidated. Joe remembered from his interview that the construction of these fuel tanks was an extremely manually intensive process, and he saw very little evidence of any Lean or Six Sigma activities within the facility he toured, but he'd reserve judgment until he made more observations.

When Joe finally arrived at the building he'd be calling home, he saw that all of the parking spaces were filled, so he ended up having to park and walk a considerable distance. Joe finally found the door he was supposed to enter and walked up two flights of stairs to a very dimly lit hallway. There were no signs to indicate which way to turn to go to the CI office, so he guessed which direction to go and, of course, he guessed wrong. When he finally arrived there, he found four people, his apparent co-workers, huddled together in a rather heated discussion. No one noticed Joe entering the office. He paused and listened, and discovered that the discussion was centered around how they were going to calculate and report required quarterly cost savings dollars to the federal government. Apparently because Barton received stimulus money, there was a requirement to report dollar savings each quarter.

Joe cleared his throat to get their attention, and the discussion stopped. A rather petite and very attractive woman asked, "Can I help you?"

Joe smiled back and introduced himself. "I'm Joe Pecci the new Continuous Improvement Manager . . . and you are?"

"I'm Judy Godfrey and I had no idea we were getting a new manager! She turned toward the group. "Guys," Judy said, "Did you know we were getting a new manager today?"

They all said, "Nope, but that's normal around here. No one ever tells us anything!" One by one they all introduced themselves and shook Joe's hand.

"Oh boy," thought Joe, "No one even knew that I was coming. Is there a communications problem here?"

One man stepped forward. "I'm Bill Cody, one of the Lean Six Sigma black belts . . . pleased to meet you." Bill was perhaps the shortest man Joe had ever met in his life. At best he was maybe five feet one inches tall. But he was also one of the bulkiest men Joe had ever met. Not a whole lot of difference between Bill's height and width, and he had a noticeable waddle when he walked.

"Nice to meet you too, Bill," said Joe.

Another man introduced himself. "Manuel Gonzalez, s-sir, nice to meet you s-s-sir. I'm also one of the b-b-black b-b-belts here," he stuttered. Manuel was noticeably trembling as he shook Joe's hand.

"Calm down Manuel, I don't bite," Joe said.

Judy said, "Manuel is like this all of the time . . . early stages of Parkinson's disease."

"Sorry, Manuel, I didn't know," Joe responded in a feeble attempt at an apology.

A third man stepped up. "Stan Wilson, Joe, good to meet you. And I'm a black belt here too, but I'm studying to become a master black belt." Stan appeared to be a very confident person.

Joe asked Judy what her role in the office was, and she said jokingly, "My primary role is to keep these guys in line." Everyone laughed. Then she explained that her role as lean assistant was to prepare all of the graphs and charts and Power Point presentations for the quality director and to perform statistical calculations that everyone requested. "I love my job," said Judy, "but I just wish I'd get more advanced notice on things from the quality director. Everything I do is a last-minute adventure, and it's frustrating to say the least."

During his interviews Joe had met the quality director, his new boss. The director seemed like a man in chaos and disarray, and he offered Joe a job on the spot. The director explained that although the operator efficiencies were high, and the quality levels met the customer requirements, Barton was late on virtually every order and they had received threatening letters from their customer base. He explained that one of Joe's functions would be to find out why orders were late and to fix this problem. In fact, he told Joe that was to be his primary role—in addition to generating significant cost savings. Since Joe's background was manufacturing, and he had an excellent track record and references, the quality director told Joe that he expected rapid improvement in on-time delivery and cost savings.

The quality director was nowhere to be found, and when Joe asked his team if anyone had seen the director today, Judy explained, "He isn't here on Mondays . . . he's on the golf course."

With the introductions complete, Joe asked, "What are you guys working on?"

Bill replied, "You don't want to know." He added, "Every quarter we have this mad scramble to come up with cost savings that we have to report to the government, and every quarter we have to dig deep into our projects to calculate how we're doing."

"Where's the finance member of your team," asked Joe. Why aren't they helping you?"

"Finance?" said Stan. "There's no member of Finance on our teams!"

"Why not?" Joe asked.

"W-we've just n-n-never included them," Manuel explained. "W-we prepare our "b-best g-guess" on s-savings and s-s-submit it to them for review. S-s-sometimes they accept it and s-s-sometimes they don't," he said.

"You mean when you write your project charter, you don't get advance agreement from Finance on the project and how you're going to calculate savings?" asked Joe.

"No way," said Stan. "They don't understand the nature of our business."

Joe reviewed one of the project charters, and sure enough there was no sign-off from Finance at all. Joe thought, "This explains why they're in a state of chaos every quarter trying their best to justify cost savings." Joe knew he had to change this right away, so he asked Judy to set up a meeting with the finance director. "Can you meet him in an hour, boss?" Judy asked. "Tell him I'll be there." Joe responded.
For the next forty-five minutes Joe's team discussed some of their old cost saving submissions. In each case the savings were tied to cycle-time reductions and/or efficiency improvements. In one project, the team reduced the cycle time in one of the process steps by one hour and claimed the cycle-time reduction as an annual cost savings.
Joe asked, "Was the headcount reduced based upon the cycle-time reduction?"

Stan replied, "No, they just moved two operators to other production lines."

Joe asked, "Then how was that seen as a cost savings?"
His question was met with blank stares. "W-w-we've always done it that way s-s-s…ir," replied Manuel. Joe could see that he had his work cut out for himself.

When Joe arrived at the finance director's office, the director was on the phone but motioned for Joe to come in and have a seat. It was apparent that he was talking to someone outside of Barton, probably someone at the corporate office. He was talking in the usual cost-accounting gibberish, using expressions like operator efficiency, purchase price variance and other cost accounting nonsense.

Finally, after ten minutes of conversation, the finance director finished his call and introduced himself. "I'm Paul Johnson, the director of finance at Barton."

Joe replied, "I'm Joe Pecci, the new manager for the Continuous Improvement office."

After exchanging a few pleasantries, Joe broke the proverbial ice by saying, "Paul, I want to talk to you about why Finance isn't a part of Barton's continuous improvement projects."

"We have never been asked to be a part!" exclaimed Paul. "I would love to have my folks be a part of your teams," Paul said.

"They're our teams Paul," Joe retorted. "So let's get together, starting today."

"Works for me," said Paul.

For the next hour they talked about the role of Finance on the team, and everything was going well until Joe told Paul that, in his opinion, the method they were using to capture cost saving was flawed. Paul was clearly taken back by this statement, reacting as though it were a personal attack on him. Joe explained that when he first started his career, he was taught the same cost-accounting methods that Barton was using, but that about twenty years ago, Joe had had a personal epiphany of sorts. Joe explained that he had been hired as general manager of a company that was being considered for closure, and Joe's job was either to turn the company around or oversee its closing. Joe's background had been all quality and engineering, so he was surprised that he was selected to lead this effort.

Since Joe had no real experience in operations management, he knew he had to rely on his two operations managers, whom he hadn't met yet. When he did meet them, he soon realized that they had no idea of how to effectuate a business turnaround. Joe remembered going to a library (there was no internet back then) to read about operations management, and he stumbled upon a book called *The Goal* by Dr. Eliyahu Goldratt. Joe took it home and stayed up all night reading it. He explained to Paul that this book changed his entire approach to manufacturing. Joe bought extra copies and had his entire staff read the book. His team had daily discussions about the content, and to make a long story short, by applying the lessons in the book, they not only saved the plant from shutting down, their plant became the model for the rest of the company.

Joe explained to Paul how within every organization, constraints existed, and that unless and until a constraint was exploited and the rest of the organization was subordinated to it, no real improvement would take place. Joe opened his briefcase and handed Paul his very own tattered and worn copy of *The Goal*, and made Paul promise that he would read it. Joe continued their discussion about how he thought Barton was misreporting cost savings. He asked Paul why he thought it was OK to report localized labor-hour reductions as a cost savings, since they did not remove the labor from the company.

Paul's response floored Joe: "Because the customers accept it as a reduction."

"But do you, Paul?" asked Joe. "Do you believe in your heart that these things you're reporting are actually cost savings?" Joe asked. "What if later on the customers come back to us and tell us that we must reduce our prices based upon the reported cost savings?" Joe added. "What will we tell them Paul?" asked Joe.

Their conversation continued on, and Joe explained the concepts associated with the Theory of Constraints and Throughput Accounting (TA) and how TA is much better for daily decision-making than traditional cost accounting. When Joe left Paul's office, he reminded him to read *The Goal*, and Paul promised Joe that he would, but he also made Joe promise to tell him more about how he had led the turnaround of the manufacturing facility he had described to him earlier in their conversation.

Joe left Paul's office and headed back to his own office. Joe knew that if Barton was going to be successful at improving on-time deliveries, there had to be a radical shift in organizational thinking on how to approach this effort. Joe also knew that he could not do this by himself; he needed to develop his team and teach them a better way. When Joe arrived at his office, he could see that his team was still struggling to come up with cost savings for the past quarter. Joe asked them to come into his office so they could talk. One by one, they came in and took a seat. Joe's first question to them centered around how they selected their improvement projects.

"We generally are told by the quality director what our projects will be," Bill explained.

"And how does he select them? Has he ever explained that to you?" Joe asked.

"N-n-n-no . . . h-h-e-e just tells us that the VP of Operations w-wants us t-to w-work on th-th-this or th-that," explained Manuel.

Joe turned to Judy to ask her to contact the VP of Ops, but she was one step ahead of him. "Can you meet him for lunch, boss?" said Judy.

"Yes," Joe replied. "Just tell me where and when, and I'll be there." Ten minutes before Joe was to meet the VP of Ops, Judy got a call from the VP asking if Joe could meet him for breakfast instead in his office. Joe actually liked this idea better because he could also get to see the production layout firsthand.

"Tell him yes, Judy," said Joe, and then told Judy that he was leaving for lunch. He said he would be back in a couple of hours.

It was clear to Joe that one of the things he had to do was to get everyone on the same page and that page was different than the one they were on. He decided to skip lunch because he had something more pressing that he needed to do today.

Joe brought up his search engine to find the nearest bookstore and dialed the number. "Well, how many copies do you have?" asked Joe. "Twenty-one? I'll take all of them . . . hold them for me . . . I'll be there in about twenty minutes,"

And so off Joe went to the bookstore to pick up twenty-one copies of *The Goal*. He decided that since reading *The Goal* together had worked so well when he was appointed general manager of a turnaround, why reinvent the wheel? Joe picked up his books and then decided that he was hungry after all and needed to grab a quick bite to eat. Joe really didn't know where to go in this new city for lunch, so he just drove around until he spotted a small, out-of-the-way bar. He decided to take a copy of the book in with him and brush up on some of the key concepts. He sat at the bar, laid down his copy of T*he Goal* and put on his reading glasses.

It didn't take long for the bartender to ask Joe what he wanted to drink. Joe told him he was working and that he'd better just have a soft drink. Joe asked the bartender what kind of food they served for lunch, and he told Joe that all they had were sandwiches and chips. Joe ordered a ham sandwich and settled down to read his book. His sandwich appeared shortly thereafter, and the bartender asked Joe what he was reading. Joe held up the book and to his surprise the bartender said, "Great book—one of my favorites."

"You've read The Goal?" Joe was stunned.

"I sure have," the bartender replied.

"I'm Joe Pecci, the new continuous improvement manager at Barton," said Joe as he shook the bartender's hand.

"Nice to meet you, Joe, I'm Connor Jackson."

"So how do you know about The Goal, Connor?" Joe asked. "I mean, I don't think I've ever met a bartender who knew anything about the Theory of Constraints."

Connor replied, "It's a long story . . . so sometime when you have more time, come back in and I'll tell you."

"I'll just do that Connor . . . and by the way, this is the best ham sandwich I've ever tasted."

Joe finished his lunch and drove back to the office, only to find it empty. "Where is my team?" Joe thought. Then he realized that it was almost five o'clock. Joe had gotten lost in his book and read about 200 pages while he was at the bar. "Oh well," Joe thought to himself," I guess I might as well go back to my hotel and call my wife to let her know how my first day on the job went."

Chapter 2
Joe's Second Day

Joe Pecci woke up early on his second day at Barton Enterprises anxious to meet with the VP of Operations. Joe knew nothing about him; he didn't even know his name. The VP was supposed to interview Joe, but at the last minute he was called to the corporate office in New York that day to explain why so many customers were complaining about their late deliveries. And since Joe's new boss, Phil Smith, had told Joe when he hired him that his number one priority was to improve on-time deliveries, this meeting took on a whole new level of importance. Joe had paced his hotel room floor last night well into the wee hours of the morning thinking about and preparing for his meeting with the VP. Joe made a list of key topics including performance metrics, the production layout, and of course, the late orders. Joe's meeting was scheduled for 7:00 AM, which was an hour and a half from now, so he decided to go into Barton and just look around the production area.

Joe walked in unannounced to the third shift operation at Barton. He imagined that if Barton were like other companies, its third-shift operation would be much different than the first shift, and the second shift would be still different. In many companies it's like having three different organizations, with each shift essentially having its own culture. As he walked in, radios were blaring, but he didn't see many people working. In fact, he didn't see many people at all. He saw one guy with his feet propped up, leaning back in his chair, reading a newspaper, and another practicing his golf swing. He also saw lots of inventory of partially completed tanks especially in front of one particular operation, where he did see one person working very hard. As he moved closer to the operations, the newspaper was quickly put away and the imaginary golf course disappeared. Apparently they thought Joe must have been someone important.

Joe tried to imagine the flow of product through this production line, but couldn't visualize it. It looked like a functional island type arrangement where all similar operations were grouped together. He recalled that during his interview he really didn't get much of a tour of the facility, so he didn't know much about the tank building process. Joe was startled when he heard a voice behind him say, "May I help you?"

Joe quickly turned around and said, "Ah, yes. Hi, I'm Joe Pecci, the new manager of the continuous improvement office."

"Nice to meet you, I'm Bradley Fox, the third shift supervisor, and boy do we ever need your help around here." Bradley was a young, very clean-shaven man, probably around the age of thirty.

"I certainly hope I can help you Bradley, Joe replied. Do you have time to show me your process?"

Bradley immediately said, "I would be happy to, Mr. Pecci."

"Please, Bradley, call me Joe."

"OK, Joe, follow me."

As Joe and Bradley walked, Joe couldn't help but notice how very disorganized the production line was with so much inventory everywhere! "OK," said Bradley, "This is where it all starts. We push these big molds into this staging area and prep the surface with a coating of release agent so we can remove the tanks from the molds at the end of the line."

Joe noticed that the fiberglass molds were not in the best of condition, with chips missing at various points on the surface. When Joe pointed these out, Bradley told him, "They still work and besides, we can fix that defect after we take the tank out of the mold. The name of the game is to make as many tanks as we can. Otherwise we get in trouble for low efficiencies," Bradley added.

Joe thought to himself, "Hmmm, there's that efficiency metric again." Then he asked Bradley, "But doesn't it take a while to make the repair on the tank?"

Bradley looked around and said, "Yeah, but that's the way the boss told us to do it and he likes things done his way. He told us that if his overall efficiencies go too low, he gets called on the carpet by corporate, so we do it his way."

Joe thought to himself, "Performance metrics motivating the wrong behaviors. I've seen it so many times. It's sad."

Bradley continued the tour of the disjointed production line, showing Joe each isolated step in the process. On this particular tank type, the top and bottom of the tanks were produced separately and then joined together later on to form the semi-finished tank. When Joe and Bradley reached the operation where the joining took place, there was a stack of tops and bottoms of tanks waiting to be joined together. Joe made a rough mental count of the number of individual tops and bottoms and saw that there were six tops and six bottoms in front of the joining operation. On the other side of the joining operation, there were no tanks to be seen. Joe knew that joining was the bottleneck, or constraint operation, in this particular process, and two things were abundantly clear. (1) Barton was not exploiting the constraint, and (2) they were not subordinating the other process steps to the constraint, at least not on this production line. When Joe asked Bradley what the processing times were for each process step, he didn't know. He explained to Joe that he thought that it took about twenty-three work days to get a tank through the whole process from beginning to end, and since Barton employees worked five days per week, it should take roughly five weeks to get a single tank through. But then Bradley added that it rarely happened that quickly.

Joe made a quick mental calculation and realized that at least one set of tops and bottoms were fabricated at least thirty weeks ago! When Joe asked him why it took so long to build these tanks, Bradley never hesitated and blurted out, "Mostly because of parts availability!"

"What kind of parts, Bradley?" Joe asked.

"You know, basic parts that we use in every kind of tank—things like baffles," said Bradley.

Joe made a mental note about parts shortages and thought to himself, "Barton needs a different kind of parts supply system to eliminate 'stock-outs.' Joe noticed the light on in the VP of Ops' office, so he thanked Bradley for his time and quickly walked toward the office area. He had so many "new" questions for the VP, and so many questions in general.

Joe knocked on the partially opened door, and the VP motioned for Joe to come in. He was answering an important email from corporate and said he'd be right with Joe. Joe sat patiently waiting until the VP finally stood up and introduced himself. "I'm Sam Henderson, VP of Operations."

Joe shook hands with Sam and said, "I'm Joe Pecci, the new Manager of Continuous Improvement. Nice to finely meet you, Sam."

"Joe, thanks for stopping by this morning, but I'm afraid we'll have to cut this visit short. I've just been summoned to headquarters again to talk about late deliveries, and I have to leave in about thirty minutes to catch a flight to New York. That means we have about fifteen minutes max to get acquainted. So Joe, tell me about yourself . . . and have a donut—they're freshly baked this morning."

Frustrated, Joe thought to himself, "I've been waiting since yesterday to meet this guy and now he has to leave." Joe said, "Sam, let's wait until you get back from New York to get acquainted. Right now I've got some questions for you. And I have a book for you that you that you might want to read on the plane."

Joe handed Sam a copy of *The Goal* and told him he thought this might help him with his meeting in New York. Sam just looked at Joe with a stunned look on his face.

"Sam, I came in early today to look at your tank process this morning and I'm confident I can help you with your on-time delivery problem." Sam leaned forward, eager to hear more of what Joe had to say. Joe continued, "But in order for it to work, you have to do exactly what I tell you to do, when I tell you to do it."

Sam was completely taken back by Joe's bold and audacious statement, but simply said, "Go on Joe, tell me more."

Joe continued again, "I want to teach you about something called the Theory of Constraints. Have you ever heard of it?"

"No, Joe I have not. Can you explain it quickly? I have to leave in about three minutes."

Joe replied, "Sam, it's going to take longer than three minutes, but if you'll read this book before you get back, we can pick up this conversation when you return."

Sam replied, "Joe, I've got to be honest with you—I'm getting sick and tired of making these frequent trips to corporate, and since what we've been doing here isn't working, I promise you that I'll read your book while I'm gone. OK?" Joe nodded in approval. With that said, Sam left with briefcase in hand turning back only to wave goodbye.

Joe decided it was time to go and have a sit down with his new boss, Phil Smith, Quality Director, and now was as good a time as any—assuming that Phil wasn't out playing golf today. Joe entered Phil's building, walked to his office, stuck his head in and asked Phil if he had a few minutes. Phil motioned for Joe to come in and have a seat. He was busy on his computer looking at some graphs and run charts, and he never looked up at Joe.

"Is this not a good time Phil?" Joe asked.

Phil just let out a grunt and said, "Is there ever a good time?"

Joe said, "I wanted to talk with you about how my black belts are apparently having improvement projects selected for them by Sam and how they are having to scramble every quarter to identify cost savings. I also wanted to give you a book to read."

"A book?" said Phil. "I don't have time to read a book!"

Joe replied, "Well Phil, based upon what I've seen this morning, this is one book you can't afford not to read. It will change your entire approach to this business," Joe added. Joe handed Phil his own copy of *The Goal* and asked him to please read it. Phil grunted again and took the book from Joe. "Will you read it Phil?" asked Joe. Phil said that he would try to find some time, but that he would read it. Joe got up and told Phil that he'd try to get on his schedule so that he and Phil could talk more about project selections and discuss the book.

Joe slowly walked back to his office thinking about his second day while he walked. He stopped to chat with a few people he hadn't met before, just to get more information on how things worked here. Before he knew it, it was almost noon before he reached his office.

Joe's phone was ringing as he entered his office door, but he was too late and missed the call. He looked at the caller ID and saw that it was Sam Henderson. "What in the world does Sam want?" Joe thought. Joe picked up the phone to call him back, but he could see on the screen that Sam was calling him again. "Must be something serious," Joe thought as he answered it.

"Hi Sam, what's up?"

Sam's voice sounded as though something terrible had happened. "Joe, I'm in big trouble and I really need your help at the plant. The board has given me two months to turn around our on-time delivery or they're going to fire me! So can you help me Joe? I'll do anything you say!" said Sam in an obvious panic.

"Sam, of course I'll help you," Joe replied. "Meet me in your office tomorrow morning at 6:00 AM and we'll talk. In the meantime, I want you to read that book I gave you."

"Sure Joe, anything. See you in the morning!"

And with that, Joe hung up and sat down to plan tomorrow's early morning meeting with Sam. Joe thought about the best way to present what he wanted to say. "I think I'll start out with my piping system drawing so that Sam can have a visual appreciation of what a physical constraint looks like. If he can see the simplicity of what a constraint looks like in this simple drawing first, then I'll draw a picture of an actual process so he can relate it to the piping-system drawing."

So with that, Joe drew the piping system he had just imagined on a flip chart. Joe thought to himself, "Section C of the piping system is what limits the throughput of water. If you wanted to increase the flow of water through the system, the only way to do so is to focus on Section C.

Of course", Joe thought, "Sam should see right away that he has to increase the diameter of Section C."

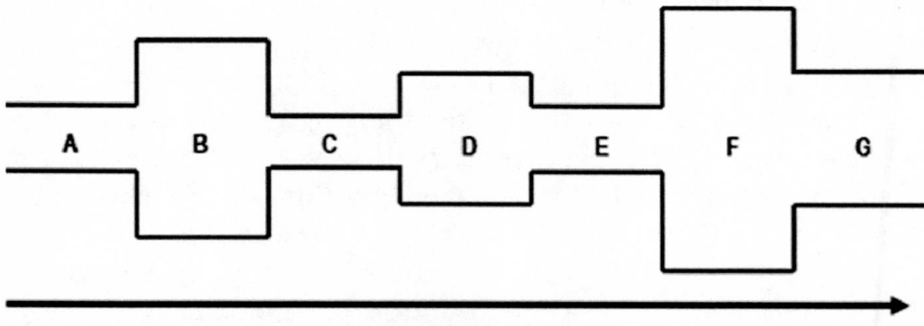

Water Flow

Joe then sketched out a simple four-step process with processing times for each step in this imaginary process. He thought, "I'll ask Sam to identify which step limits the flow of product through this process. Sam should see right away that Step 2 is the system constraint because the long processing time of seventeen days is the equivalent to Section C of the piping system." Joe was getting excited about tomorrow morning's meeting with Sam. "What else?" Joe asked himself.

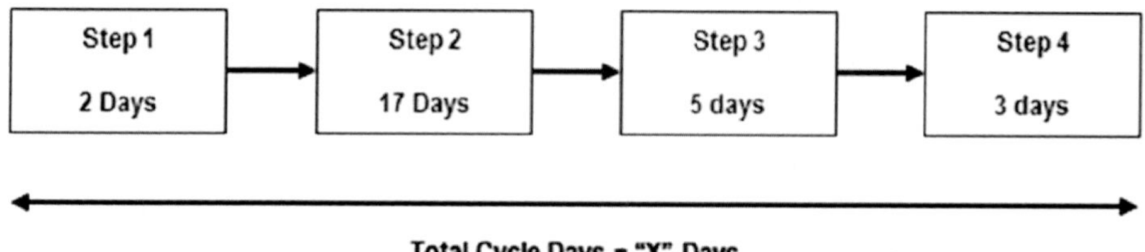

Joe knew he needed to make Sam see that focusing improvements on any place other than the constraint was simply wasted effort. Joe continued with his thoughts, "Increasing the diameter of any section other than Section C will not result in more throughput of water. Likewise, focusing on any step besides Step 2 of the process will do Sam no good with respect to increasing the throughput of product through the process." Joe continued thinking, "Sam also needs to understand that running Step 1 of this process at a higher than required efficiency will only result in a stack-up of inventory in front of Step 2. In other words," Joe thought, "Sam must understand the importance of Goldratt's Step 3, subordinating everything else to the constraint."

"Maybe I'll have a discussion about why selecting the right performance metric is so important," Joe thought. He then decided that he would take Sam to the shop floor and, knowing what he himself had just learned, ask Sam to identify the constraint in the process that Joe had seen early this morning with Bradley. Joe thought some more and decided that he needed to make a flip chart with Goldratt's Five Focusing Steps on it. "I'll spend time explaining each step to Sam so that he completely understands the five steps." Joe thought, "I sure hope Sam reads The Goal before our meeting tomorrow morning."

Goldratt's Five Focusing Steps
1. *Identify* the system constraint.
2. Decide how to *exploit* the constraint.
3. *Subordinate* everything else to the above decision.
4. If necessary, *elevate* the constraint.
5. If in the previous steps a constraint has been broken, go back to Step 1, but do not allow inertia to cause a system constraint.

Joe had a thought as he left the office for the day, "I think I'll go visit Connor on my way to my hotel."

Chapter 3
Joe's Meeting With Connor

"Where in the hell is it?" Joe said to himself as he drove down street after street searching for Connor's bar. Joe couldn't remember exactly where the bar was, and he hadn't noticed the name of it when he was there before. All he knew was that it was a small, out-of-the-way bar that had great ham sandwiches. "I wish I would have been more observant and looked at the name of the bar where Connor worked," thought Joe.

As Joe drove around trying to retrace his route from yesterday, he noticed a sign that said "Jonah's Bar and Grill" jutting out from behind a tree. Could this be the bar? Could there be this connection between Connor and the main character in The Goal—Jonah? Joe decided it was worth a look and as he turned the corner, lo and behold, there was Connor's bar and it was named Jonah's.

As he walked in the door, he saw Connor behind the bar in a conversation with three men. Since there weren't any seats left at the bar, he sat at an empty table nearby. Connor seemed to be in what appeared to be a rather intense conversation, and he didn't notice Joe. A waitress came by and asked Joe what he wanted to drink. He thought for a moment and then asked her, "Do you by any chance have any Chianti?" The waitress wasn't sure, but said she's go ask the bartender. She went to Connor and asked and then pointed in Joe's direction. Connor recognized Joe and waved to him. The waitress came back and told Joe that they did have Chianti and that Connor would be right over with it. Much to Joe's surprise, Connor not only delivered the glass of Chianti, he brought a bottle and another glass.

"Mind if I join you, Joe?" said Connor.

"Not at all," said Joe. Joe thought it was strange that a bartender would be allowed to drink with the patrons.

"So, Connor, how long have you worked at Jonah's?" asked Joe.

"I've been here about six years," replied Connor.

"You won't get in trouble with the owner for sitting here drinking with me will you Connor?" asked Joe.

Connor laughed and replied, "Not at all Joe. I am the owner."

Joe laughed. "So you said the last time I was here you would tell me how a bartender like you had come to know about The Goal, and you said it was a long story. Well here I am and I do have time to listen now, if you care to tell me."

Connor said, "OK, but bear with me Joe . . . this could take awhile."

The two men talked with each other for several hours. It seems that back in the mid-1980s Connor was flying through Dallas on his way to Los Angeles for a job interview. He struck up a conversation with a man waiting to board the same flight to LA. They talked mostly about Connor's upcoming interview and his background and experience. As luck or fate would have it, they ended up seated next to each other on the flight to LA. So they continued their conversation, again talking mostly about Connor's background and experience—sort of prepping for Connor's interview. Just before they deplaned, the man handed Connor a business card and a book and made Connor promise to call him when he got home and tell him how his interview went. Over the next several days Connor read the book, but had never looked at the business card until he got home. To his amazement the card had the name Goldratt on it, and the book was the then, newly published blockbuster, *The Goal*.

True to his promise, when he got home, he called the man, and within three days he had a new position as a TOC consultant. During that time Connor had the opportunity to work in many different industry types learning the tools of the trade from one of the best consultants ever. About ten years later, Connor decided to venture out on his own and left to form his own consulting business. Over the years Connor had done very well on his own and had invested his money wisely to the point that he no longer needed to work. It seems that on his last consulting engagement, here in Waterford, Mississippi, he had dinner at a small bar in Waterford named Jonah's and decided that night that it was time to retire. He made an offer to buy Jonah's on the spot and he has been there ever since. Joe asked Connor if he missed the consulting life, and Connor just said, "Sometimes I do, but

I'm very happy doing what I do here."

Joe was eager to learn more about Connor's experiences as a TOC consultant and what made him so successful. He asked Connor if he had ever been a Lean Six Sigma master black belt, but Connor just laughed and said, "I studied the Lean and Six Sigma concepts but never became certified in either. I never had time for anything like that. When I found TOC, I found something that really worked for me, and I was too busy fixing companies . . . No Joe," Connor continued, "I'm what you call a Jonah's Jonah."

"A Jonah's Jonah—what on earth is that?" asked Joe.

"Sorry, it just means that I am certified to teach others how to be a Jonah," replied Connor.

"Sorry, Connor," said Joe, "I have no idea what a Jonah is, let alone a Jonah's Jonah. I mean I remember the character Jonah from The Goal, but that's about it."

"Well Joe," said Connor, "A Jonah is basically someone who has mastered all that the Theory of Constraints has to offer," Connor continued, "This would include Throughput Accounting, the TOC Thinking Process (TP) tools and—"

"Wait Connor, you've lost me again," said Joe. "I know about Throughput Accounting, but what about the TOC Thinking Process Tools? What are they?" asked Joe.

"Sorry Joe, I guess I'm taking too much for granted," replied Connor. "Allow me to explain in a bit more detail."

Connor took his time and even though Joe new about TA, he still explained the basics. Connor then explained the TOC TP Tools. "The TOC TP tools are logic-based 'thinking tools' that are used to solve problems, develop strategies and resolve conflicts," said Connor. "These tools were developed by Dr. Goldratt. They can be used in a stand-alone fashion or they can be combined to form a rational problem-solving and change-management system," Connor explained. "Their real purpose is to facilitate the translation of people's basic instincts and intuition into a logical and rational format, and they do so in a nonthreatening way," continued Connor. "They can be used to construct common-sense solutions to problems as well as facilitating the resolution of basic conflicts between people, departments or organizations. They can be used for consensus development among people who are trying to resolve problems."

Joe didn't really understand what Connor had explained at all, but in order to avoid embarrassment, he acted like he did. "Connor," asked Joe, "Do these tools have names?" Connor replied, "Yes, as a matter of fact they do." Connor grabbed a piece of paper and wrote them down for Joe as follows:

1. The Current Reality Tree
2. The Conflict Resolution Diagram
3. The Future Reality Tree
4. The Prerequisite Tree
5. The Transition Tree

Connor explained that some of the tools involved necessity-based logic and some involved sufficiency-based logic. The necessity-based ones use the format of—"In order to have this, I must have that. While the sufficiency based ones use simple if-then statements.

Joe asked, "But how do you use them, and is there an intrinsic order for using them?"

"Joe, it's getting late, and I think we've done enough for one day," said Connor. "I promise you, in time I will explain when and how to use all of them."

Joe agreed, put his coat on, said goodbye to Connor and left to go back to his hotel room to put the finishing touches on his presentation to Sam. On his drive back to his hotel, Joe kept thinking about what a resource Connor could be if he could just convince him to come out of retirement. . . just for a while. Maybe he would.

Chapter 4
Joe's Meeting with the VP of OP'S

Joe woke up early the next morning in anticipation of his meeting with Sam Henderson. He had been up late last night getting his presentation ready for Sam. One thing he added to the presentation, after his meeting with Connor, was a discussion on Throughput Accounting (TA).

Joe decided that in order for Sam to grasp the full implications and gain an understanding of TOC, he needed to be able to make the connection to bottom line improvement. Without understanding the basic concepts of TA, Joe concluded that Sam would never grasp why the Theory of Constraints works as well as it does and what it can do for Barton. Joe thought to himself, "I sure do hope Sam read at least some parts of The Goal and that it stimulated his thinking about how it might apply to Barton Enterprises."

As Joe pulled into the parking lot around 5:30 AM, he noticed that Sam's car was already in his designated parking space. "That's a good sign," thought Joe. He unloaded his flip chart and easel and headed for Sam's office. When he arrived, Sam's office light was on, but no Sam. He put his presentation materials down and went looking for Sam, and it didn't take long to find him or at least hear him. Sam was in what sounded like a very heated discussion with Bradley Fox, the third shift supervisor that Joe had met yesterday. As he got closer to them he could hear what the subject was—manpower efficiencies! Sam's voice echoed throughout the production area and anyone within range could hear Sam's rants. "I don't want to see anyone ever idle again!" bellowed Sam. "Are we clear on that, Bradley?"

"Yes sir," replied Bradley.

"If I do, heads are going to roll!" Sam shrieked.

Sam finally noticed Joe and motioned to him to come closer. "I was just explaining to Bradley how important it is to keep everyone busy so that our efficiencies remain high. Without high efficiencies, we'll never get product out the door on time," Sam explained.

Joe thought to himself, "I guess Sam didn't read the book after all. I need to have a private conversation with him right away before he does any more damage." And so with that, Joe and Sam started off to Sam's office to begin Sam's operational makeover. As they walked, Joe recounted the conversation he had just heard between Sam and Bradley. Well maybe conversation isn't the right word since Bradley had very little input; it was more of a lecture. Joe thought, "I'm actually glad I heard this exchange because I know exactly where to start now."

"These guys just don't get it," said Sam. "You'd think as many times as I've told them to keep everyone busy that by now they would understand. I just don't get it."

"Sam," said Joe, "did you ever think that what you're asking them to do might not be the right approach?"

"How could it be wrong to have everyone working?" Sam asked.

"Let me explain," said Joe. And with that, Joe set up his easel and flip charts. "What you see on this page is a simple piping system," Joe explained.

"Piping system?" Sam exclaimed, "Why on earth would you show me a piping system? What does a piping system have to do with building tanks?" asked Sam in a frustrated voice.

"Please bear with me Sam," Joe said.

"Ok, but I don't see how a piping system has any relevance to building tanks," said Sam.

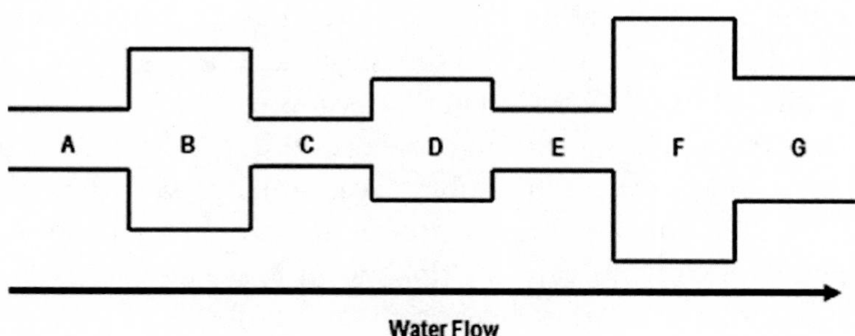

"If you wanted more water to flow through this series of pipes, what limits its flow? Or another way of saying it is—what is constraining the throughput of water through this system?" asked Joe.

Sam looked at the simple drawing and said, “It’s pretty obvious that it’s Section C because it has the smallest diameter pipe.”

“Correct,” said Joe. “So Sam, if you wanted to increase the flow or throughput of water through this system, where would you focus your efforts and what would you do?” asked Joe.

“I would focus on Section C and simply install a larger diameter pipe,” Sam explained.

“And how would you know how big to make the new diameter of Section C?” asked Joe.

Sam thought for a moment and said, “I guess that would depend on how much more water I needed.”

“Right,” answered Joe. “Would increasing the diameter of any other pipe increase the throughput of water through this system?” asked Joe.

“Nope, changing any other diameter would have no impact on how much water comes out the other end,” said Sam. “Can you get to the point of this Joe?”

With that, Joe went on to his next sheet, his drawing of the simple four-step process that he had prepared the night before. “OK Sam, this is a drawing of an imaginary four-step process used for building widgets.

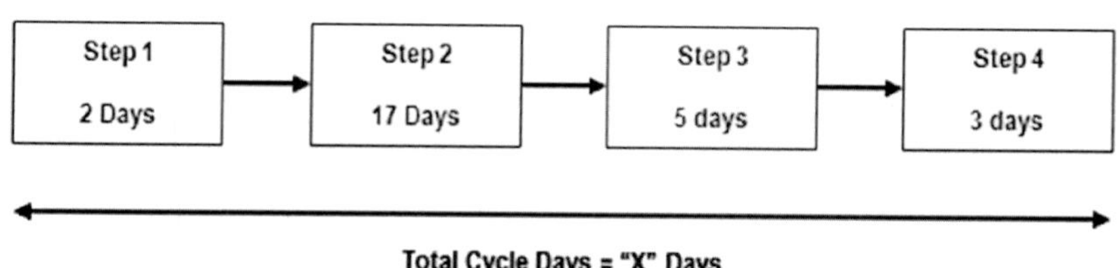

“Sam, keeping the thought of the piping system in your mind, what prevents this process from having more throughput, and what might you do to increase throughput?” Joe asked.

Sam looked and looked at the process drawing for a good five minutes and finally blurted out his answer. “Step 2 is the bottleneck, so I would say it is limiting our throughput.” Sam continued, “So I guess the only way to increase the throughput would be to reduce the time it takes at Step 2 . . . am I right?”

“Yes Sam, you are dead right! Great job Sam!” said Joe. Joe continued, "In the piping system example, I asked you how would you know how big to make the diameter of Section C, and you rightfully said it would depend on how much more water was needed. How about the same question for Step 2? How would you know how much to reduce the processing time in Step 2?"

Sam thought for a minute and finally said, "I guess that would be based on customer demand?"

"Correct!" Joe said. "OK, Sam, would the process put out any more product if, say you reduced Step 3 from five days to two days?"

"Nope," said Sam. "Only reducing the time at Step 2 would do it, right Joe?"

"Yes, Sam, you're right again!" said Joe. "Now Sam, what would happen if you ran Step 1 to its full capacity of one part every two days?"

"Not sure what you mean by that question, Joe . . . can you ask it a different way? asked Sam.

"Sure, Sam. If you tried to run Step 1 to maximize its efficiency (capacity) what would be the inevitable result." asked Joe.

"Obviously our efficiencies would look good and we'd make more money . . . right, Joe?" said Sam.

"Wrong, Sam!" said Joe.

Sam was a bit taken back by Joe's forceful response and immediately asked the question, "Why, Joe? Why wouldn't we make more money? If I'm increasing efficiencies, why wouldn't I make more money?"

Joe continued, "We'll talk about efficiencies later, but for now you need to understand that the only thing that happens when you run Step 1 at maximum capacity is that you stack up inventory in front of Step 2." Joe explained,"This happens because Step 2 can only process incoming parts at a rate of one part every seventeen days," Then he asked, "And does the throughput of the process increase even by one part when you run Step 1 to its maximum capacity?"

"No, I guess it doesn't Joe, you're right. It just ends up building more Work in Process (WIP). It makes perfect sense Joe. Efficiencies look good, but throughput remains the same. How stupid of me!" said Sam.

"No, Sam, you're not stupid at all. It's just the way you and most managers have been taught and measured," Joe explained. "One important thing to remember is that we are not interested in making localized improvements, we're interested in making system-wide improvements. There's a world of difference between the two." Joe continued, "I think it's time to talk about a different way of looking at accounting and how we make money." And with that, Joe flipped to his next sheet on Throughput Accounting.

Just as Joe was about to begin his explanation of Throughput Accounting, his cell phone rang. "Good morning, this is Joe Pecci, how can I help you?"

It was Paul Johnson, the Director of Finance. "Joe, I'm about halfway through The Goal, and I'd like to talk to you about what I read about Goldratt's version of accounting. How soon can we meet?"

"How timely," Joe thought. "Paul, what are you doing right now?"

"Nothing important. Why?"

"Could you come to Sam's office?" Joe asked.

"Sure, but why?" said Paul.

"I'll explain when you get here," said Joe.

"OK, be there in about ten minutes."

Joe told Sam that he had invited Paul to join in on this next conversation, and Sam's facial expression immediately changed. "What's wrong Sam? Joe asked.

"Well Joe, Paul and I don't really get along very well." said Sam. "He's always making me look bad in front of the board. He's always challenging me on why my people aren't always busy."

"Look Sam," said Joe, "it's going to be very important that everyone here is on the same sheet of music going forward, so having Paul hear what I'm about to explain is absolutely necessary. How about a cup of coffee while we're waiting for Paul?" said Joe. "Sounds good, Joe," Sam replied.

About fifteen minutes later Paul finally arrived. Joe said, "Paul, before we talk about accounting, I'd like to go over something else that Sam and I have been talking about this morning." And with that said, Joe put Paul through the same piping diagram and process Q & A as he had done earlier with Sam. Paul grasped the concepts very quickly and asked some very pertinent questions during the discussion. It was apparent that Paul had read a lot more of *The Goal* than Sam had.

"What is the goal of Barton Enterprises?" Joe asked.

Sam replied first, "To satisfy our customer."

"That's definitely important, Sam, and it's a critical success factor, but it's not our goal," said Joe.

Paul was next, "Our goal is to make money!"

"Precisely!" said Joe. Joe continued, "And how do we make money?"

"By making sure our efficiencies and profits are good," said Sam.

"There's that efficiency term again," Joe thought. "These guys are really hung up on efficiencies." Joe then began his explanation of Throughput Accounting by simply defining throughput, inventory and operating expense on his flip chart. To avoid confusion, Joe used the definitions exactly as they were written in *The Goal*.

Goldratt's Throughput Accounting

1. **Throughput (T)** is the rate at which the system generates money through <u>sales</u>. If you produce something, but don't sell it, it's not throughput. T is obtained after subtracting the totally variable costs such as cost of raw materials, etc.
2. **Inventory (I)** is the money that the system has invested in purchasing things which it intends to sell. I includes the $'s tied up in WIP and Finished Product Inventory.
3. **Operating expense (OE)** is all the money the system spends in order to turn inventory into throughput including all labor costs.

Paul raised his hand and asked, "Why does Goldratt's definition of throughput include sales?"

"Good question," said Joe. "Quite simply, if you produce product and it just sits in a storage rack, it isn't making any money. In fact, it's actually costing you money."

"Costing money! How is it costing you money? I don't understand." Sam asked.

Joe replied, "Doesn't unsold inventory have a carrying cost associated with it Paul?"

"Well yes," replied Paul, "I guess it does, but it does have value too."

"It only has value when it's sold and we receive money for it," Joe replied."OK, go on, I guess I see your point," said Sam.

"With these three financial measurements, making daily decisions on how to run this facility will become much easier and the decisions will be much better," said Joe.

"But what about things like ROI, net profit, productivity and inventory turns? We have to know these too," said Paul.

"Yes, we do Paul," said Joe as he flipped to his next sheet. Joe let both Sam and Paul take in these new definitions and excused himself to use the rest room.

Goldratt's Throughput Accounting Formulas

1. **Net profit (NP)** = T - OE = T-OE
2. **Return on investment (ROI)** = NP/I
3. **Productivity (P)** = T/OE
4. **Inventory turns (IT)** = T / I

When Joe returned, Sam was the first to comment. "Joe, for the first time in my adult life, I can finally understand something about accounting! These definitions make it so clear to me. How come I've never seen these before?"

"Hold on," said Paul, "We have to report all of these results back to Corporate and these definitions are totally different than our standard definitions! Corporate will never permit us to use these definitions!"

"But they're so easy to understand Paul, why wouldn't they?" said Sam.

"Sam, there are GAAP rules that we must follow and report to the government. Nope, we can't use these," said Paul.

Joe could see that he was about to lose Paul so he interjected, "Paul, we have no intention of reporting these numbers to Corporate. We will use these definitions and formulas to make decisions here at our facility." Joe continued, "Do you agree that for most people they're much easier to understand and relate to than the traditional cost accounting formulas?"

"Well yes they are," said Paul," but I need to study them more and see how they tie in to what we're doing."

"Paul," said Joe, "I'm going to suggest you read another book that bridges the gap between Throughput Accounting and traditional cost accounting. The title is The Measurement Nightmare by Debra Smith. In fact, I have a copy sitting on my desk that you can borrow. Will you read it Paul?" asked Joe.

"Sure, I'll read it. In fact, I have to get to a conference call with Corporate Finance, so I'll stop on my way and pick it up," replied Paul. And with that, Paul left.

"Now, where was I with Sam?" Joe thought, "Ah yes, back to the constraints." "Sam," Joe said, "I'd like to go to the shop floor and walk through your tank-building process, if you don't mind."

"Great," said Sam, "Let's go."

"Wait a minute Sam," said Joe, "let's first talk about how you receive and schedule your customer orders."

"OK . . . maybe I should go get Mary Jones, our Production Control Manager." replied Sam. "She knows much more about that kind of stuff than I do." Sam called Mary and asked her to come to his office. Mary arrived shortly thereafter and Sam asked her to explain the order entry procedure to Joe, which she did quite nicely. Mary was a very detailed person, and a few times she got down into the weeds, and Joe had to bring her back to the basics.

Joe could see that Sam was getting more and more confused. "Just a minute Mary," Joe said. "I need to make a phone call." He called Stan Wilson.

"Good morning Stan, do we have a Value Stream Map (VSM) of the J40 tank process?" Joe asked. "I see . . . could you come over to Sam's office for a minute? . . . OK Stan, I'll see you in ten minutes."

"Sorry, Sam and Mary, I just asked one of my black belts, Stan

Wilson, to come over and help us visualize this process," said Joe. "Have either of you ever seen a VSM?" he asked. As it turned out, neither Sam or Mary had ever seen one before. "I always start any improvement initiative with a VSM so that I can see the process flow that includes the order entry system, the major suppliers and our own process," said Joe. "On one diagram the VSM shows us how everything fits together, and I think it will help crystallize what we want to do here. I'm going to ask Stan to put one together today so that we can visualize what we're working on," he added.

"Good morning Stan, I assume you know Sam and Mary?" Joe asked.

"I know of them, but have never actually met them. Nice to meet both of you," Stan said as he shook their hands.

"Have a seat, Stan," said Joe. "Stan, we've been discussing the J40 tank process this morning and I'd like you to work with Mary and develop a VSM today. Can you do that?"

"Sure boss, piece of cake!" replied Stan. "Let's go Mary," said Stan, and Mary and Stan left to build a VSM.

"While those two are doing that Sam, let's talk about performance metrics," said Joe.

"OK, what would you like to know, Joe?" asked Sam.

"Basically, what performance metrics are you using, and what do they mean to you. Also what do you believe is the purpose of a performance metric? Does that make sense to you Sam?" asked Joe.

Sam nodded and said, "Basically there are two primary metrics that we use, manpower efficiency and on-time delivery," said Sam. "Of course we have quality and safety metrics too where we measure first pass yield and accident rates."

"And how are the efficiencies and on-time delivery trending?" asked Joe.

"Well, we're doing really well on our efficiencies, but terrible on our on-time delivery," said Sam. "Remember yesterday I was called to Corporate to explain why my on-time delivery is so poor?"

Joe nodded,. "You also said you were getting tired of making these trips," Joe recalled.

"I most definitely am," replied Sam.

"OK Sam, in your opinion what is the purpose of performance metrics?" asked Joe.

"That's a great question, Joe," replied Sam. "In my opinion, performance metrics are intended to measure what's important in a company," said Sam. "So how do you feel about the performance-metric manpower efficiency?" asked Joe.

"I think it's a great metric because it tells me whether my people are staying busy or not," replied Sam.

"But does it help you achieve more throughput Sam?" Joe asked. "Or does it help you achieve better on-time delivery?"

"I guess not, since our on-time delivery sucks big time," replied Sam. Sam came back with a question. "What do you think the purpose of performance metrics are, Joe."

"I'm glad you asked me, Sam. The primary purpose of performance metrics is to motivate the right behaviors," said Joe. "And in this case, driving efficiencies upward in nonconstraints only serves to drive up inventory and lengthen cycle times."

"So Joe, are you telling me that by trying to increase overall efficiencies, I am actually setting the stage for poor delivery performance?" asked Sam.

"Sorry to say, Sam, that's exactly right."

"So how can we turn this around, Joe?"

"Let's take a walk, Sam."

"Sam, now that we're out here on the production floor, I want you to remember the drawing of the simple four-step process I showed you on the flip chart and what we talked about," said Joe. "Let's start at the first step in your process and walk through the whole process." As they walked through the process, Joe pointed out the need to move the process steps close together so that the product flow would be better defined. They continued walking until they came to the joining process. Joe said, "Tell me what you see, Sam."

Sam replied, "I see a problem, Joe."

"And what problem do you see, Sam?"

"Well, first of all, it's clear so far that our joining operation is the constraint," said Sam.

"Why do you think it's the constraint, Sam?" asked Joe.

"Because of all the inventory sitting directly in front of it," said Sam.

"And why is this inventory here Sam," asked Joe.

"Probably because the joining operation is the slowest step in the process," Sam replied.

"And . . . ?" Joe asked.

"Because we're not subordinating everything else to the constraint," said Sam.

"Excellent Sam!" said Joe. "But there's more to it than just that. You see Sam, you're being measured by a performance metric that is causing you to exhibit the wrong behaviors. In order for you to satisfy the efficiency metric, you're essentially being forced to overproduce on every step in your process—sort of like you're being held hostage by this metric. Goldratt said it best when he said, 'Show me how you measure me, and I'll show you how I'll behave,' " said Joe.

Joe explained that although the joining operation was indeed a physical constraint, the real culprit here was the policy constraint of using manpower efficiency as a performance metric. Because Sam was being measured by the performance metric efficiency, he was forced to build product at higher-than-needed amounts in the non-constraints that are feeding the constraint. Joe explained that this, in turn, caused the overall cycle time of the process to be extended, resulting in delayed shipments.

It was all so clear to Sam now. He said, "So if I want to improve on time deliveries, I must do two things. First, I have to reduce the amount of time in the joining operation, but equally important, I must subordinate the other processes to the speed of the constraint. Right?"

"Yes, Sam, you are correct," replied Joe.

"Effectively, in order for us to speed up, we must slow down," said Sam.

"Absolutely," said Joe.

"What a day!" said Sam. "What a wonderful day. Let's go have some lunch, Joe, and it's on me."

At lunch Sam had many "what to" and "how to" questions about his operation. He and Joe discussed the importance of rearranging the process into a cellular configuration, the need to organize the production line using 5S events and a host of other subjects and topics. As Joe described Sam's current process layout he referred to it as the Butterfly Syndrome. Joe explained that as you watch butterflies move about, they do so in a haphazard way, fluttering about aimlessly with no apparent direction in mind. Joe proposed that one of the first things needed was a rapid improvement event to create a coherent cellular arrangement—one that enhanced the flow of product through it.

Joe also expressed the need for a simple scheduling system based upon pulling product through the process instead of the current push system. Joe referred to it as Drum-Buffer-Rope (DBR). They discussed the need to identify and eliminate waste and to establish one-piece flow. But the overriding message during their extended lunch was the need to use an integrated TOC, Lean, Six-Sigma approach in all that they do. That is, use TOC to identify the constraint and then apply Lean and Six Sigma to reduce waste and variation, but do so only in the constraint. If and when the constraint moves, the improvement efforts move with it, and the process of ongoing improvement (POOGI) continues. Joe explained that one of the primary reasons Lean and Six Sigma initiatives were failing at such an alarming rate at Barton was the belief that improvements everywhere yield improvements to the system. That is, instead of focusing improvement efforts on the key leverage points of a business, there seemed to be a maniacal attempt to fix everything, and this approach simply doesn't work.

The more Joe described the future, the more excited Sam became until finally Sam said, "Joe, when can we get started? My career survival clock is ticking."

"In due time my friend, in due time," replied Joe.

The two of them had lost complete track of time, and before they knew it, it was 5:30 PM.

"Feel like going for a drink Sam?" Joe asked. "There's someone I'd really like you to meet."

Within minutes they were pulling into the parking lot of Jonah's Bar and Grill. As they walked toward the building, Joe told Sam about Connor and how he had actually worked as a TOC consultant and had helped develop many of the tools they would be using to transform Barton into a money-making machine focused on their customers and of course, the constraint.

"I'm excited to meet him, but why in the world is he working at this out-of-the-way bar Joe?" asked Sam.

"I'll let Connor answer that question," laughed Joe.

Chapter 5
Sam and Connor Meet

As Sam and Joe walked into Jonah's, Sam couldn't help but notice the artwork, diagrams and photos hung neatly on the walls. Some were quite abstract while others were figurative, but all seemed to reflect apparent manufacturing processes, or at least that's how Sam interpreted them. "How odd," thought Sam, "to see things like this hanging on the walls of a bar of all places."

Joe noticed that Connor was, once again, in a discussion with the same men he had seen Connor with the last time he was here. Joe and Sam found an empty table and motioned for the waitress.

"Chianti again?" asked the waitress.

"Sounds good to me," replied Joe.

"And for you?" she asked.

"Just bring me a beer," Sam replied.

"Any particular brand?" she asked.

"No, just any Light beer would be great," said Sam.

"Interesting place Joe," said Sam. "I've never seen a bar with this kind of décor."

"If you think the décor is interesting, wait until you meet Connor," said Joe.

"I can't wait," said Sam. "Today was a real eye-opener for me, Joe. And I have to tell you, I'm really excited to get started. It's very apparent to me now that I've been going about manufacturing totally wrong," said Sam. "And the sad part is, it's all common sense."

"Don't beat yourself up too much, Sam," said Joe. "It might be common sense, but it's also counterintuitive for most people. The concept of slowing down in order to speed up isn't something that most people come up with on their own."

"But once you see it, once you have your shazam moment, your epiphany, it hits you like a ton of bricks," reflected Sam.

"Tell me something Sam," asked Joe, "What was the most important thing you learned today?"

Sam reflected for a moment, and then he said,. "Joe it wasn't just one thing, it was a series of things that were all tied neatly together. The first thing was the whole notion of the existence of a constraint that dictates the throughput of any process."

Sam continued, "Tied closely to that was the importance of selecting the right performance metrics, and that the primary purpose of these metrics is to motivate the right behaviors. I had just never thought of performance metrics in that vein before," said Sam. "Although we didn't get into a deep discussion on manpower efficiency, it's apparent to me that the only place that efficiency has any meaning at all is in the constraint. It means very little or nothing in the non-constraints." "Yes Sam, it's a mistake many companies make," said Joe. "As you look back at your lecture to Bradley this morning about keeping everybody busy, do you think you owe him an apology?" Joe asked. "Yes Joe I do, I know now that he really wasn't doing anything wrong."

Joe listened as Sam continued today's recap. "I learned that the primary failure of our continuous improvement effort here at Barton is that we have been focusing on the inconsequential nonconstraints instead of the critical constraints. The constraints are the key leverage points in our processes, and by attempting to 'solve world hunger' by working on everything, including nonconstraints, it's simply been counterproductive," explained Sam. "It's now clear to me that we should focus all of our improvement efforts on our leverage points."

Joe smiled and encouraged Sam to continue., "Go on Sam, you're making me smile. "How about throughput accounting Sam, what did you think of it?"

"Joe, what you taught me about accounting today might have been the best thing of all," mused Sam. "I mean for the first time in my career someone showed me a great way to make financial decisions." He added, "The way I see it, and correct me if I'm wrong, Joe, there are three questions I have to ask when I'm considering a change. The first question is, does what I'm considering doing increase throughput?" Sam paused. "The second question I need to ask is, will it reduce inventory? And the third question I need to ask is, will it reduce operating expense?"

"Yes, Sam, you have it exactly right!" exclaimed Joe.

"Mind if I join you, Joe?" came a voice out of nowhere. It was Connor Jackson.

"Well hi Connor. I didn't want to disturb you when we came in because I saw you were having a pretty intense discussion," said Joe. "Connor, I want you to meet Sam Henderson, our VP of Operations at Barton."

"It's a pleasure to meet you. Connor Jackson here."

"Sam Henderson, and the pleasure is all mine," said Sam. "Joe has told me all about you, and I was really looking forward to finally meeting you."

"So who were those guys you were talking to Connor? asked Joe. "It looked like a pretty intense discussion,"

"Those guys are a couple of VPs from one of the companies in town," said Connor. "They come in fairly regularly just to shoot the bull about their companies and how their TOC implementation is going. I've been giving them some free advice for the last six months, and sometimes they don't agree with the advice I give them, so I have to set them straight," Connor explained.

"I thought you didn't consult any more Connor." said Joe.

"That's not consulting. That's just having fun doing what I love," said Connor.

"You guys look like you were in a pretty heavy discussion as well," said Connor.

Sam replied, "We were just reconstituting everything that Joe taught me today about the Theory of Constraints. It was amazing to learn all of these common sense new things."

"I'll let you get back to your conversation then," said Connor.

"Please stay, Connor," said Joe. "Unless of course you'll get in trouble with the boss," Joe winked at Connor.

"Are you sure you don't mind?" Connor asked.

"Mind?" said Sam. "We'd love to have you stay."

"Well then, let me spring for another round of drinks," said Connor.

"So, Sam, I don't know much about Barton Enterprises. Tell me what your company does," asked Connor.

"Sure, Connor. We make fuel tanks for commercial and military aircraft," said Sam. "Almost everything we make is done so manually."

He continued. “Barton has been around for almost fifty years, and we’re one of the major suppliers to the aviation industry.”

“And how long have you been with Barton, Sam?” asked Connor.

“I’ve been at Barton for almost twenty years, and I’ve been the VP of Operations for the last ten years,” said Sam. “And I just found out today that my approach to this business has been all wrong. Hasn’t it, Joe?”

“It’s not that it’s been wrong, Sam,” replied Joe. “It’s just that there’s a better way.”

“So Sam, what’s giving you the most heartburn? What’s keeping you up at night?” asked Connor.

“Oh, that’s easy,” replied Sam. “We can’t seem to deliver our products on time.”

“Let me guess,” said Connor. “One of your primary performance metrics is operator efficiency.”

“You must have been talking to Joe,” Sam replied as he looked at Joe.

“Nope, I’ve just seen it so often over the years—when companies try to drive efficiencies higher and higher, it becomes inversely proportional to on-time delivery,” said Connor. “The harder you push for higher efficiencies, the more inventory enters the system. The more inventory in the system, the longer the cycle times. And the longer the cycle times, the later the deliveries,” explained Connor.

“This all makes so much sense to me!” said Sam. “I just hope we can make improvements in time to save my job.” Sam looked worried.

“How much time do you have, Sam?” asked Connor.

“I’ve been given two months to fix on-time deliveries or the axe is coming,” replied Sam.

“Two months?” said Connor, “Two months is an eternity! Especially with Joe’s help,” he added.

With that, a look of relief replaced Sam’s look of desperation. “Guys, where do I start?” asked Sam. “How do I know what to change first and then second and then—”

“Stop, Sam. Joe and I will tell you what to do and when to do it,” replied Connor.

“ ‘Joe and I?’ ” said Joe. ”You mean you would be willing to help us, Connor?” asked Joe in an excited voice.

“Yes, but under certain conditions,” replied Connor.

"And those conditions are?" said Joe.

"Well, for one, I can't spend lots of my time at your plant. I do have my own business to run," said Connor.

"OK," Joe and Sam said together."

"But will you have time to at least come to see the process once before we start?" asked Joe.

"Yes, I want to do that soon," replied Connor. He continued, "The second thing is we need to lay out a strategy—a roadmap, if you will—before we begin making random changes. I don't want to go and just make changes without thinking through our strategy first," said Connor. "And thirdly, you must do exactly what I tell you to do, when I tell you to do it. That's critical."

"Gee, where have I heard that one before, Joe?" said Sam.

The three continued talking until Sam's cell phone rang. "Hello, this is Sam Henderson, can I help you?" said Sam.

"This is Paul Johnson. I just got a call from Cecil Graham, our Chairman of the Board, and he isn't so happy with you, Sam. He has scheduled a trip to our plant in two weeks to check on our progress since you met with him and the other board members," said Paul.

"Two weeks? He expects progress in two weeks?" exclaimed Sam.

"Yes, I told him about our meeting with Joe, and he's very interested in why Joe thinks that our accounting practices here at Barton need to be changed," explained Paul.

Sam put his phone on the external speaker setting so Joe and Connor could hear this conversation. "He also wants to see quantifiable evidence that progress is being made with on-time delivery," said Paul. "So I suggest you get your ass into the plant and make some improvements right away, Sam," Paul said in a sarcastic tone.

"You run your part of the business and I'll run mine, Paul!" said Sam in a loud voice.

"I am," replied Paul, "It's your performance we're all worried about." And with that the phone went dead. Joe and Connor looked at each other and smiled.

"It's going to be a lot of fun, Joe," said Connor.

Sam hung up the phone after a few more choice words for Paul. Then he explained the details of the call to Connor and Joe. "I've got to get to the plant and make some things happen guys. I've got to leave," said Sam obviously having a panic attack.

"Sam, sit down. Remember my second condition?" asked Connor. "No changes until we develop our roadmap," he said.

"But my clock is ticking, Connor, and two weeks is right around the corner," said Sam anxiously.

"What time is it?" asked Connor.

"It's 9:30 PM. Why Connor?" asked Joe.

"I can have my assistant close up tonight. Let's go have a look at your plant right now, if you don't mind," said Connor.

"But there won't be much going on, on third shift . . . ," said Sam.

"I actually think it might be the best time since it will be quieter, and we'll be able to see the results from first and second shift," replied Connor.

"Let's go," said Sam, and off the three of them went.

When they arrived at the plant, Sam walked Connor and Joe through the entire process, and Joe noticed right away that the queue in front of the joining operation had grown by one top and bottom since he last saw it. This meant that at least one tank had been built about thirty-five weeks ago and that the backlog of tanks would continue to grow until Barton got rid of their push system and the terrible metric of efficiency. When they completed the tour, they went to Sam's office to talk about what they had seen.

"What do you think Connor?" asked Sam.

"I think you have a mess, but it's also "fixable," said Connor. "Do you have a flip chart and an easel, Sam?" asked Connor.

Sam went next door and retrieved the one Joe had used earlier. Sam kept flipping through the pages searching for a clean sheet, when Connor noticed the piping diagram Joe had sketched and said, "Wait, flip back to that last sheet."

"What is that?" asked Connor.

"It's something Joe explained to me to demonstrate the concept of a constraint," said Sam. "You want to explain this, Joe?" asked Sam.

"No, Sam, you explain it to Connor," Joe instructed. Sam explained the sketch in detail to Connor, and Connor said, "I've never seen this presented quite like this before. I really like it!"

"Nice job, Joe," said Connor.

"It really helped me see what a physical constraint actually looked like," said Sam.

Connor approached the flip chart and started writing down things that he had observed during the tour—like excessive WIP, a very disjointed process, the problem caused by the efficiency metric, the push system, and so on. Connor flipped to the next sheet and labeled it "Immediate Actions."

Immediate Actions

1. **Shut down all steps in front of the constraint.**
2. **Re-arrange the process into a cellular layout to achieve flow.**
3. **Cross-train all non-constraint operators on the joining process.**
4. **Do not start another top and bottom until the queue in front of the joining operation equals one top and one bottom.**
5. **Do steps 1, 2, 3 and 4 right now.**

When Sam saw the first step Connor had written he became agitated. "Connor, I can't shut down the upstream operations—my efficiency numbers will deteriorate!"

Joe interjected, "Remember condition number three Sam?"

"I remember, but what about my efficiencies?" asked Sam.

"To hell with your efficiencies Sam!" replied Connor. "Do you want efficiencies or do you want on-time delivery? You can't have it both ways, Sam."

"Okay, Okay," said Sam. And with that he motioned for all of his operators to gather at the joining operation.

"Folks, I want you to meet Connor Jackson and Joe Pecci," said Sam. "Joe is our new Continuous Improvement Manager and Connor is an expert on process improvement. They're both here to help us improve our on-time delivery," said Sam. "What they're about to explain to you might seem counterintuitive, but believe me, it is exactly what we need to be doing. And with that I'm going to turn it over to Joe and Connor."

Connor started, "Good morning, everyone. What Sam said is exactly true—in that what we're going to tell you is very counterintuitive," said Connor. "That is, at first it might not make any sense to you. But I want all of you to listen with an open mind," he said. "Will all of you do that for us?

"We, but mostly you, are going to change the way things are done around here, and we don't have much time to do it," said Connor. "So with that in mind, I'm going to ask Joe to make a brief presentation about something called the Theory of Constraints. Joe?"

"Good morning everyone, and hello, Bradley," said Joe. Bradley waved in acknowledgment.

Over the next twenty minutes Joe presented the same material he had presented to Sam, minus the Throughput Accounting piece. When he finished, he asked if there were any questions.

Sally, one of the third-shift operators raised her hand and said, "We've all been wondering why we just keep building and building these tops and bottoms when they just get hung up in joining. Are we going to change that?" she asked.

"We most certainly are Sally," said Joe. Great question!"

Another voice came from the crowd. "I have a question," a man said. "Why in the world do we have one part of the process here and another part there?" he asked. "It just seems more like if we had them closer together, we could do a better job."

"What's your name?" asked Joe.

"Timmy," the man replied.

"That too is a great question!" said Joe. The questions kept pouring in, and Sam leaned over to Connor and whispered, "These people know what we need to do. I've never taken the time to listen to them before. What an eye-opener for me."

"Sam," said Connor, "I'd like you to meet your subject-matter experts—the folks who will be telling us how to set up and run this line," he added.

"Now I want to turn this back over to Connor," said Joe. "We're going to be making some immediate changes to how we run this line. Connor?" said Joe, "It's all yours."

Connor flipped to the last page on the flip chart that listed the immediate actions this new team would take. Connor added one more action to the original list, "Never let the constraint sit idle," and he changed the wording on action six." Upon looking at the list, Sally asked, "Which step is the constraint?"

Immediate Actions

1. **Shut down all steps in front of the constraint.**
2. **Re-arrange the process into a cellular layout to achieve flow.**
3. **Cross-train all non-constraint operators on the joining process.**
4. **Do not start another top and bottom until the queue in front of the joining operation equals one top and one bottom.**
5. **Never let the constraint sit idle.**
6. **Do steps 1, 2, 3, 4 and 5 right now!**

Connor immediately replied, "Can anyone answer that question for Sally?"

The joining operator, Tom, said, "That's easy. It's me!" and everyone laughed, but he was right!

Then the questions came one right after the other until finally Connor stopped them and said, "Let's get to work." So with all non-constraint operators ready to work, Connor led the discussion on re-arranging the process.

"How do you want it set up Connor?" asked one of the operators.

"That's not my call. It's yours," he said.

"Our call?" responded a few voices. "You mean we can set it up like we think it should be?" they asked.

"Yep, that's exactly what I mean," replied Connor. "The only thing I ask is that you include everyone and that you diagram it on a flip chart sheet," he said. "One other thing—I want half of you to start cross-training on the joining operation. You guys decide who does what," Connor added. One thing Connor knew was that in an exercise like this, everyone would flock to their informal leader, and they did.

Half of the team spent the rest of their shift moving process steps around until they finally got it the way they wanted it, while the rest of the team spent their time cross-training on the joining operation.

By shift's end, the line was fully set up and ready to run. Connor asked for volunteers to demonstrate the new production line to the first shift operators and almost everyone volunteered. There was excitement and pride in the air at Barton, maybe for the first time in many years. Two operators, realizing that someone would need to show the new process to second shift, volunteered to come in early. Sam was dumbfounded at the apparent enthusiasm he was seeing. He actually wiped away a tear of joy because in his mind he now knew his mission was possible with this new team atmosphere. The pace of activities was fast and furious. Sam knew that there would be some detractors, but he also understood the power of peer pressure.

Connor finally said, "Guys, I think you can take it from here. I've got to go get some sleep."

"Wait Connor, when can we get together to develop our strategy—our roadmap?" asked Sam.

"Come by the bar tonight and we'll start," said Connor.

"Should I bring anything, Connor?" asked Sam.

"Yes, as a matter of fact you can," said Connor. "We'll need to know what kind of chronic problems you've had that get in the way of you making more tanks."

"You mean besides me, right Connor?" Sam joked.

"I'm talking about things like parts shortages, tools, equipment, policies and procedures—things like that. Got it Sam?" asked Connor.

"Got it chief!" Sam replied.

"See you guys tonight," said Connor, and he left. "Oh, by the way, bring a flip chart with you," Connor called back over his shoulder. "We've got some strategy to work on."

It was quite a day for Sam. He knew that his efficiency numbers were going to take a hit, but in the interests of on-time delivery improvements, he was willing to risk it. He now had hope, at least for now, that he could make the necessary improvements and keep his job. But would he be able to make a change in his performance before Cecil Graham came in less than two weeks? He was hopeful, but he was still worried. Sam was tired, and he decided to go home and get a couple of hours of sleep so he could be there for second shift.

Joe was tired too, but he decided he needed to get his black belts together for some training and to have a discussion about what had happened on third shift. At 7:00 AM Joe went back to his office and noticed that all four of his people were in for the day. "Good morning everyone," said Joe. "I need to have a meeting with all of you in ten minutes." One-by-one they all filed into his office with Stan leading the way.

"You look tired, boss, didn't you sleep well last night?" Stan asked.

"No, I spent the night here as a matter of fact," replied Joe.

"Didn't you pay your hotel bill, Joe?" said Stan jokingly.

"No, I was at the plant all night. It's one of the things I want to talk about," said Joe.

Joe asked his black belts to talk about the recent projects they've been working on and their results.

Bill spoke up first and said, "I've been working on 'Leaning Out' the new hire process, and we actually took three days off the process," he said proudly.

Manuel was next, "I've b-been w-working on the p-parts acquisition process, and w-we r-reduced it b-by one w-week on average."

Stan jumped in and said, "I've been working with Engineering on how to speed up their specification update system, and we've made some progress." It seemed that Engineering was often late in posting spec changes, and tanks ended up getting built to out-dated specs. "Oh, and boss, I've got that VSM for the J40 process about done, would you like to see it?"

"Not right now Stan, we'll look at it later, and by the way, you'll probably have to redo it after what we did last night," replied Joe. After listening to everyone, it was clear to Joe that none of these projects were centered on critical processes and none would do anything to improve on-time delivery.

"Guys, let me ask you a question," said Joe. "Which of your projects will do anything to help us deliver any more products or reduce scrap or rework?"

"Not mine," said Bill.

"M-mine w-won't either," said Manuel.

"Mine might in the long run," said Stan.

"Guys," said Joe, "Let's go into the conference room and talk. You come too, Judy."

Joe set up his easel and flip chart and proceeded to present exactly the same materials he had presented to Sam, including the Throughput Accounting piece and the list of immediate activities that Connor had written on his sheet. Joe went into more depth about the Theory of Constraints and gave them each a copy of *The Goal*, which they were required to finish in three days or less. Before ending for the day, he said, "Let's go to the J40 line so I can show you everything we did last night, or should I say, early this morning."

When they arrived, Joe saw Sam in his office and took a detour in his direction with his troop of improvement folks following him like baby ducks.

Sam looked up and motioned for Joe to come in. "You won't believe it, Joe. You just won't believe it!"

"Believe what, Sam," asked Joe.

"What my people on first shift have done to our production area!" Sam exclaimed.

"What is it, Sam? What have they done?"

"They have transformed it!" replied Sam. "They took what we did on the J40 line and expanded it to most of our other lines. Joe, I'm so proud of my guys!"

"Sam, you've met Stan, but I want you to meet the rest of my team," said Joe.

"I've met Judy before, when she was the chairperson of the United Way team. Hi Judy," said Sam.

"This is Bill Cody and this is Manuel Gonzalez, they're both black belts," said Joe.

"Nice to meet both of you. You have quite a boss in Joe," said Sam. "He's taught me more in the last two days about running a production facility, than I have learned in twenty years."

"Enough of the bullshit Sam, let's go see your production area," said Joe.

As they turned the corner, Joe could see a flurry of activity—many people working to rearrange the production lines. As he looked closer, it was clear that every line had been set up to improve the flow, but he also noticed the joining operation in each line working hard to process the tanks. "So," Joe thought, "The constraint is not sitting idle and the constraint operator was teaching other workers how to do his job." All of a sudden Joe saw a friendly face—Bradley Fox, the third shift supervisor. "What are you still doing here Bradley?" Joe asked.

"I was so excited with what we learned and what we did on third shift, I just had to stay and help first shift carry on with what we'd started," replied Bradley. "This is really some cool stuff, Joe," he said. "And Sam even apologized to me for dressing me down the other night about having people sit idle."

"I think we've all learned some new things lately, and there's more on the way," replied Joe.

Joe turned to his black belts and said, "I want each of you to pick a production line, find the hourly Lead and introduce yourself to him. This is where you guys will be living from now on," said Joe.

"But what if Mr. Henderson doesn't want us working on projects out here?" asked Bill.

"Trust me Bill, he wants us all out here," said Joe.

"Go find your contacts and find out what kind of problems they have," said Joe. "Stan, since you already started a VSM on the J40 line, you take that one," Joe instructed. "Bill, you take the J50 line, and Manuel, you take the J60 line. Let me know what you find out there, but make sure it's a problem that the Lead has identified and not one you choose," said Joe.

Sam and Joe saw that the transformation had begun. It looked like an ant hill with ants scurrying around looking for food. They decided to go find some coffee and talk about their meeting with Connor tonight.

"What do you think Connor meant by developing our strategy, Joe?" asked Sam.

"I think we're going to hear about a different side of the Theory of Constraints called the TOC Thinking Processes," said Joe. "I've heard about the Thinking Processes, but I know very little about them."

The two continued talking and working on the homework Connor had assigned them. They carefully made a list of all of the things that got in the way of producing more tanks, and at the top of the list Sam had inserted the performance metric efficiency.

Joe's three black belts knocked on the door, and Sam motioned for them to come in.

"Boss," said Stan, "We've got our assignments from the Leads on each line. Would you like to hear them?"

"Yes, we would," chimed in Sam.

"Manuel, why don't you go first," said Stan.

"M-my p-project on the J60 line isss a problem w-with r-reejects coming out of j-joining, said Manuel.

"Is there one particular reject that stands out, Manuel?" asked Sam.

"N-not sure, butt I think it's m-mold r-r-related d-defects, but I'll c-crunch the data and f-f-f-find out," said Manuel.

"Bill, what have you got?" asked Joe.

"My Lead said there were two major problems with the J50 tanks—parts availability and unsticking of the fabric," said Bill.

Stan added, "My Lead also said parts, so why don't I work on parts and Bill can work on the unsticking problem?" Stan suggested.

"I like the idea," said Joe. "How about you, Sam?" he asked.

"I think it's great, and thanks in advance for all of your help," said Sam.

The list for Connor was now complete with this input, so Joe and Sam grabbed their briefcases and the easel and flipcharts and headed for Jonah's. "See you there Joe," shouted Sam. They knew that their transformation was well under way.

Chapter 6
The Strategy Session at Jonah's

Sam and Joe pulled into the parking lot at Jonah's full of anticipation and uncertainty. Neither one knew what to expect from Connor today, but they were excited to get going. Sam helped Joe with the flip chart and easel, but when they came to the door, there was a sign on it saying Jonah's was closed.

"What the hell?" said Joe, "Weren't we supposed to come this evening, Sam?"

"That's what we said . . . I sure hope everything is OK with Connor," said Sam.

The lights were on, but the door was locked and the sign clearly said CLOSED in capital letters.

"I guess we'd better leave," said Joe. But as they turned to walk to their cars, the door opened, and they heard Connor's voice. "And just where do you two guys think you're going? We've got a lot of work to do tonight, so get your butts in here before someone sees the open door," said Connor. "I closed the bar tonight so we could focus our attention on developing our strategy, " he said.

"You didn't have to close for us, Connor," said Sam.

"What about your lost revenue from closing the bar?" asked Joe.

"It'll be fine, guys, come on in," said Connor.

"How did things go after I left the plant Sam?" asked Connor.

Fantastic!" replied Sam. "My guys really stepped up for us. They have finished converting all of the lines over to the same cellular arrangement as the J40 process without any direction from either of us, Connor. Never seen anything like it before," said Sam. "I've never seen a more motivated bunch of guys in my life," he continued. "I am certain that we have turned the corner in terms of speeding up the process. And Joe assigned his black belts to the three highest production lines to work on what the hourly Leads think are their most pressing problems," concluded Sam.

"And what do the Leads say those problems are? No, let me guess," said Connor. "I would say that you have a parts availability problem . . . is that one of them?" asked Connor.

"Yes, that's probably the biggest issue," said Sam.

"I'm guessing that rejects is another problem?" asked Connor.

"Right again, Connor," said Sam.

"And the third problem is probably some kind of chronic Engineering problem?" asked Connor.

"Yes, but how did you know?" asked Sam.

"Just a lucky guess," said Connor. Then he followed up with Joe and Sam. "So, did you guys get your homework assignment done?"

"Yes, we sure did, but how do you plan on using what we identified that prevents us from making more tanks?" asked Joe.

"Good question, Joe," said Connor. "Joe, remember when I told you about the TOC Thinking Process tools? And how they could be used to develop and execute a strategy?" asked Connor.

"Uh huh, I remember you mentioning them to me," replied Joe.

"Well, we're going to use one today called the Intermediate Objectives Map (IO Map)," said Connor. "The IO Map is a logic diagram, and it's based on what is called necessity-based logic. The IO Map starts with a goal at the top, and in our case the goal is something like, 'Making Enough Tanks to Satisfy Demand, or Delivering Tanks on Time," whatever we decide it should be," said Connor. "The goal is defined by the process owner, and that's you Sam. "OK, I understand," said Sam.

Connor continued, "Immediately below the goal are three to five Critical Success Factors (CSFs) that must be in place to assure that we achieve the goal. On the map it then follows, 'in order to achieve the goal, we must have . . . ' and you list the CSFs," said Connor. "So for example, suppose the goal was delivering tanks on time, and one of the CSF's was 'All parts available when needed.' Then the IO Map would be read as, 'In order to deliver tanks on time, we must have all parts available when needed.' And you would identify the remaining CSFs and read them the same way. "This is all so interesting," said Sam, "And it makes so much sense."

"Immediately below the CSFs are entities called Necessary Conditions (NCs), which must be in place to guarantee achievement of the CSFs," continued Connor. "For example, suppose the CSF was 'All parts available when needed.' Then the IO Map would be read as follows—'In order to deliver tanks on time (the Goal), I must have all parts available when needed (a CSF).' And 'in order to have all parts available when needed, I must have a strong parts-replenishment system in place,' " said Connor. "So you can see, there is a logical, necessity-based flow of needs. Does this make sense to you guys?"

"It most certainly does, Connor," said Sam, "May I try one?" asked Sam.

"Yes, by all means, please do," Connor replied.

"OK, here goes," said Sam. " 'In order to deliver tanks on time (the Goal), I must have minimal defects on each tank (CSF),' And 'in order to have minimal defects on each tank, I must have a strong detection system,' " said Sam.

"What else do you need, Sam?" asked Connor.

"You mean I can have more than one necessary condition?" asked Sam.

"Yes, you can't have an unlimited number, but definitely two or three," Connor said.

"OK, what if the other condition one was something like a 'strong mold-repair system?' " said Sam. "Would that fit?"

"I think it might be better if that was a lower level NC," said Connor.

"Oh, so you can have lower level NCs to supplement the first level NCs?" asked Sam.

"Yes, but I generally don't go below the second or sometimes the third level of NCs," Connor explained.

"OK, let me try this," said Sam. " 'In order to deliver tanks on time (the Goal), I must have minimal defects on each tank (CSF).' 'In order to have minimal defects on each tank, I must have mold-related, defect-free, tank surfaces (NC).' 'In order to have mold-related, defect-free, tank surfaces, I must have a strong mold-surface inspection and repair system (lower level NC),' " said Sam. "What do you think Connor."

"I think they might be a little wordy, but you definitely have the idea, Sam. Great job!" said Connor. "So let's get set up and put this IO Map together."

The three of them worked tirelessly. They definitely had disagreements and conflicts. But by the end of the evening they had a finished product. It wasn't a perfect product by Connor's standards (Sam and Joe are finding out he is somewhat of a perfectionist), but it definitely would get them started. There were four Critical Success Factors and up to three levels of Necessary Conditions.

After they completed the first draft of the IO Map, there was a discussion about what to do next.

"Normally," Connor said, "we would now develop a current reality tree based upon all of the Undesirable Effects (UDEs) that exist within the system. But because time is an issue, I think it's best to just simply develop action plans to correct the most obvious items and maybe the easiest ones. For example, one of the lower level NCs under 'Constraints Meeting Cycle Times' is that there must be work relief on all constraints. I think that's something Sam should be able to fix right away, right, Sam?" asked Connor.

"Already in place," said Sam.

"Another one might be guaranteeing that the mold surfaces are free of defects, which should significantly reduce rework on the finished tanks," said Connor.

"We'll have that in place hopefully by tomorrow," said Sam. "Also, by shutting down the upstream parts of the process so that the excessive WIP in front of the joining operation is burned off, we should be in compliance with Little's Law hopefully in about a week," said Sam.

"Great point Sam. I forgot we had addressed that yesterday," said Connor.

"That leaves two Critical Success Factors that we haven't addressed, the parts availability issue and the tanks scheduled to meet demand," said Connor.

"We've been trying to fix the parts-availability problem for a long time, and nothing seems to work," said Sam. "We use the Department of Defense-type MIN/MAX system, and we're all of the time running into stock-outs and shortages that just kill our throughput," he said.

"I think I might have a solution for you, but it's going to take some work," said Connor.

"Who's responsible for the supply system, Sam?" asked Joe.

"His name is Jerry Dumas and he works for Paul Johnson," said Sam. "He's been given strict orders to hold down the parts inventory as a cost-savings initiative, and he takes it very seriously. I think he gets a bonus based on how much money he saves in parts, and Paul backs him up," said Sam. "I'll meet with him tomorrow," Sam added.

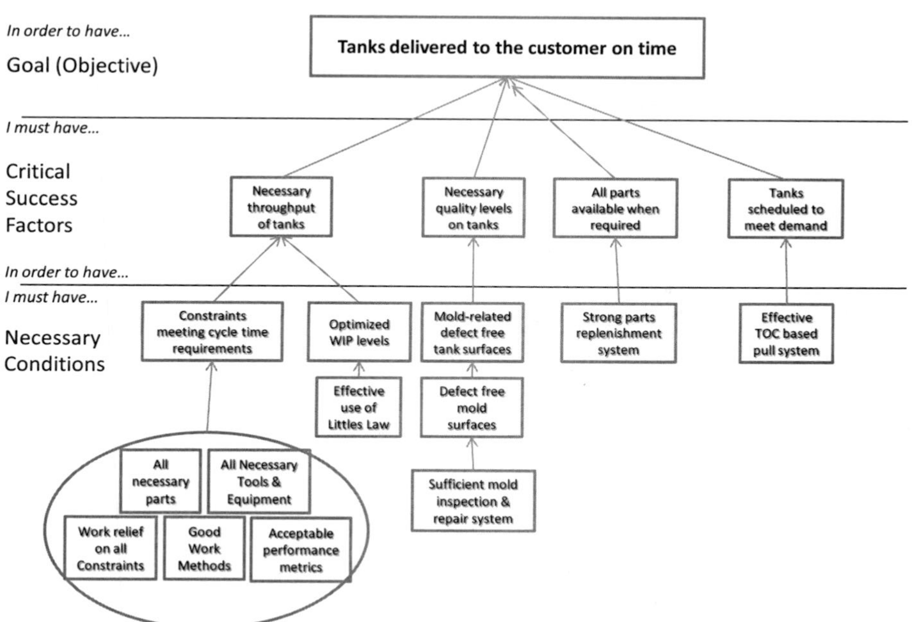

"Let's wait to meet with him until after we talk about a TOC replenishment model," said Connor. "And we also need to address the scheduling system," he said. "TOC has a solution for that as well called Drum-Buffer-Rope (DBR) which we should be able to implement relatively easily."

"How does this Drum-Buffer-Rope work, Connor?" asked Joe.

"Look guys, I don't know about you two, but I'm exhausted. Let's call it a night, OK?" said Connor.

"I'm just getting my second wind," said Sam, "So I think I'll run into the plant and see how second shift is making out with all of our changes."

"I'll go with you, Sam," said Joe.

"Thanks for everything, Connor," said Sam.

"Guys, let's get together tomorrow afternoon. Things are usually slow around 2:00 PM," said Connor. "I'll give you the lowdown on the TOC replenishment model and Drum-Buffer-Rope."

"OK, Connor, we'll see you tomorrow afternoon," said Joe.

Sam and Joe arrived at the plant around 10:30 PM, anxious to see how things were moving. When they stepped into the production area, everyone appeared busy just as they had hoped. "Hi, boss," said Stan Wilson.

"What are you still doing here, Stan?" asked Joe.

"Just hanging out, having fun," said Stan. "We've rearranged the production line on the J40 based on an idea from one of the workers, and it's made a difference. The nonconstraint operators are now doing all of the paperwork for the constraint operator, so he can keep working," said Stan. "It's saving about forty-five minutes per shift boss.

"I've started a notebook of ideas, and we formed a team to decide on which ones we can do and which we can't," continued Stan. "The WIP in front of joining has decreased from seven tanks to five since yesterday on third shift," Stan said.

"Wow, Stan, that's a big drop!" said Sam.

"Well, Sam, I don't think they need us here tonight. Let's go get some sleep," said Joe.

"See you tomorrow, Joe, and Stan, don't stay all night, please," said Sam.

"OK, boss, see you in the morning. Good night," said Stan.

Chapter 7
The Second Meeting with Connor

"Oh my gosh, it's nearly 7:30, and I didn't get a wake-up call from the front desk. Sam must be wondering where I am," exclaimed Joe as he jumped out of bed and headed to the bathroom for a quick shower. Thirty minutes later Joe pulled into the parking lot at Barton. Sam's car was not in his usual parking space. "So maybe he had slept in as well," thought Joe. Joe flung his briefcase over his shoulder and headed to the production area. "Hmmm, that's strange, Sam's office is open, but he's not here," thought Joe.

"Can you help me, Joe?" said a familiar voice behind him. It was Sam and he was loaded down with multiple bags of something.

"What's all this?" asked Joe.

"It's donuts for this amazing team we have assembled," replied Sam. "It's time to reward great behavior, Joe, and your guys are the central focus this morning."

"I had no idea you were going to do this Sam. Why didn't you tell me?" asked Joe.

"Do what, Joe?" asked Sam, "I have no idea what you're talking about," He added, "Joe, take credit where credit is due."

"What the hell are you talking about, seriously Sam," said Joe in a very convincing voice.

"You really don't know do you, Joe?" asked Sam.

"Hell no, Sam," said Joe. "Would you please tell me what's going on?" Joe added.

"Joe, it seems that your black belts took it upon themselves to come in on second shift and hold three simultaneous 6S events on their three assigned lines with no direction from you," explained Sam. "Now that's dedication, if you ask me."

"Well, how did they do, Sam?" asked Joe.

"Come on, I'll show you," said Sam.

Joe was amazed at the new appearance of the three production lines. He noticed Manuel and motioned for him to come toward him.

"G-good morning, s-s-sir," said Manuel.

"What made you guys think of doing this last night, Manuel?" asked Joe.

"W-w-wee were s-s-sit-ting in our office y-yes-s-sterday, and S-s-s-stan a-s-s-sked us-s what w-wee thought c-c-could b-bee done t-to improve th-th-the l-l-lines, and I s-s-s-suggested s-s-s-six s-s-s-s t-t-to him. H-h-hee l-liked the idea s-s-so m-much th-that he s-s-s-suggested w-wee s-s-start l-l-last n-night," said Manuel.

"Where are Stan and Bill, Manuel" asked Joe. Manuel pointed in the direction of the J40 line where he saw both of them talking.

Suddenly, Sam's voice rang out, "Hey everybody, meet me in the break room for a meeting." When the day shift workers (and some third-shift leftovers) entered the break room they saw stacks and stacks of donuts and other pastries.

"Everyone," said Sam, "In appreciation of everyone's hard work these last few days, I just wanted to show my appreciation to you."

His comments were met with immediate and deafening applause and a standing ovation! "We love you, man!" came a voice from the back of the room. "Someone is finally listening to us," said another.

Sam looked around the room and he noticed several people missing—Joe's three black belts. "Does anyone know where Stan, Bill and Manuel are?" asked Sam.

"I do," said a voice in the rear. "They're working on the constraint. We told them to come in here, but they said, 'The constraint can't ever be left idle.' "

Sam's head dropped and shook from side to side in amazement that such dedication existed all of this time, and he had never seen it. He asked, "Can someone go get them please?"

Another voice from the back, "No, but I'll go relieve them. The constraint hasn't been idle in two days, and we don't want to start now," said the voice.

Two more voices said, "We'll go relieve the other two."

When Stan, Manuel and Bill walked into the break room, they were met with applause and whistles, and all three of them just smiled.

Finally another worker in the front stood up and said, "These three guys have done more to help us in the last two days than anyone has since I've been here, and I just want to say thanks," and with that he walked over and shook their hands. One-by-one, all of the workers walked by and shook their hands, patted them on the back, looked them in the eye and said, "Thank you!"

"My guys have come so far in two days that it's amazing," said Sam.

"Everyone has!" said Joe. And with that, they were back on the shop floor.

What the three black belts had done was create point-of-use tools and equipment, a parts drop-off area, designated spots for things to be placed, and a variety of other improvements. Joe could see what a difference it had made to the area, but more importantly to the people. They had even developed 6S audits as a way of sustaining these gains. One thing was certain, there was a focused team in place that covered all three shifts and virtually every worker. For the first time possibly ever, there was a sense that their opinions mattered and that they were viewed as the true subject-matter experts. Most of them understood the basics of the Theory of Constraints that had been presented to them and had actually embraced it unlike any workforce Joe had ever seen. Sam was in a state of shock to realize that all this time, during his ten years as the VP of Operations, this workforce could have been helping him if he had just reached out to them. Instead he had been into command and control management, but now he realized just how inappropriate that style really was.

"Sam, let's take a look at some data on just how late your orders typically are," said Joe.

Sam rummaged around his desk and pulled out the last monthly report which clearly stated, "On-Time-Delivery—61%," which was terrible.

"Now Sam, let's see if we can project where we might be in a little be over a week from now when Cecil Graham arrives," said Joe.

They walked to the floor and checked on the queue, which had been seven tops and bottoms when they started, and to their surprise, the backlog was now down to four. They walked to shipping and asked how many of the J40s, J50s and J60s had shipped in the last two days. Two each of each type had shipped, which was a weekly record, and they still had two shipping days to go! This increase meant that on these three tank types, they were only one tank behind for each type. When Sam saw this, Joe couldn't contain him as he started jumping up and down for joy.

As they walked back through the production area, they noticed that the J40 joining area wasn't working. "Uh oh, what's wrong?" asked Joe. After the two of them talked to the operators, they realized that they had run out of baffles and that the next shipment wasn't due in for at least two days. When they checked the stock level for baffles at the J50 and J60 tanks, the J50 tank had one baffle left and they were inserting their last one. at the J60 tank.

Sam and Joe ran to the supply area and checked to see if there were any baffles left in stock. "We don't keep them in here," said Sandy Peters one of the stock room clerks. "When we get them we take them to the shop floor."

"When will the next shipment be in?" asked Sam.

"I suppose seven days after we order it," said Sandy.

"You mean there's none on order?" asked Sam.

"Nope, we're not allowed to reorder until we are down to our last ones on the floor," explained Sandy.

"What do you mean you're not allowed?" asked Sam.

"Just exactly what I said," said Sandy. "Mr. Dumas has given us strict orders and procedures to follow. He told us he's trying to keep our inventory of parts at the lowest level possible . . . Sorry guys, rules are rules."

"Let's go talk to Dumas and get to the bottom of this right now," said Sam.

"No Sam, remember Connor told us to wait until we had developed our parts- replenishment plan before we talk to Purchasing," said Joe.

"But Joe, we're in a stock-out condition right now!" said Sam.

"Surely Connor would want us to fix this by whatever means possible!" exclaimed Sam.

"Let's wait, Sam," replied Joe.

As Joe and Sam walked back to Sam's office, they shook hands and chatted with various workers along the way. Virtually every operator on the floor was very concerned about the parts issue and had even gone to Supply to ask them about their parts-shortage problems. Sam reassured all of them that they would resolve the issue, and that they were meeting with Connor tonight to develop a plan to do just that.

The workers all seemed confident that we would fix it, so their spirits remained high.

All of a sudden Sam and Joe heard the loud sound of a bell ringing out in the production area, and they went to see what that was all about. Apparently, the shop floor suggestion committee had received a recommendation about a way to alert everyone when a part was ready to depart the constraint. The joining operator had suggested that ringing a cow bell would be a good way to alert the nonconstraint operators so that they could come to help move the completed tank and then help insert the new top and bottom into the joining mold. "What a simple, yet ingenious way to communicate," Sam said to Joe. "These guys are amazing me more and more every day."

When Joe and Sam finally made it back to Sam's office, Sam noticed he had a couple of voice mails on his phone. He put his phone on speaker because he saw the name Jerry Dumas on the listing of missed calls.

"Listen to this, Joe," said Sam as he played back the message.

"Sam, this is Jerry Dumas, Procurement Manager, and it has been brought to my attention that you and many of your workers have been bothering my people in Supply about parts shortages." The message continued. "I would appreciate it if you would stay away from my people, as they are following my instructions. We have a business to run, and from where I sit—and from what I hear—you have enough to worry about."

"That's it Joe," said Sam. "I'm going to Paul Johnson right now!"

"No Sam, just maintain your cool until we meet with Connor this evening," said Joe.

"OK, but I'm at my wits' end with Paul and his cronies!" said Sam in an angry voice.

"I know," said Joe, "But let's honor Connor's third requirement—'Do exactly what I tell you to do, when I tell you to do it.' Okay, Sam?"

"OK, Joe, OK," said Sam.

"We'll be meeting with Connor in a few hours, and we can explain the urgency of our situation," said Joe. "I'm pretty certain Connor will have good advice for us." Joe added, "I'm going to go give my guys a well deserved pat on the back, and I'll be back in a few hours to go to Jonah's."

Joe arrived back at his office and called his black belts in for a chat.

"Guys, I want to tell you how proud I am of your efforts and the initiatives you took on your own. You made a huge impact on the production floor, and I can tell you from Sam that he appreciates what you've done." Joe continued, "Sam and I are going to meet with Connor tonight to discuss the parts-shortage problem. So Stan, since that's your project, if you're interested in joining us, you're welcome to come. I'm sure Sam and Connor won't mind at all," Joe added.

"I'd love to go, boss, where are you meeting?" asked Stan.

"At a little bar named Jonah's on Central Street around 6:00 PM," said Joe.

"Count me in boss, I'll be there," said Stan.

Joe was getting ready to leave to pick up Sam when his phone rang—it was Sam. "Joe, we have temporarily solved the baffle-shortage problem," said Sam.

"How did you do that?" asked Joe.

"I'll explain it when you get here, and you'll love it."

Joe was really anxious to hear just how the baffle-shortage problem had been temporarily fixed, and he hurried over to Sam's office.

"OK Sam, let's hear it," said Joe. "How did you solve the parts problem?"

"Well actually I didn't do anything. It was this amazing bunch of people and their self-initiated suggestion program that came up with this temporary fix," said Sam. "Do you remember that Stan had been working on a way to get Engineering Change Notices to the floor sooner so that we didn't build the tanks wrong, only to have to rebuild them?" asked Sam.

"Yes I do . . . Why?" asked Joe.

"Well, we have about eight tanks that fell into this category, and guess what they have on them that we can use in our tanks?" said Sam.

"Of course—the baffles," replied Joe.

One of the joining operators mentioned that to Stan, and he took care of the rest," said Sam. "He developed a method to remove the baffles that we need on the lines, and he has already gotten Engineering approval to use them," said Sam. "This guy is a fireball, and if I were you I'd get him a performance bonus through HR," Sam suggested. "He's certainly earned it in my book."

"I will definitely do that Sam. Thanks for the suggestion," said Joe.

"Now we'd better get going, or we'll be late for our meeting with Connor."

When they arrived at Jonah's, Sam spoke to Connor. 'Hi, sorry we're running a little late, but we had some things to take care of to keep our production lines running," said Sam.

"Let me guess, you ran out of some standard part that you use on your tanks," said Connor.

"Gosh, Connor, how do you know so much about my operation when you've only been there once?" asked Sam.

"Look, after all of these years consulting, you learn to not only look at the current problems, you also look for potential future problems," said Connor. "When I was at your plant, I asked questions about your supply system, and I was told you use a traditional MIN/MAX replenishment model," Connor explained. "One thing I know about these type systems for supplying parts is that there will be parts stock-outs," said Connor. "You also told me that what's his name, the purchasing manager, was being measured on the basis of how much money he could save, and the more he saved, the bigger his bonus was. So when you combine both of those factors, it's a recipe for disaster for parts availability," said Connor.

Joe asked, "So how do we fix it?" Just then Stan Wilson came in and walked over to their table.

"Oh, by the way, Connor, this is Stan Wilson, one of our Lean Six Sigma black belts," said Joe. "Stan has the project of fixing the parts supply process, so I hope you don't mind him being here."

"Not at all, nice to meet you Stan," said Connor as they shook hands.

"OK, so let me explain your parts distribution system to you," said Connor. "And remember, we must solve this problem or you're going to fail," he added. "You recall on the IO Map, parts availability was one of the Critical Success Factors toward achieving our goal of on-time delivery. The current supply system in use at Barton is the traditional minimum/maximum used at many military and commercial installations," continued Connor. "The rules associated with these systems are very simple," and Connor wrote them on the flip chart.

Rule 1: Determine the minimum and maximum stock levels for each part.

Rule 2: Don't exceed the maximum stock level for each part.

Rule 3: Don't reorder until you reach or go below the minimum stock level for each part.

"The driving force behind these MIN/MAX rules is deeply imbedded in the cost- world belief that in order to save money, I must reduce how much money I spend on parts. To do this, I must never buy more than the max and never order until I reach the min," explained Connor. "It's the age-old conflict of saving money versus making money."

Connor continued, "The theory for the MIN/MAX concept is that parts are stored at the lowest possible level of the supply chain. Parts are used until the minimum quantity is exceeded, and then an order is placed to replenish. Let me draw you what it looks like, so you can follow me better," said Connor.

"The parts order goes up the chain from the bin they're kept in to the production supply room to the central warehouse where it's ordered," he said.

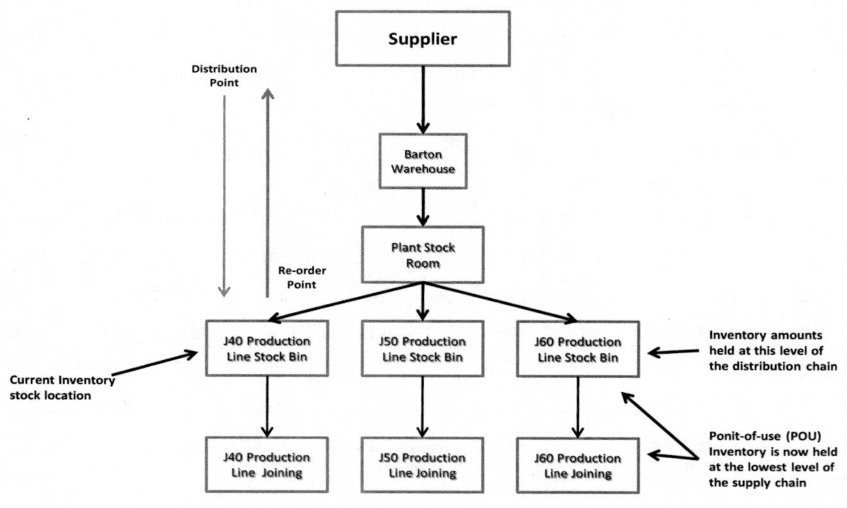

"This is a visual flow of what I just described, and as you can see, the distribution of parts is from the top down, and the reorder is from the bottom up," said Connor. "The parts come in to Barton's warehouse from the suppliers, and from there they are distributed to your plant stock room. The parts are then distributed to the appropriate line-stock bins until they are needed in the joining operation," Connor continued. "Probably once a week the bins are checked to determine the inventory level in each of the bin boxes. If the bins are at or below the minimum defined level, then an order is placed for that part number. Get the picture so far, guys?" asked Connor.

"I absolutely do," said Joe, "It's just like all of the other TOC tools, common sense."

"I agree," said Sam.

"Since orders are coming from multiple bin locations, there is probably a consolidation process that takes place before parts are reordered, so that a volume discount can be obtained," said Connor.

"Once this consolidation process is completed, then the orders are placed for the required parts." Connor went on. "Now, even though this type of system 'appears' to control the supply needs of your plant, in reality there are negative effects that we see and feel with the MIN/MAX system.

"The first problem," said Connor, "is that you are constantly in a reactive, rather than a proactive mode because this system is almost guaranteed to have frequent 'stock-out' conditions, which you are seeing in your production area," explained Connor.

"Why do the stock-outs occur?" asked Sam.

"Good question Sam." Connor replied. "Stock-outs occur when the lead time to replenish the parts exceeds the minimum stock that's in the bin," he explained. "And because of variation in demand, stock-outs can occur in shorter or longer times than the MIN/MAX model might suggest. The problem is that when you do have a stock-out, your production stops. And I learned from talking to your Leads and operators, it happens frequently."

Connor continued, "I would assume that because your purchasing manager is rewarded for keeping inventory low, he has set reorder minimums at a very low level without considering the parts lead time. Does what I'm saying make sense to you Sam?"

"Oh yes, it makes perfect sense to me, but how do we fix it?" asked Sam.

"OK, so what do we do to fix this system?" responded Connor

"The TOC distribution and replenishment model states that most of the inventory should be held at the highest level in the distribution chain (that's the warehouse) and not at the lowest level (the bins)," Connor explained. "You still hold some inventory at the point of use, but the majority should be held at Barton's warehouse," said Connor.

"There's more to this replenishment model, but these are the basic principles," said Connor. "The bottom line is this—instead of using some minimum quantity to trigger the reorder of parts, the reorder process should be triggered by daily usage and the time required for the vendor to replenish the parts. That is, simply replace what you've used on a very frequent basis rather than waiting for some minimum quantity," said Connor. "Now when you use this frequent order system, there will always be enough parts on hand to produce tanks, and no stock-outs will occur!

"Connor, I can actually picture this working so well for us and to think we will have not stock-outs by simply increasing the replenishment frequency is just mind boggling to me," said Sam.

And as an added bonus," Connor said, "the average overall inventory will be significantly lower. This is the case because under the MIN/MAX system, the maximum quantity is automatically ordered, while with the system of frequent orders based on usage, the amount of inventory required drops significantly and no stock-outs occur," concluded Connor. "So now you guys can go meet with your purchasing manager and explain all of this to him."

"Let me do a process check Connor," said Joe. "We change the reorder location and the frequency of reorders and voilà, no more stockouts and much less inventory . . . do I have that right?"

"Yes, that's exactly right Joe," said Connor. "I know it seems too simply to believe, but it's really that simple."

"One more thing, guys, added Connor, "our next project will be to implement a Drum-Buffer-Rope (DBR) scheduling system, and as you'll see, if we have parts shortages, DBR will never work," said Connor. "I have to go out of town for a few days, and I won't be available until I get back," he said. "When I come back, we'll get together and discuss DBR. So until then, fix the parts supply problem. And now gentlemen, I need you to leave so I can pack for my trip."

"Where are you going Connor?" asked Joe.

"I'm going south, and that's all you need to know," said Connor.

As Sam and Joe walked to their cars, they chatted about how best to approach Jerry Dumas and whether it might be better to have both Jerry and Paul in the same room together. Sam believed that they should meet with Jerry first and then if necessary, meet with Paul. Joe didn't agree. He felt that both should be together when they presented the proposal so that both Paul and Jerry would be "enlightened" together. So they decided that rather than rushing into a meeting, they should meet tomorrow morning and formulate their strategy.

"You know, Joe," said Sam. "You haven't been here very long, but you've made such an impact already."

"I think you mean Connor has made an impact Sam," replied Joe.

"No Joe, you're the driving force here, not Connor," said Sam. "Connor has just shown us new tools and techniques based upon TOC, but it was you who convinced me about the power of managing the constraints." Sam continued, "Don't get me wrong, we wouldn't have moved as far and as quickly as we have without Connor, but without you coming to Barton, I would be out looking for a new job."

"Thanks, Sam, your words mean a lot to me. I'll see you in your office at 6:00 AM sharp Sam?" asked Joe.

"Yep, see you then," replied Sam.

As usual, Joe and Sam arrived well before their scheduled time of 6:00 AM, anxious to see how things were going on the production lines. "Good morning Sam," said Joe. "Morning Joe, let's go take a look," replied Sam.

"Holy shit!" exclaimed Sam, "Look Joe, the queue in front of joining on the J40 is down to two!"

"Let's go look at the delivery status," said Joe.

What they found amazed both of them. On their three major lines (J40, J50 and J60) the number of late orders had dropped to zero in a little under two weeks!

"Hi Sam and Joe," said a familiar voice.

"Hi Bradley, what a great job you guys are doing!" Sam said.

"We have a big problem, Sam," said Bradley. "We've used up all but two of the recycled baffles, and once they're gone, we'll have to shut down our three major lines," said Bradley.

"We think we have a solution to the part's shortage problems we've been having, but it won't happen overnight," said Joe.

"When is the next shipment of baffles due in?" asked Sam.

"I can't seem to get an answer from the supply folks," said Bradley.

"We'll follow up this morning and let you know what we find," said Sam.

"Let's go plan our meeting with Procurement, Sam," said Joe.

Sam and Joe spent the next hour contemplating and planning this important meeting and finally decided to only meet with the Procurement Manager, Jerry Dumas. Their strategy was to first demonstrate how well the processes were running and then get into a discussion about the parts supply system. If they didn't get anywhere with Jerry, then they would set up a meeting with Paul. They both knew that overcoming resistance to change would be their most difficult barrier, but they were ready for the challenge. They remembered Connor's words about how DBR would not work until the parts problem was fixed.

Sam was checking his emails before they went to see Jerry. "Joe," he said, "I've got an email from Connor and you're copied on it."

"What's it say Sam?" asked Joe.

"Weather is beautiful, and the golf is fantastic!" said Sam.

"I wonder where he is," said Joe.

Sam continued reading the email. "I have another tool that I want you to play with to remove waste and variation from your processes," said Connor's email. "The name of this tool is the Interference Diagram (ID)." Connor's email explained how to set up and use the ID, and he had even included an example of one he had used in the past.

"What a powerful looking tool," said Sam.

"We'll talk about the ID when we get back from our meeting with Jerry. Let's go," said Joe. And off they went to see Jerry.

"No, Jerry's not here today," said his administrative assistant. "He and Paul had to go to Corporate for a meeting on inventory reduction, and he won't be back until Monday," she said.

"Great! Just great!" said Sam, obviously frustrated.

"OK," said Joe. "Could you put us on his calendar for first thing Monday morning please? Come on Sam, let's go look into this Interference Diagram."

"What are we going to do, Joe?" asked Sam.

"I don't know, but we'll figure something out," replied Joe.

So Sam and Joe walked back to Sam's office to check out the new tool from Connor.

Chapter 8
The Interference Diagram

Sam downloaded the Interference Diagram and the development instructions that Connor had sent him, and he printed a copy to review with Joe. "OK, Joe, let's see what we've got here," said Sam. The ID Connor had sent was from a company that, like Barton, was trying to increase their production output, so it was definitely relevant. The instructions were surprisingly simple, as described by Connor.

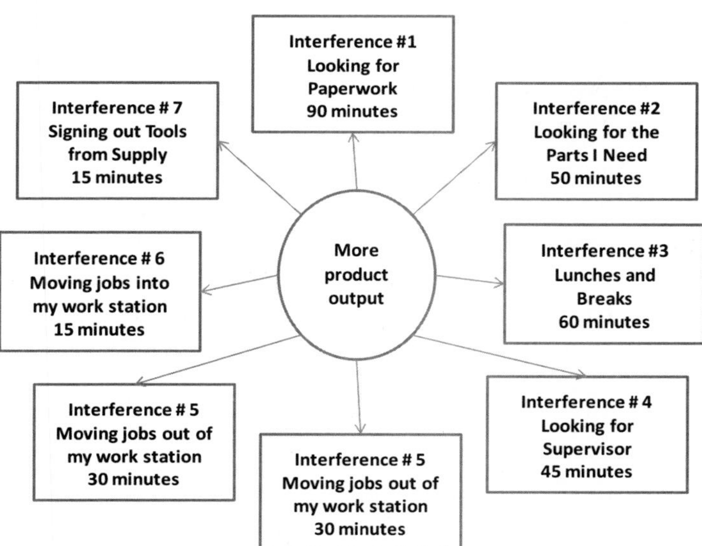

Connor had written, "The Interference Diagram (ID) is a thinking tool that offers the ability to define those 'interferences,' or obstacles, that block or hinder your ability to achieve a specific goal or outcome." He continued, "The ID tool is used to verbally and visually surface these interferences.

"The concept and structure of an Interference Diagram is simple," Connor wrote. "The figure I have attached to this email displays the structure of the ID. First, in the center of a white board or flip chart, write down what you want more of or what your goal is. Next, think to yourself, 'What stops me from getting more of what I want?' The answer to this question becomes the interferences that you write on the diagram in the small boxes surrounding the goal."

"The ID sounds simple enough to create, don't you think Sam?" said Joe. "It really does Joe, I can't wait to get started with it," Sam replied. "There's more Sam, let's not get impatient," said Joe.

Connor went on, "Ask the same question again, and write down your next response. Continue to list your interferences until you are satisfied that your list is fairly complete, or at least sufficient to move on. Guys," he explained, "this works best if you keep your interference statements short and sweet and be sure to let your subject matter experts (SMEs), the people building the tanks, populate the interferences, and ask them to estimate the average time per day or week that they spend on each interference and keep the time values consistent, such as minutes per day or week," explained Connor.

"Once you've gotten all of the interferences and time estimates, create a Pareto chart which I always prefer, or a pie chart to make it clear to everyone the priority order for interferences," said Connor. "If you haven't met with Purchasing yet, you might want to show them the completed ID, and I feel certain that parts availability will be sitting at the top of the list or close to it," said Connor. "The ID and the Pareto chart could very well help you sell the TOC replenishment system to them."

"You know Joe, one of the things I really like about Connor is that he always seems to have solutions for seemingly impossible problems," said Sam. "I agree Sam," said Joe.

In conclusion," wrote Connor, "the Interference Diagram is a great tool to find and exploit the hidden capacity of a constraint operation. In this example it's a tool that helped a company analyze how they could get more from the constraint by verbalizing and visualizing those things that the constraint could or should stop doing in order to free up more time to do more of want they wanted—get more output," he concluded. "Good luck, guys, and I'll see you in a few days."

"Sam, I think I'll get my guys over here to help with this and learn about this new tool," said Joe.

"Sounds good, Joe, and I'll round up everyone for a training session," replied Sam.

Joe's black belts all arrived, as did the production operators, leads and two supervisors. Once they were all seated in the break room, Sam started the session.

"As all of you know," said Sam, "we've made tremendous strides in a very short time, totally transforming our production process, and you're all to be congratulated on the fantastic work you've done so far. We've actually caught up on our late orders to our primary customers!" Spontaneous applause filled the room.

"But," Sam continued, "we have more work to do, and we need your help. We're going to show you a new tool that we think will take us to the next level. This tool is called an Interference Diagram (ID)."

For the next twenty minutes Sam explained how to construct an ID, and then he asked for volunteers to help construct one. At least twenty hands went up, demonstrating the air of confidence and spirit of cooperation that now permeated Sam's production area. "Wow," said Sam. "We need to keep this team to no more than six to eight people, so I'd like you, as a group, to select your representatives." Within ten minutes the selections had been made and Sam adjourned the meeting. Sam then led this new team to his conference room to get started.

"The first thing we need to do is agree on what we want more of," said Sam.

"Isn't it obvious what we want more of?" said one of the team members.

"We want more throughput," said the operator.

"I think we want better on-time delivery," said another member.

"Without more throughput, we'll never get better on-time delivery," replied the first member.

"He's right," thought Sam, "In order to get better on-time delivery, we have to have more throughput." Everyone agreed that more throughput should be in the ID's center circle.

Then Stan spoke up, "With all due respect, I think you and Joe have other things to do, and I think we can take it from here."

And with that, Joe and Sam retired to Sam's office to discuss their strategy for next Monday's meeting. They could see the team heading to the shop floor, collecting opinions from the other operators. They both liked the idea of involving everyone with the construction of the ID.

Several hours later, Stan asked Joe and Sam to join the team in the conference room to see what they had done with their Interference Diagram. Hanging on the wall before Joe and Sam was a complete listing of the major reasons why throughput was too low on the J40 tank. One-by-one, the assembled team, led by Stan, explained what was preventing them from achieving more throughput on the J40 tank.

Stan explained, "Of course, these are the interferences that are impacting the J40 constraint, but the team all agrees that these are the major interferences for all tank types." Stan continued, "We have already addressed a couple of these, like relieving the constraint through breaks and lunches and filling out paper work. The nonconstraint operators are doing both of these now, so we've already saved about 120 minutes per day.

Stan continued, "One thing the team wanted me to mention was that these are very conservative estimates, and that on any given day, some of these interferences could be much longer than we have listed. Also, these times are based upon a two-shift operation, since third shift is not fully manned."

J40 INTERFERENCE DIAGRAM

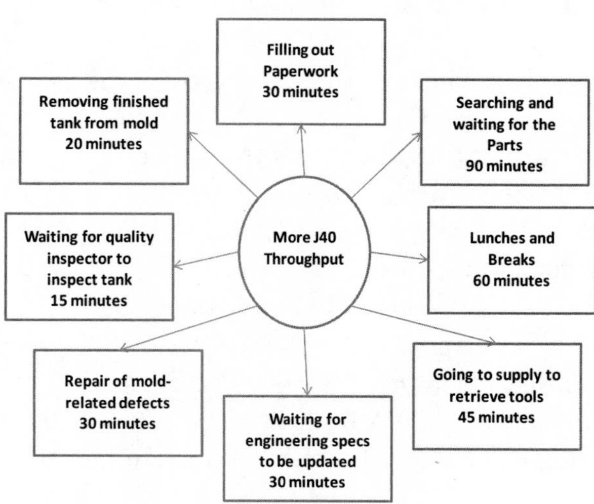

Stan said that the team also used the data to create a Pareto chart to demonstrate the priority order of how these interferences should be attacked.

The team calculated that there were 960 minutes of available time for two shifts (eight hours per shift times two shifts times sixty minutes per hour equals 960 minutes). Conservatively, one third of their time (320 minutes out of 960 minutes) was wasted due to the interferences they identified. From the Pareto chart it was clear that the top two interferences were related to supply. Waiting for parts and waiting for tools accounted for about 135 minutes of lost time per day on average, which comes to about 14 percent of the total lost time.

The team also said that they had ideas on how to reduce the other wasted time, and that they would put a plan together and present it to Sam and Joe. Nothing these days seemed to amaze Sam and Joe anymore after what had already happened, but the smiles on their faces were quite noticeable.

This team and all of the other operators had really taken ownership of the on-time delivery problem, and the improvements to throughput were obvious. In fact, the queue in front of the joining operation now stood at one tank, which meant that it was time to restart the front end of the operation and begin producing tank tops and bottoms.

When Sam mentioned this to the team, Stan replied, "We've already started prepping the molds. And by the way, in the last three days we have managed to repair the surface of both molds so that we can reduce the number of mold-related defects." Sam and Joe realized that they had a responsibility to take care of those interferences that the team couldn't impact, like waiting for parts and tools from supply.

With the data the team had developed, Sam and Joe now had the "back-pocket" information needed to meet with Jerry Dumas on Monday to discuss Barton's parts-replenishment problem.

"Sam, how do you think we should approach Jerry on this parts issue," said Joe.

"I think we should show him the data we have and dump it on his lap," replied Sam. "I'm just sick and tired of the games that are being played at Production's expense and I want it to hit him right between the eyes." Sam was showing his obvious frustration. "What do you think Joe?" asked Sam.

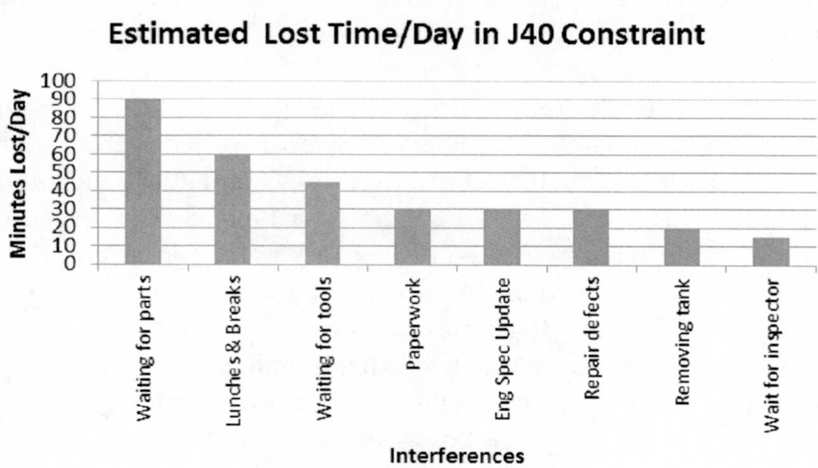

"Sam, if there was one thing we should have learned from The Goal, it's how Jonah operated." Joe said. "What I mean by that is, Jonah never gave anyone the answer to a problem, he just asked the right questions so that the only logical conclusion was what he was thinking. I think we need to think through our approach and act more like Jonah," said Joe. "We have until Monday morning to come up with that approach, so let's give it some thought and then get back together. I'll call you later and we can compare notes."

Joe thought about the meeting he and Sam would have with Jerry and how Jonah might have handled it. He knew there would be a conflict between Jerry's desire to minimize inventory and his need to have all parts needed to keep the lines running.

"I wonder what Connor would tell me to do?" Joe thought. "What the hell, why speculate, I'm going to call him. This is just too important a meeting to make a mistake," and he dialed Connor's cell number.

"Hello?" said a voice on the other end of the phone. "Connor, this is Joe and I know you told me not to call you, but I have an important question to ask you," said Joe.

"OK Joe, but make it quick, I've got a five footer to save par, and dinner is on the line," said Connor.

"Is there a TOC tool that can be used to solve an apparent conflict in thinking?" asked Joe.

"Yes, Joe, there's something called a Conflict Resolution Diagram (CRD), also known as an Evaporating Cloud (EC), but I don't have time to explain it to you right now," replied Connor. "Get on a search engine, Joe, and you'll find lots of references to it," said Connor. "I have to go Joe, it's my turn to putt. Let me know how it goes."

And so off Joe went to his computer and found and read numerous references on the internet to the CRD. He discovered that the CRD was a necessity-based logic structure that is used to resolve issues without compromising the objective—that is, it facilitates win-win scenarios rather than win-lose. The bottom line intent with a CRD is to expose hidden the assumptions of an argument to generate breakthrough ideas.

Joe thought, "This is exactly the tool we need to hopefully convince Jerry that he is blocking our throughput and on-time delivery." Joe decided that he needed to sketch out a CRD for the parts-shortage issue and then bounce it off of Sam. Joe started by articulating the common objective that both he and Jerry shared. Joe thought, "We both want parts to be available to be able to produce tanks," so he filled in the objective box A. Next Joe filled in the requirements boxes B and C. He continued his thought process. "From my perspective, in order for Barton to have parts available to produce tanks, we must have a strong parts-replenishment model. From Jerry's perspective," thought Joe, "in order to have parts available to produce tanks, we must work within the current parts system." Joe then thought about the prerequisite boxes D and E, and from his perspective he filled in box D with—"In order to have a strong parts replenishment model, we must have parts policies and procedures changed." For box E, Joe wrote—"In order to work within the current parts system, we must have the parts policies and procedures stay the same."

"That's the conflict," thought Joe. "I want the policies and procedures changed (D) and Jerry wants the policies and procedures to remain the same (E). OK, it's a good start," thought Joe. "What do I do now? Ah, yes, I need to state the assumptions behind D and E—the "because" statements."

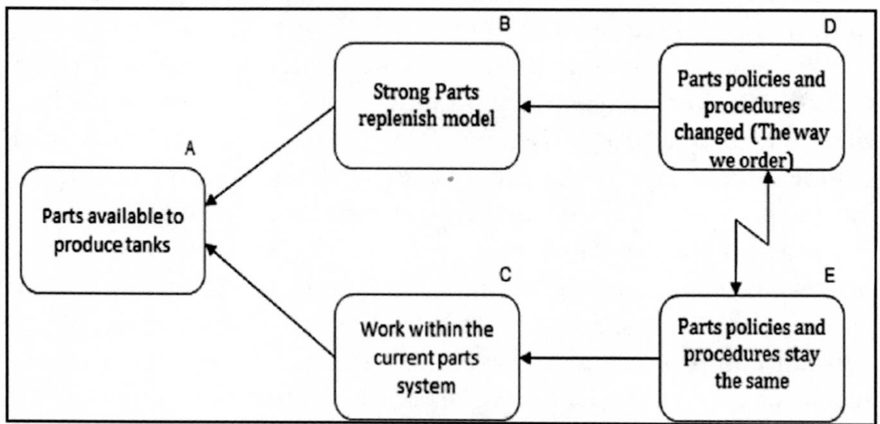

Joe made a list of assumptions for B-D as follows:

B --> D

1. Current system creates parts shortages.
2. Current system does not meet the need.
3. There is a gap between need and have.
4. The system is expensive. High expenses, high inventory
5. System is based on MIN/MAX and not actual consumption.
6. Policies and procedures are outdated.

These assumptions represented the causal connections, or "because" statements of the relationship between box B and box D of the CRD. Joe thought, "In order to have a strong parts-replenishment model, I must have parts policies and procedures changed because the current system creates parts shortages." One by one, Joe tested the assumptions to make sure they fit, and he concluded that they did. Next Joe made a list of because statements for the other side of the conflict as follows:

C --> E

1. Current system minimizes the inventory in the system, which costs Barton less.
2. Current system maximizes the on-hand cash for Barton
3. Current system maximizes Jerry's bonus

Joe thought, "Assumption number three seems a bit controversial, but it is a real fact," so he left it in the list. Joe was happy with his lists of because statements, so he moved on to the next step in the process, finding an injection that would invalidate the key assumptions. Joe thought for a moment and concluded, "If Jerry's objective is to minimize the inventory in the system and maximize the on-hand cash, then we need to convince him that the TOC replenishment model actually reduces the overall inventory in the system. And since Jerry's bonus is based upon having less inventory in the system, his bonus could actually be larger than it currently is."

"That's it!" exclaimed Joe. "Convince Jerry how the new system would result in a larger bonus for him! I've got to go see Sam right now," said Joe, and off he went to show Sam what he had come up with.

"Hi, Sam, have you got a few minutes?" asked Joe.

"I sure do, Joe, what's up?" replied Sam.

"I think I have a way of convincing Jerry that he needs to change his parts- replenishment system," said Joe.

"Great!" said Sam, "Let's hear it."

Joe showed Sam his Conflict Resolution Diagram and explained how it was supposed to work. Joe went through the assumptions for each part and then explained the injection, or breakthrough solution, he thought they should use.

"This is great, Joe, where did you learn about CRDs?" asked Sam.

"From Connor . . . well, not exactly from him, but he told me to look it up on the internet," said Joe.

"You spoke to Connor? I thought he was down south playing golf." said Sam.

"He is, but I decided to call him anyway," replied Joe. "He wasn't very happy about it, but our backs were against the wall here, and we needed a way to break this conflict . . . I sure hope he made that putt," muttered Joe.

"What putt?" asked Sam.

"Never mind, I'll tell you about that later," said Joe.

Then the two of them reviewed the CRD and especially the assumptions impacting Jerry.

C --> E

1. Current system minimizes the inventory in the system, which costs Barton less.

2. Current system maximizes the on-hand cash for Barton

3. Current system maximizes Jerry's bonus

"What do you think, Sam?" asked Joe.

"I think this will work, but I want to make one recommendation, if you don't mind," said Sam. "I'm thinking assumption number three, the one about maximizing his bonus, should come off of the list," said Sam.

"Why, Sam, why do you think that?" asked Joe.

"I'm thinking that we want him to figure that out by himself," said Sam. "If he looks at assumptions one and two, shouldn't his own personal conclusion be that his bonus will be bigger?" explained Sam. "And if he realizes that, he just might own this new TOC replenishment system and drive it forward at a faster rate than we could ever do," said Sam. "Let's face it Joe, he is motivated by his bonus, but he doesn't need to know that we know that."

"Sam, you're absolutely right! I am so glad I bounced this off of you today," said Joe.

Sam and Joe spent the rest of the afternoon planning their meeting with Purchasing and how they were going to present their proposal. First, they would define the current state by showing a run chart of weekly on-time delivery. Jerry would see immediately that the most recent data point was over 90 percent compared to their historical 68 percent average. Next they would go through their basic TOC presentation including Throughput Accounting so that Jerry could make the connection between improved throughput and on-time delivery. They would then review their Intermediate Objectives Map with him to show him the relevance of why we need to improve the part's availability. Finally, they would show him the Interference Diagram and Pareto chart so that he could see first-hand how not having parts available when needed would hurt throughput. This would set the stage for a discussion on the TOC parts-replenishment model. They expected pushback from Jerry, so they would be prepared with the Conflict Resolution Diagram when that happened.

"I think we're ready Joe. It looks really good to me," said Sam.

"I think so too," said Joe. "See you bright and early Monday morning, Sam."

"What are you doing this weekend, Joe?"

"My wife Jennifer is coming in this weekend to look for a house," replied Joe.

"If you want to have the wives meet this weekend, give me a call," offered Sam.

"Will do, Sam and thanks for the offer."

Chapter 9
The Meeting with Jerry

Monday morning was full of anticipation for Joe and Sam. It was finally time for their long-awaited meeting with Purchasing to discuss the parts supply issue, the number one interference to throughput and on-time delivery.

"Morning Sam," said Joe.

"Morning Joe. Are we ready?" asked Sam.

"Sam I don't think I've ever been more ready and better prepared for a meeting than this one," replied Joe.

"I agree," said Sam.

"How do things look this morning, Sam?" asked Joe.

"I'm a little worried about the efficiency report that comes out every Monday," said Sam in a worried voice. "I know it's going to show a distinct drop in efficiencies, and I'm sure Paul will be all over me when it does—not to mention his corporate counterparts."

"Sam, your on-time delivery is approaching 100%!" exclaimed Joe. "Surely that will mean more than a drop in efficiencies."

"You don't know how Paul works—he's a back-stabber," said Sam. "Any chance he gets to make me look bad, he's going to jump on it."

It was finally time to go meet Jerry and, as expected, Joe and Sam were early getting to his office. Sam knocked on Jerry's door and then opened it. Jerry was sitting at his desk with a smug look on his face, and beside him was a very petite, fortyish, stunning woman of Asian descent.

"Good morning, Jerry," said Sam.

"Good morning Sam and Joe," replied Jerry. "Gentlemen I want you to meet Becky Chen," said Jerry. "Ms. Chen is from Corporate Purchasing and she is here to help us reduce our inventories."

Both Sam and Joe shook her hand and told her they we pleased to meet her and looked forward to working with her. She thanked them and smiled.

"Shall we get started Jerry?" asked Sam.

Ms. Chen took control of the meeting and explained her mission of reducing on-hand inventory by at least 20 percent.

"Ms. Chen, do you have a plan to do that?" asked Sam.

"Please call me Becky," she said, "and no, I want to work with you to develop one, so I'm open to all ideas," replied Becky.

Joe said, "Becky, we think we have an idea that will not only significantly reduce inventory, but it will guarantee that we never have a parts shortage problem."

"Really?" replied Becky. "I will be very anxious to hear about that."

Sarcastically, Jerry said, "Me too," and then he laughed out loud.

"Something funny?" asked Sam.

Joe grabbed Sam's arm and squeezed indicating that he needed to maintain his cool.

"You are, Sam," said Jerry. "I mean you're months behind in deliveries, and here you are trying to convince us that you have a plan to save the world. Sam, get real, do you really think you can significantly lower inventories and increase on-time deliveries?" asked Jerry sarcastically.

"I know we can with yours and Becky's help," said Sam in a firm voice.

"We do have a plan to show you, but might I recommend we move to the conference room so we can make this a working session?" asked Joe.

"I think that's a wonderful idea," said Becky as she rose and started walking toward the door.

Joe thought, "My gosh is this woman petite and so very pretty."

The four of them moved to the conference room, where Joe had anticipated the meeting would go and had their easel and flip chart in place.

Sam started, "Becky and Jerry, in order for us to present our plan, we need to give you some background on where we were before the last several weeks. Is that OK with you two?" asked Sam.

"We know where you've been," said Jerry in his typical sarcastic tone. "Let's just hear your supposed proposal," he added.

"Jerry, I disagree," said Becky. "I think we need to take the time to listen to what Sam and Joe have to say, especially if they think it's important." Go on Sam," said Becky.

Joe thought, "Finally we have a voice of reason in our midst."

Sam continued by showing an on-time-delivery run chart that was hovering around 65 percent, ranging from a low of 51 percent to a high of 72 percent. "Not a pretty picture is it Becky?" asked Sam.

"No Sam, it looks pretty bad," said Becky. "Why is it so low?" she asked in a soft, questioning voice.

"We'll get to that," said Sam.

"It's because you can't seem to keep your people working Sam, tell us the truth," said Jerry.

Becky gave Jerry a look that said, "Will you be quiet and listen!"

Sam continued, "Joe here, joined Barton recently, and I have to tell you that in a very short amount of time he has changed my whole approach on how to run a manufacturing organization."

"In what way?" asked Becky.

"He has taught me all of the things I have been doing wrong for so many years Becky," said Sam. "And the funny part is—everything he's taught me is just so commonsensical! With your permission, Becky, I'd like Joe to explain it the same way he did for me," said Sam.

"Come on guys, can we just quit wasting our time and give us your proposal?" Jerry remarked.

"Jerry!" said Becky, obviously getting frustrated by Jerry's constant interruptions and sarcastic tone. "You need to shut up and listen for a change," she told him.

"Maybe this will help," said Sam as he put up a new run chart showing the huge jump in on-time delivery to nearly one hundred percent.

"That can't be real, Becky," said Jerry, "They've obviously fudged the numbers!"

"For the last time, Jerry, be quiet and listen to what these guys have to say, or I swear I'll stick a sock in your mouth," said Becky.

Sam and Joe both covered their mouths to hide their smiles. Sam thought, "It's about time someone put Jerry in his place! For such a petite and delicate looking woman, Becky is fearless and certainly isn't afraid to tell anyone what's on her mind."

"Go on," said Becky. "This is an amazing turn of events and I'm very interested in hearing how you have achieved these results, especially in such a short period of time."

"Joe, could you walk Becky and Jerry through your presentation please?" said Sam.

"My pleasure," said Joe. And with that, Joe presented his piping system and four-step process example. Joe asked the same questions he asked Sam, and it was clear that Becky grasped the concepts very quickly.

"Where did you learn this?" asked Becky.

"In this book," said Joe as he handed both Becky and Jerry their own personal copies of The Goal. "I really encourage both of you to read this book because it's a game changer," said Joe.

"I have lots of time in my hotel room, so tonight I will definitely get started on it," said Becky, "And Jerry, I suggest you read it too. I hope there's a section on meeting etiquette," she said sarcastically to him.

Joe then discussed the basics of Throughput Accounting and, once again, Becky understood everything completely.

"My guess is that TA isn't supposed to replace our standard cost-accounting reporting to the government, but rather it helps you make daily decisions. Am I right?" asked Becky.

Joe and Sam realized that Becky was not just another pretty face, but rather a thinker, and Lord knew we needed more thinkers—and listeners.

"Go on Joe, this is all so new and interesting for me," said Becky. "In fact, when he returns from his European trip, I plan to speak directly with Gregory Daniels III about what's happening here," Becky continued.

"Sorry, Becky," said Joe, "I'm new with the company, who is Gregory Daniels?" "Mr. Daniels is our CEO and President of Barton Enterprises," said Becky. "He is a very progressive thinker, and I'm certain he will be interested in what I have to tell him about the progress you guys have made," said Becky.

Jerry's facial expression changed radically when he heard this, and his level of receptivity immediately spun up. "Let's hear more," said Jerry, and all three heads turned in surprise. "If Mr. Daniels will find this interesting, I'd better pay attention," said Jerry. Everyone laughed as Joe continued.

Joe explained how Sam had rallied his production people to the point that they were in complete control of their own destiny. He explained all of the changes that had taken place on the shop floor that had accounted for the dramatic and immediate improvement in on-time delivery. Joe then presented the Intermediate Objectives Map to Becky and Jerry, and Becky was the first to comment. "Joe, this looks like a great strategic tool. Where on earth did you learn this?"

Laughingly Joe said, "In a bar."

"In a bar?" asked Becky, "What kind of a bar is it?"

"It's the most unique bar in the world—a place where senior executives meet on a regular basis to discuss ideas," said Joe. "If you have time this week, Sam and I can take you there."

"I wouldn't miss it for the world," said Becky.

"How about tonight?" asked Joe.

"You're on," said Sam.

Joe then presented the Interference Diagram, and both Becky and Jerry were really interested.

"This is another amazing tool," said Becky. "On one document, everything that gets in the way, the barriers to what you are trying to accomplish are visually displayed," said Becky. "I have never seen anything like this in my life—another product of 'The Bar'?" questioned Becky.

"Yes," said Joe.

"Connor taught us how to use this tool," said Sam.

"And exactly who is this Connor?" asked Becky.

"Oh, sorry, Becky, Connor owns the bar," replied Sam.

"How in the world would a bar owner know about things of this nature?" asked Becky.

"We'll let Connor explain that to you Becky," said Joe. Continuing, Joe said, "We have been using this ID to remove the apparent barriers so that we could reduce time lost in the constraint."

"Jerry," said Becky, "I see that parts availability is listed here, and I remember seeing it on the IO Map as well," said Becky. "Just how big of a problem is parts availability?"

With that question Joe flashed the Pareto chart on the screen, and it was met with an immediate gasp by both Becky and Jerry.

"Here I am with the mission of reducing parts inventory, and now I see that we have parts shortages that account for the largest percentage of time lost," said Becky.

"Wait Becky, Sam and I think we have a way of achieving a significant reduction in total inventory dollars while virtually eliminating stock outages," said Joe.

"I've got to hear about this. Now you've really got my attention," said Becky.

"Mine too," said Jerry.

"Hmmm, maybe we won't even need the Conflict Resolution Diagram," thought Joe.

"OK, here's what we think will solve our problem of parts shortages and still meet your objective of reducing the overall inventory of parts," said Joe. Joe methodically walked them through the TOC Replenishment Model they had learned from Connor.

Both Becky and Jerry listened intently to what Joe presented until Becky asked another question. Becky had taken prolific notes during Joe's presentation and asked, "Can I get a copy of all of this material, Sam?"

"You most certainly can—hard copy or electronic?" asked Joe.

"Both, if you don't mind," said Becky.

"Me too," said Jerry.

"Not a problem," said Joe, "Just give me your email addresses, and I'll send them to both of you when I get back to my office."

"We have one more tool we'd like to show you Becky," said Sam.

"From the bar again?" Becky asked, smiling.

"Actually, this one came from a golf course, but Connor did teach us this one too," said Joe.

"A golf course?" asked Becky. "You guys are making me laugh."

"You were saying you had one more tool, Joe?" asked Becky.

"Yes, it's called a Conflict Resolution Diagram, and as the name implies, one of its uses is to resolve conflicts," said Joe.

"What's the conflict you're trying to resolve, Joe?" asked Becky.

"The conflict between staying with the current parts-ordering system versus moving to our proposed system," said Joe.

"Joe and Sam, I really don't see this as a conflict. Why do you think it is?" asked Becky.

"Because with every dramatic change, there are opposite forces pushing against each other," said Joe. "On the one hand you have people who want to preserve their current comfort zone, while on the other, you have people wanting to create a new way. It's a natural human reaction to change, Becky," explained Joe.

"Jerry, do you see any reason at all why we couldn't implement this new system right away?" asked Becky.

"No, and one thing you probably didn't know or take into consideration is that my bonus is based on how much money is tied up in inventory," said Jerry.

"Gosh, if we had known that, we would have started with it," said Sam as he turned and winked at Joe.

"So when can you guys meet with Jerry and me to develop the details of this new system?" asked Becky.

"Whenever you want to, Becky," said Sam.

"How about one o'clock?" said Becky. "And Sam, do you have time to show me where all of this magic has taken place?" she added.

"I most certainly do," said Sam.

The meeting broke up with Sam and Joe feeling like proud new fathers of a new baby. Sam and Joe led the way with Becky and Jerry following them. Joe looked back over his shoulder, and it appeared as though Becky was actually scolding Jerry. At one point they had stopped and faced each other, and Becky had her index finger directly in Jerry's face and she was not looking happy. Jerry's head was dropping downward, almost in shame.

"Sam, I think we have a new friend and confidante," said Joe.

"I think you're right," said Sam.

Sam took Becky on a tour of the operations, stopping to explain changes they had made. They chatted with most of the operators along the way and finally came to the constraint. Becky introduced herself and gave the operator major kudos. The operator just looked at Becky and said, "All of this happened because Sam listened to what we had to say" He went on, "You wouldn't believe how much this place has changed in such a short amount of time—not just physically, but the morale is higher than it's ever been in the twenty years I've been here."

Just then Joe noticed that Stan was out on the floor flashing photos of the new process, and Joe motioned for him. "Becky, I want you to meet Stan Wilson, one of our Lean Six Sigma black belts," said Joe.

"Becky Chen, pleased to meet you," she said with a firm hand shake.

"Nice to meet you, too," said Stan.

"Stan, do you by any chance have photos of the process before we made all of our changes?" asked Joe.

"Sure boss, I always take before and after photos," said Stan.

"Would you like to see them Becky?" asked Joe.

"Yes, I would so I can get a picture of the magnitude of the changes you guys have made," replied Becky. Stan scrolled through his before and after photos and even Joe was surprised at the change. "Stan, can you send me these photos?" asked Becky as she handed him her business card. "Sure thing," said Stan.

"So after you fix the parts replenishment system, what's next?" asked Becky.

"We're going to be implementing something called Drum Buffer Rope," said Joe, "a TOC-based pull system designed to improve the synchronization and flow of tanks into and out of our processes."

"How does that work?" asked Becky.

"I'll tell you what, Becky, let's wait until you meet Connor tonight, and we'll let him tell you about that," said Joe. "We're actually going to have a planning session at his bar tonight, Becky, and you and Jerry can hear it firsthand—you'll sort of be a part of its development," Joe added.

"I never thought I'd be so excited to go to a bar, but you guys have me on pins and needles," said Becky. "What time are we going, Joe?"

"What time would you like to go, Becky?" asked Joe.

"As early as possible."

"Excuse me, let me call Connor and see what time he can have us," said Joe. Joe called Connor and the two of them talked for about fifteen minutes. Joe told him about the meeting with Becky and Jerry and how excited Becky was to meet him. "Thanks Connor," said Joe and he hung up.

"Connor said he could meet with us around 2:00 p.m., since that's when his lunch crowd usually thins out," said Joe.

"Great," said Becky. "Is that OK with you, Jerry?" she asked.

"Damn it, I've got a conference call with Corporate at 2:00, so I won't be able to make it," said Jerry.

"We'll fill you in, Jerry, don't worry about it," said Becky.

Just then, Sam received a call from Paul Johnson.

"Sam," said Paul, "You've got a lot of explaining to do! Your efficiencies have dropped significantly in the last two weeks. The one thing you were doing right!" he added.

"I can explain, Paul," said Sam.

"Not to me," said Paul. "Cecil Graham, our Chairman of the Board, will be here the day after tomorrow. You can explain it to him."

"I thought he wasn't coming until next week, Paul, said Sam.

"Well he was until I called him and told him about your efficiencies!" said Paul as he hung up the phone.

"That snake in the grass!" said Sam.

"What's wrong Sam?" asked Joe. "You seem really upset about something."

"It's that damn Paul. He just threw me under the bus again," said Sam, obviously very upset.

"What do you mean, Sam? What did he do this time?" asked Joe.

"We all knew that what we were doing was going to negatively impact efficiencies and boy did it ever," said Sam.

"Yes, we all knew that was coming," said Joe. "So what did Paul say that has you so upset?"

"It's not so much what he said, it's what he did that pissed me off!" replied Sam emphatically.

"Which was . . . ?" asked Joe.

"Our efficiencies for the week dropped from where they were, which was around 82 percent, down to just above 60 percent," explained Sam. "So who do you think the first person he called was?"

"It should have been you, but based upon your reaction, it wasn't you, was it Sam?" said Joe.

"No!" replied Sam, "he called Cecil Graham, and who do you suppose is paying me a visit the day after tomorrow?" said Sam sarcastically.

"Mr. Graham is coming here this week?" asked Joe in an excited tone of voice.

"Yes, and why are you so happy, Joe?" asked Sam.

"Sam, listen to me, when he sees what's happened to your throughput and on-time delivery, my guess is he's going to be very happy," said Joe.

"Joe, you don't know Cecil Graham. He and Paul are like best friends, and who knows what else Paul told him," said Sam. "No Joe, he's coming to give me the axe, I'm sure of it."

Becky approached Sam and Joe. "Guys, I wasn't trying to listen in to your conversation, but I couldn't help but hear what you both said," she said. "Sam, I know Cecil Graham very well, and I agree with

Joe on this one," said Becky. "Cecil and I have been friends for a long time, and believe me, once he hears what's been going on here, well let's just say making money is more important to him than his close ties to Paul," said Becky.

"I'm very disappointed with Paul, considering he probably doesn't have a clue about what's happened to your on-time delivery." Becky continued, "Cecil Graham is the Chairman of the Board for Barton Enterprises, but he is also a principal with Barton's parent company, American Investors, Inc.," said Becky. American Investors is one of the richest private equity companies in the world, and they do know how to make money. My gut tells me that Cecil will take the time to listen to what you two have to say and keep it in the context of making money rather than whether or not a performance metric has risen or fallen," said Becky.

"I haven't known you very long Becky, but I do respect your opinion, and if you feel strongly about Mr. Graham like you say, then I'll calm down," said Sam.

"Thanks for your vote of confidence Sam, that means a lot to me," said Becky. "So what time are we going to meet Connor?" asked Becky.

"I told him we'd be there around 2:00 p.m.," said Joe.

"I need to meet with Jerry before I go, so let me run along and do that," said Becky. "I'm going to go back to the hotel and freshen up a bit before going to Connor's, so I guess I'll meet you there. Is Connor's bar easy to find, Joe?" she asked.

"Why don't I swing by your hotel and pick you up, Becky," said Joe.

"That would be great because I'm terrible with directions," said Becky.

"I'll pick you up around 1:45, Becky," said Joe.

"I'll be waiting out front for you, and thanks Joe," said Becky.

"Sam, trust me, everything will be just fine," said Joe.

"Let's take a walk around the floor and see how things are going before we leave for Jonah's," said Sam.

As they approached the J40 line, one of the Leads approached them and said, "Boss, we've got a problem."

"What kind of problem, Tommie?" asked Sam.

"Well, we only have one more baffle left, and we're about to need two more, one for the J40 and one for the J60 line," said Tommie. "I checked with the stock room and got the same old runaround about not ordering them until we're down to the last one," he explained.

"OK, Tommie, we'll see what we can do and thanks for letting us know," said Sam.

"Joe, I keep thinking about what Connor said with respect to Drum Buffer Rope," said Sam.

"What's that, Sam?" asked Joe. "He made it very clear that if the parts problem wasn't fixed, then DBR would never work and as we just saw, it's not fixed," said Joe. "Sam, I really believe that with Becky and Jerry's help, we'll fix it," said Joe. "Sam, Jerry is Paul's puppet and whatever Paul tells him to do, he's going to do," replied Sam. "And you know that for some reason, Paul is out to get me!" said Sam. "This won't stop us from planning our Drum-Buffer-Rope system Sam," replied Joe. "I know, I just want everything to work as it should," said Sam.

It was now 1:30 p.m. and time for Joe to go pick up Becky at her hotel. As he pulled into the hotel, there she was. She had on a blue miniskirt and high boots and looked stunning to say the least. When Becky saw Joe she waved and smiled. "Hi Joe," said Becky as she opened the door and plopped herself down on the passenger seat.

"Hi Becky," said Joe. "You look fantastic."

"I don't very often get to go to a bar with so many intelligent men, so I thought I'd at least look decent," said Becky. "Let's go meet Connor," she said as they drove away.

On the ride to Jonah's, Becky and Joe talked small talk until Becky said, "Joe, I've been thinking about everything I saw and heard today at Barton, and I have some questions for you."

"Go ahead, ask me anything you like," said Joe.

"You tell me if I'm wrong, but with everything you and Sam have done in the plant, it seems like your throughput has taken a huge jump," said Becky. "Yes it clearly has," said Joe.

So another way of saying that is you now have some excess capacity, right, Joe?"

"I'd say you're right, Becky, we can clearly produce more tanks with the same number of people," said Joe. "So we do have much more capacity than we did two weeks ago."

"So if you have excess capacity, don't you think it's time that we contacted Sales to see if we can get additional orders?" asked Becky.

"That's a very astute observation," said Joe.

"Have you ever met Benji Teamon, Joe?" asked Becky. "No, I'm afraid I haven't," said Joe. "Who is he?" he asked.

"Benjamin Teamon is the Director of Sales for Barton," said Becky.

"Benji is clearly the best sales person I have ever met, but he's always on the road," she added. "I should call him, find out where he is and invite him here to see the new Barton," said Becky.

"That's a great idea, Becky," said Joe as she dialed Benji's number.

"Hi Benji, it's Becky . . . I'm doing just fine thank you," she said. "Where are you now, Benji?" Becky asked. "Oh sorry, I should have guessed you would be making a sales pitch somewhere," she said. "Benji, when you get a free minute, I think I may have a real opportunity for you . . . OK Benji, call me back later," said Becky.

"So Joe, how difficult would it be for you to calculate your new capacity?" asked Becky.

"Not difficult at all, just let me meet with Sam, and I'll give you a number," said Joe.

"Here's what I'm thinking, Joe," said Becky. "I'd like to be able to give Benji a concrete number of tanks that he can sell, and if he can close a couple of deals with your new capacity, your bottom line will probably soar," she said. "And when your bottom line sours, I promise you, nobody at all will care about low efficiencies," she added.

"When you meet with Sam," said Becky," you guys also need to estimate your new turnaround time on orders. That by itself could be a significant differentiator in this market," she adds. "This should take the pressure off of Sam and let him get a great night's sleep for a change."

And with that, Joe pulled into Jonah's. "Here it is, Becky, the infamous Jonah's."

"Joe, one other question for you before we go in," said Becky. "The drawings of the piping system and the process that you have on flip charts—is there any way you could reproduce those in PowerPoint for me?" asked Becky.

"Why sure, Becky, why do you want them on PowerPoint?" asked Joe.

"I have an idea that I'll tell you about later," said Becky. "How soon can you have them ready?"

"Depending upon how late we stay here tonight, I can probably have them ready for you in the morning," said Joe.

"And the IO Map and Interference Diagram, too?" asked Becky.

"Yes, those too," said Joe. "But what are you going to do with them, Becky?"

"I'm going to make a sales pitch of sorts," replied Becky.

"Anything else, Becky?" asked Joe.

"Oh yes, the Conflict Resolution Diagram," said Becky.

"OK, you'll have them all in the morning," said Joe.

Chapter 10
Becky Meets Connor

Sam was already inside Jonah's, and he rushed over to greet Becky and Joe when they walked in the door. "Hi Becky, I'm so happy that you could make it today," he said.

As Sam was on his first time to Jonah's, Becky was a bit taken back by all of the wall dressings. On every wall there was either a logic diagram, a graph or an abstract painting of something that had to do with manufacturing or a process of some kind.

"Oh my God," said Becky, "I've never seen anything like this in my life! And the funny thing is, I love it!" she said.

Joe pointed in the direction of the bar where Connor was, once again, in a discussion with two suits. "That, my new friend Becky, is Connor Jackson," said Joe.

"We are really anxious for you to meet him," said Sam. "He is unlike any person you've ever met."

"I don't think I've ever looked forward more to meeting someone than I am Connor," said Becky as she continued to gaze at the adorned walls.

"I've got a table, so let's go sit down, and Joe, I've gotten you a glass of Chianti," said Sam. "What would you like to drink Becky?" asked Sam.

"Chianti works for me," said Becky. "Not too many people I know drink Chianti, it's my favorite wine," she said.

Connor was in an unusually long discussion today with three new men and hadn't noticed Sam or Joe yet. He looked at his watch and looked around the bar and saw everyone at the table. He took off his apron, grabbed a bottle of Chianti Classico and headed toward Sam, Joe and Becky.

"Hi guys," said Connor. "And who might this lovely lady be?" he asked.

"This is Becky Chen, Connor, the woman I told you about on the phone," said Joe.

Becky stood up and shook hands with Connor. “It is such an absolute delight to finally meet you Connor,” said Becky. “I’ve heard so much about you since I got here that I feel like I already know you” she said. “You’ve become quite the celebrity at Barton.”

“Well Becky, I don’t know about my celebrity status, but I can tell you one thing, these two guys here have made some remarkable progress in an extremely short period of time,” said Connor.

“I agree Connor, it is a remarkable accomplishment!” said Becky.

“So Becky, tell me about you,” said Connor. “What’s your background and education?”

“Well, I got my bachelor’s degree from Stanford in math and physics and my master’s degree from Princeton in economics,” Becky said.

Joe interrupted, “While you two get to know each other, I need to have a conversation with Sam. So if you’ll excuse us, we’ll be back in a few minutes.” Joe turned to Sam. “Let’s go outside so I can smoke,” he said.

“I didn’t know you smoked,” said Sam. “I do too, by the way.”

When they got outside, Joe told Sam about his conversation with Becky about the need to know what their new capacity is.

“Why does she want to know about that, Joe?” asked Sam.

“She wants to get us more work in here, and she’s already put in a call to Benji Teamon,” said Joe.

“More business?” said Sam. “We’ve been having trouble just getting the current business out the door . . . I don’t know about trying to do more, Joe,” said Sam.

“Think about it, Sam,” said Joe. “We were able to increase throughput by an amazing amount, and we haven’t even fixed the parts problem. Imagine what we will do when that gets fixed,” he said. “My guess is that we could take on at least 30 percent more business without a problem.”

Sam thought for a moment, made a quick mental calculation and said, “You know what Joe, I think you’re right, but let’s be conservative and keep it at 20 percent.”

“OK, Sam, let’s go back in,” said Joe.

Becky and Connor were laughing when Sam and Joe walked in, seeming to be enjoying each other’s company.

“Sam and Joe, this is one pretty amazing woman we have here,” said Connor.

"We think so too," said Joe.

"Want another glass, Becky? It's on the house," said Connor.

"Don't mind if I do," said Becky.

"Wow," thought Joe, "I'm only a third through my first glass, and she's on her second already."

"How about you Joe?" asked Connor.

"No, I'm the designated driver tonight, so I'd better pace myself, replied Joe. "Plus, we need to talk about Drum Buffer Rope sometime tonight."

"One question," said Connor. "Is the parts supply problem fixed yet? Because if it isn't, there's no need to talk about Drum Buffer Rope," he said.

Sam replied, "No Connor, I'm afraid we still have the problem, but we're working on it."

"Hold on," said Becky. "Tomorrow morning we will have all of the vendor- replenishment lead times and new calculated minimum stock levels in place," she said. "I met with Jerry Dumas, our purchasing manager, and told him that I didn't care if he had to work all night, we had to have that information available in the morning."

Joe and Sam looked at each other and held up a high five for Becky.

"Becky, you don't know what that means to us," said Sam.

"The parts replenishment problem is the last major hurdle we have to overcome to solidify our on-time deliveries," echoed Joe.

"Your presentation on the TOC replenishment model convinced me," said Becky.

"The only problem is, we're probably going to shut down during the middle of first shift tomorrow because we don't have enough baffles to finish the tanks," said Sam.

"Took care of that too, guys," said Becky whose words were starting to slur a bit as she finished her second glass of wine.

"How did you fix that?" asked Joe. "I instructed Jerry to have some parts overnighted into Barton so that we wouldn't shut down," she said.

"Another glass?" asked Connor.

"Sure, why not," said Becky. "Connor, I skipped lunch. Any chance you could make me a sandwich? Joe tells me your ham sandwiches are to die for," she said. Connor motioned for the waitress to come to the table, and he ordered it for Becky.

"Guys, I know I shouldn't be telling you this, but it's something you probably need to know," said Becky. "I just want to be honest with you. I'm not exactly who you think I am," she said, obviously being a bit loose-lipped because of all the wine on an empty stomach.

"What is it Becky?" asked Joe.

"I actually am working directly with Cecil Graham," she replied.

"Sorry," said Connor, "Who is Cecil Graham?"

"Cecil Graham is the Chairman of the Board for Barton Enterprises, but he's also a principal with Barton's Parent Company, American Investors, Inc. (AII)," said Becky. "And as you may or may not know, AII is one of the richest private equity firms in the world." Becky continued. "I actually am working with Cecil in the capacity of someone performing a due diligence on Barton," she explained.

"Barton is up for sale?" asked Sam.

"No, no, but private equity firms are always looking for good new investments. I am representing Chen Holdings, my own upstart private equity firm," Becky said.

"What?" said Joe and Sam together. "Let me get this straight, you, Becky Chen, are thinking about buying Barton?" asked Joe.

"I'm just looking right now, guys, nothing concrete at all," she replied.

"While you and Sam were outside talking, I was explaining this to Connor, and he convinced me that I should let you in on this little secret," said Becky. "But gentlemen, this can go no further than the four of us.

"By the way," said Becky, "Have you figured out how much new capacity you've freed up like I asked you to?"

"I think we can safely say that it should be around twenty percent," said Sam.

Both Becky and Connor burst out laughing until Becky said, "That's exactly the number Connor said you would say. Sorry guys, that just struck me as being funny. Connor estimates that conservatively, you should see a minimum forty percent increase."

"Forty percent?" asked Sam, "Why do you think it would be that high?" asked Sam.

"Do the math Sam, twenty percent is just way too conservative," said Connor. Connor and Becky explained how they had both come up with their numbers, and both Sam and Joe had to admit that their own estimate was way off base on the low end.

Just then Becky's phone rang, and she excused herself to take the call. When she was outside, Sam said, "What the hell is going on, Joe?"

"I wish I knew," said Joe.

"All I know is we came here to talk about Drum-Buffer-Rope, and we find out that Barton may be purchased by another private equity firm," said Sam.

Connor interjected, "Guys, she's a very astute business woman, and I can tell you one thing, in the short time she's been here, you have changed her thinking about investments.

"I can't tell you how proud I am of both of you," said Connor. "What you two have been able to achieve in a little over a week is simply incredible. In my best days, I never did anything this quickly."

"Well thank you, Connor, but I think you of all people would understand that we couldn't have done it without you," said Sam.

"Hold on Sam," said Connor. "All I did was show you the way. You guys made it all happen!" he said. "You two have really impressed this woman and rightfully so," said Connor.

Becky made her way back to the table with a big smile on her face.

"Good news?" asked Connor.

"Great news is more like it," said Becky.

"I have a question for you Becky," said Sam. "How is it that you can be working for Cecil Graham and be looking at possibly buying Barton?"

"I never said I was working for Cecil, I said I was working with Cecil—big difference," said Becky. "In the private equity world the due diligence results dictate everything. I've gone over Barton's balance sheet and their margins are woefully low compared to where I think they should or could be, so on the surface Barton looks like a great investment," explained Becky.

"So when will this all take place?" said Joe.

"Private equity deals can go fast or they can drag on indefinitely, so I can't say," she replied. "I was just on the phone with Benji, and he seemed to think that if your new on-time delivery rates are significantly better than the industry standard, where they are right now, the market would be wide open," she explained. "He believes he would have no trouble bringing in new business. And being able to attract significant new business will be one of the keys in my decision to buy or not.

"So you guys getting the parts you need on a consistent basis is absolutely critical to sustaining your throughput gains," Becky said. "It's the reason I gave Jerry strict instructions today to get those parts in here tomorrow. So after I leave this week, I'll be checking in with you regularly to see how things are running, and if your purchasing group is giving you everything you need."

Becky added, "I want to apologize for taking up so much time today, because I know you had intended to talk about Drum-Buffer-Rope and I would still like to be part of that discussion. Any chance we could meet again tomorrow after Cecil's visit?" she asked.

"I'm game," said Connor.

"Me too," said Joe.

"Me too, as long as I still have a job," said Sam.

"Look Sam, I'll be meeting with Cecil when he arrives, so let me dispel any worries you have about your job," said Becky. "In my estimation, you are one of the lynch pins in this deal," she said. "You and Joe both are, so please stop putting pressure on yourself about losing your job. You're not going anywhere."

"Thanks, Becky, for that vote of confidence," said Sam. "You have no idea what that means to me, especially coming from someone as brilliant as you."

"Brilliant?" said Becky, "Just doing my job by listening, just like you did with your people on the shop floor," she said. "Like the guy on the shop floor we spoke to said—for the first time in his twenty years with the company, he now has hope. I know he didn't use those words, but Sam, that's what he was really saying."

"What time can we come back tomorrow, guys?" asked Becky.

"How about between 3:00 and 4:00 p.m.?" asked Connor.

"I think that will be OK," said Becky, "but give me your cell number, and I'll let you know for sure tomorrow." She added, "I may have a surprise visitor tomorrow."

"Who?" said Sam.

"I'll tell you tomorrow," said Becky. "Now, Joe and Sam, if you guys don't mind, I'd like to spend a little time alone with Connor," she said.

"But you don't have a car, Becky," said Joe.

"I didn't tell you to leave, I just want some one-on-one time with

Connor," said Becky. "There's a table over there, " she said, pointing to her left.

And with those instructions, Sam and Joe took up residence at a new table. "Here Joe, let me fill up your glass before you go," said Connor. "Me too," said Becky.

"Joe, what do you think she wants to talk to Connor about?" asked Sam.

"I don't have the foggiest notion," said Joe. "But you can bet it's a business discussion!"

"What do you think of Becky, Joe?" asked Sam.

"I think she's one of the smartest women I've ever met," said Joe.

"Forget about gender Joe, she's just one smart human being," said Sam. "Think about it Joe, she totally grasped in one day what it took us three days to understand."

"You're right, Sam, I hadn't looked at it that way," said Joe. "I forgot to tell you, she wants everything we showed her on PowerPoint by tomorrow morning.

"What's she planning on doing with it?" asked Sam.

"She told me she was going to make a presentation or a sales pitch of sorts, but I have no idea who she's going to present to," replied Joe.

"Joe, I'm actually getting excited about Cecil Graham's visit tomorrow," said Sam.

"Me too," said Joe.

An hour passed by with Becky and Connor still locked in a serious discussion. Connor even went and retrieved another bottle of Chianti Classico.

"I wish I had at least some idea of what was going on between the two of them," said Sam.

"Like I said, Sam, it's a business discussion, and it probably includes something about us," said Joe.

Just then, Becky turned and signalled for Sam and Joe to rejoin them at the table. "Joe, could you drive me back to the hotel now?" said Becky "I've got some work I've got to do, and if you could send me the slides I asked you for earlier, I would appreciate it,"

"Sure thing, Becky, as soon as I drop you off, I'll go back to my hotel and get them ready," said Joe.

"I can't tell you guys what a totally enjoyable day I've had today," said Becky. "And Connor, it was such an absolute pleasure to have finally met you," she said.

"Same here Becky, and we'll be in touch," replied Connor.

"Good night Sam," said Becky.

"See you in the morning, Sam," said Joe.

"Good night you two. Sleep well," said Sam. "Night Connor, see you tomorrow afternoon," he added.

"Becky, you really have my curiosity peaked with you and Connor holding a private discussion like you did," said Joe.

"I wish I could tell you about it, but I can't Joe, so please trust me," replied Becky. "You and Sam just need to keep doing what you're doing, and please let me know in the morning if you received the parts you needed," said Becky.

"I will, Becky, and please sleep well," said Joe.

"Not sure how much sleep I'll get tonight—big day tomorrow," said Becky. "And Joe, you and Sam need to check your email in the morning because I'm inviting you to a very important meeting with Cecil," she said.

"What's this meeting about, and who all will be there?" asked Joe.

"You'll find out on the email tomorrow," said Becky. "Thanks for the ride and the company, Joe. Good night and sleep well, and don't forget to send me the slides," said Becky. "Good night Becky and I'll send them shortly," replied Joe.

Joe went to his hotel, prepared all of the slides and photos that Becky had requested and sent them to her. He waited for a confirmation from her, but nothing came back. "What in the world is Becky up to?" wondered Joe. He tried to imagine what she was doing, and several scenarios went through his mind, but he dismissed them all.

"I guess we'll all find out something tomorrow," thought Joe, and he went to bed.

The next morning, remembering what Becky had told him last night about an important meeting he would be invited to, Joe immediately checked his emails when he arrived for work. The meeting invitation popped up on his planning calendar for 10:00 a.m. in the main conference room. The agenda called for Paul to present the current state of Barton's business with a review of on-time deliveries and his favorite subject, efficiencies. It also spelled out a review of the parts inventory value and Barton's plans to reduce it, again presented by Paul. The rest of the agenda called for Becky to present her observations about Barton's state of the business.

"I need to go meet with Sam right away and see where we are with the parts situation, specifically the missing baffles," thought Joe.

"Good morning, Sam," said Joe.

"She's good, Joe," replied Sam.

"Who's good?" asked Joe.

"Becky!" replied Sam. "She did exactly what she said she would do. We've got all of the parts we need to keep on running," he said. "Joe, we're completely caught up on orders and are now building future, anticipated orders."

"Wow, Sam," said Joe. "This is better than I ever imagined."

"You bet it is," said Sam.

"Did you check your emails yet, Sam?" asked Joe.

"No, why Joe?" asked Sam.

"We've been invited to a meeting at 10:00 this morning with Paul, Becky, Cecil Graham and Benji Teamon," said Joe.

"What's this meeting about, Joe?" asked Sam.

"Open it up and look at the attached agenda, Sam," replied Joe.

Sam quickly opened the email and read it. "Looks like another opportunity for Paul to slam me," he said, assuming a defensive posture.

"Look Sam, you have nothing to be defensive about with where you are with on-time deliveries," said Joe. "Let's go walk the line and see how things are going ."

Things seemed to moving quite nicely on all three of the major production lines with the flow well defined and parts not a problem at the moment. When they got to the constraint, the operator was pacing frantically back and forth, looking in all directions.

"What's wrong, Timmie?" asked Sam.

"I've been waiting for over an hour for the inspector to come by and inspect the tank," Timmie replied. "I went and talked to him, and he said he'd be over as soon as he finished inspecting one of the other processes, but that was an hour and fifteen minutes ago." Timmie was frustrated because he knew that an hour lost at the constraint was an hour lost to the system which could never be retrieved.

"I'll get him over here right away, Timmie," said Joe.

"Thanks, boss," replied Timmie.

"What we need is an alert system to let the inspector know that the joined tank is ready to be inspected," said Sam.

"Yes, but what we also need is for the inspectors to understand our new focus on constraints and the reason why," said Joe. "I'll have Stan get on both of these needs right away."

As scheduled, at 10:00 a.m. Joe and Sam went into the conference room and took a seat, waiting for the others to arrive. At 10:15 Becky, Cecil, Benji and Paul all arrived. The traditional hand-shakes took place, but when Becky shook Joe's hand, he could feel a small piece of paper being transferred to his palm. Becky put her index finger to her lips indicating that this must be a secretive message meant only for him and Sam. Joe read the note which said, "No matter what you hear, don't say a word until I ask you to." Joe passed the note to Sam, and both of them looked at each other and just shrugged their shoulders.

Paul started the presentation, "Good morning, everyone. Happy to have everyone here this morning. As you know, Barton has been having significant problems with on-time delivery of tanks to virtually all of our customers," said Paul. "Some of our key customers have even been threatening to take their business to our competitors." As he explained this, he flashed a run chart of the historical on-time deliveries. "We have been stuck somewhere around 60 percent for the past three years, and I see no signs that we're getting better," he said.

Joe could tell that Sam's blood pressure was rising, and he squeezed Sam's arm indicating that he must not respond.

Paul continued, "One of our bright spots during this time was that we have been able to maintain high efficiencies," as he flashed a run chart of efficiencies on the screen. "That is, until the last couple weeks," said Paul. "As you can see, our efficiencies have dropped from our historical average of 80 plus percent down to around 60 percent for the last two weeks," he said. "In a nutshell, we are in deep trouble, and unless we take immediate action, I'm afraid our margins are going to suffer," said Paul. "As you can see, our EBITDA is an anemic 8 percent, and I am estimating that by the end of this month it will drop closer to 6 percent," he said looking directly at Sam.

Joe could see that Sam was ready to explode in anger, but surprisingly he restrained himself, thanks to Becky's note.

It was now Becky's turn to speak. "Paul is absolutely correct in reporting that Barton's efficiencies have taken a serious nose dive in the past week or two, but I'm afraid that Paul has only reported half of the story," said Becky.

Paul fidgeted in his seat as Becky continued. "What Paul did not tell you was that while the efficiencies were falling, Barton's on-time deliveries rose to never-before-seen levels," as she flashed her own run chart demonstrating the incredible spike that had occurred in the past two weeks.

Paul's eyes were wide open as he stared at the graph. "Where did you get these numbers?" Paul asked frantically.

"From the best place possible—from all of our customers," replied Becky. "Unlike Paul, I reviewed the data and then called every one of Barton's customers to confirm what I had seen in shipping," she explained. "In every case, the customer was overwhelmed with this new level of customer support." Joe glanced at Sam and could see a smile being covered by his hand.

"Paul, why is it that Becky knew this and you didn't?" asked Cecil. "It's your job to report the entire picture of what's going on, and you clearly didn't take the time to do this!" said Cecil in a very angry tone.

"Well, er, uh . . ." said Paul, struggling for words that didn't form.

"Becky, in your opinion, why is it that we have made such a turn for the better in on-time delivery," asked Cecil, "while our primary metric efficiency, the one we have always relied on to monitor the state of the business, fell so dramatically?"

"It's actually quite simple Cecil," said Becky. "The traditional concept of efficiency evolved as an outgrowth of the standard cost system which I'm now convinced is flawed," she said. "At many other companies, efficiency has typically been applied to individual process steps or departments without regard to the effects on the system, and Barton is no different." Becky continued. "The problem with this approach to efficiency is that it focuses on local optimization rather than system optimization, and as a result, it encourages the wrong behaviors," she explained.

"I don't agree," said Paul. "We have been using efficiencies for a long time and we've never had a problem before," he said.

"You can disagree all you want, Paul," said Becky, "but how then do you explain the anemic on-time delivery and low EBITDA numbers?"

"Sam's just not getting his people to work, and that's the cause of our problems," said Paul.

Cecil glared at Paul and said, "Continue, Becky, I find this all very enlightening."

"With your permission, Cecil, I'd like Joe and Sam to explain a new concept called the Theory of Constraints to you," said Becky as she flashed the infamous piping diagram on the screen.

"Sam, why don't you take the honors on this," said Joe.

Sam began, "A little over two weeks ago, Joe Pecci came to Barton with some pretty wild ideas about how to run a business, and I have to admit, I was very skeptical when I first heard them," said Sam. "But I soon realized that for many years I had been running my operation completely backwards."

Sam did a fantastic job of explaining the new concepts to the group, and when he was finished, he turned the podium over to Joe to discuss Throughput Accounting.

Joe presented the same basic material that he originally communicated to Sam and then to Becky. He discussed the difference in focus between trying to save money by doing things like reducing parts inventory versus the impact of driving throughput higher and being able to increase the number of orders.

"So you can see sir, that focusing on saving money is nowhere near as profitable as focusing on making money by increasing throughput," Joe said.

Without warning, Paul stood up and said, "Surely you jest. Do you really believe we can actually get those sales you were talking about?"

"Yes Paul, I'm certain of it!" said Sam from his seat. "Go on Joe, talk about what's limiting our throughput," said Sam.

Joe flashed the Pareto chart that the team had developed for the J40, J50 and J60 processes on lost time, and the number one issue was clearly parts availability. Joe allowed everyone to evaluate the Pareto and then said, "We believe that if we can solve this parts issue, just by itself it will probably result in a 15 to 20 percent increase in throughput and possibly much more" said Joe.

Paul interrupted, "I repeat, do you really think you can go out and get the sales you're talking about?"

Becky had heard all she could take from Paul, and she calmly asked Benji to approach the podium and address the group.

"I'd like to answer your question for you, Paul," said Benji. "If we can continue the on-time delivery results that we've seen in the past few weeks, I can guarantee you at least a 30 percent increase in orders."

"How can you be so confident, Benji?" asked Paul in his normal, sarcastic tone.

"Because the most important competitive factor in this business is on-time delivery," replied Benji. "Actually, I was being conservative when I said 30 percent!" he said. "We already offer a product that has the best quality in the industry."

"Sam, do you think you can sustain the gains you've made this week?" asked Mr. Graham.

"If and only if we can get resolution on the parts availability problem, sir," said Sam. "And sir, we have a proposal on exactly how to fix this problem while at the same time reducing our current inventory levels by at least 30 percent," said Sam. "Would you like to hear it?"

"It won't work!" said Paul.

By now Cecil had grown impatient with Paul. "How in the world do you know it won't work when you haven't even heard the proposal?" Cecil asked him.

"Cecil," Paul said, "Sam is a manufacturing guy, not a purchasing guy, so how would he know anything about our procurement process?"

"Joe, could you present the details please?" asked Sam. And with that, Joe presented the details of the TOC Replenishment Model.

"Joe and Sam, how long would it take to implement this at Barton?" asked Cecil.

"You can't be serious, Cecil!" said Paul "You're actually entertaining the possibility of doing this?"

"No, Paul, you're the one that's going to implement it, and I want it done quickly!" replied Cecil. "Now Joe, how long do you think it would take to do this?" he asked.

"I think if we worked hard at it, we should be able to do so within a week, sir," said Joe.

"Done!" said Cecil.

"If I might add, Cecil," said Becky. "We've already taken steps to get parts in here overnight, and the first shipment arrived this morning," said Becky.

"Who authorized this?" asked Paul.

"I did, Paul," said Becky, "Do you have a problem with this?"

"He has no problem at all with what you did Becky, do you Paul?" asked Cecil.

"Uh, er, no, Cecil," muttered Paul.

"I have one more question for you, Sam," said Cecil. "How much of a manpower increase would you need for say a 30 percent increase in sales?" he asked.

"Not a single person," replied Sam proudly.

"So then, based upon the TA formulas you just presented, all of the new revenue, minus the totally variable costs would flow directly to the bottom line?" asked Cecil.

"Yes sir, every bit of it!" said Sam excitedly.

The meeting adjourned, but the conversations continued between Becky, Cecil and Benji for another hour. Becky explained everything that had happened at Barton in a little over a week to Cecil, and he was extremely pleased.

"Well Sam, what do you think?" asked Joe.

"I think we need to go to Jonah's and celebrate!" replied Sam. "I have waited a long time to see Paul squirm the way he did today, and it was well worth the wait."

"Let's go check out the lines before we go to Jonah's," said Joe.

When they got to the lines, Sam asked the supervisor, "How's everything running?"

"Couldn't be better," the supervisor said. Then he added, "Well, there is one problem."

"What's that?" asked Sam.

"We've got to have more orders," he said. "We've completely caught up with the schedule and unless we get more orders, we'll have to shut down—unless you want us to keep building without orders."

"No, no more speculative building. We'll get you more orders," said Sam. "I'll let you know tomorrow. And please tell everyone great job, from us," said Sam.

"Will do, boss, and thanks for checking on us," he said.

"Let's go to Jonah's, Joe," said Sam.

As they started to leave, the sound of the now recognizable cowbell echoed through the lines. "Let's go check out our constraint before we leave, Sam," said Joe.

As they got closer to the joining operation, Sam noticed something new. "What's this, Timmie?" he asked.

"That's our new flag system that Stan developed for us," said Timmie, the joining operator.

"I don't understand," replied Sam.

"Well you remember when I talked to you about having to wait for the inspector to inspect the finished tank?" asked Timmie.

"Yes," said Joe.

"Stan came up with the idea of having different colored flags so that everyone would know when I needed something," explained Timmie. "I ring the cowbell to alert everyone that I have a need and then place a colored flag in this holder so that anyone can figure out from a distance what my need is," he explained.

"See, when nothing is wrong, I put up a green flag," he continued. "When I know I'm going to need a part or a new batch of adhesive or something like that in the next thirty minutes, I put up this yellow flag. If I need an inspector, I use this red and white striped flag. When I'm shut down for a problem, I use this red flag, and when it's time to remove a tank from the mold, I ring the bell and put up a blue flag," said Timmie.

"How's this new alert system working for you, Timmie?" asked Joe.

"Like a charm," said Timmie, "I never have to wait for anything. I just put up my flag, ring my bell and everyone comes running."

"Joe, you've got to do something for Stan!" said Sam.

"I will," said Joe.

"Thanks, Timmie," said Sam.

"See you guys," said Timmie.

"Let's get to Jonah's, Joe," said Sam.

Chapter 11
Another Meeting at Jonah's

As Joe pulled into Jonah's parking lot, he couldn't help but notice the long, black stretch limo parked out front. "Wow, somebody important must be here today," he thought. Joe waited for Sam to park his car, and then the two of them walked together, chatting about the new flag alert system they had just seen.

"Joe, it's amazing how far we've come in such a short amount of time," said Sam.

"I've been doing this a long time, and I've just never seen anything like it," replied Joe.

"Ready to go in?" asked Sam.

"Not yet, I need a smoke," said Joe.

"I wish there was something I could do for my guys on the shop floor," said Sam. "They're really the heroes at Barton," he said. "And so are your guys, Joe, especially Stan," he added. The two of them finished their cigarettes and walked inside.

As Sam and Joe scanned the bar for an open table, the sound of applause filled the air. "Oh my gosh," said Sam. "Look who's here today," he said.

"Now I know who belongs to the stretch limos," said Joe.

As they walked closer to the sound of the applause, they could see Cecil Graham, Benji, Becky and Connor now standing and applauding. "Our heroes," said Cecil as he smiled from ear to ear.

Somewhat embarrassed, both Sam and Joe took a seat on either side of Cecil as he motioned for the waitress to bring a new bottle of champagne. "It's time to celebrate," said Cecil. "A toast—to the two guys who have changed the course of history for Barton," he said. "What you guys have done is nothing short of a miracle. And to show my appreciation, here's a small token." He handed both Joe and Sam an envelope.

"Go ahead, open them," said Cecil. Inside each envelope was a check for $10,000.

"Thank you so much, sir," said Sam, "but with all due respect, I'm afraid I can't accept this money."

"What do you mean, you can't accept it?" said Cecil.

"Let me explain sir, please," said Sam. "As much as I am honored by your gift and your recognition, I would much rather give this money to the people that have made this all happen," he said. "I was just telling Joe on the way in that the guys on the shop floor are the real heroes here, and that I wished I could do something for them," said Sam. "This money would be a small token of my appreciation to them for all they have done."

"Me too," said Joe, "Sam's right, those guys are the heroes."

"Go ahead Becky, tell them," said Cecil.

"We agree with you, Sam and Joe," said Becky. "And that's why, effective in everyone's next pay check, there will be a raise in their base, hourly pay of one dollar per hour."

"You're kidding me?" asked Joe, somewhat flabbergasted.

"No, no jokes here," said Becky. "Cecil spent some time on the shop floor after our meeting, chatting with the shop floor workers and shaking their hands," she said. "This increase was his idea, guys, so you have him to thank."

"Thank you so much sir, and speaking for Joe, I can tell you that this means the world to us," said Sam.

"I want you to call them all together tomorrow and thank them personally for me, and then announce their increase to them," said Cecil.

"With pleasure," said Sam.

"One other thing, Joe," said Cecil, "I happen to have heard about the great job your black belts and your Lean assistant have done, so here is something for each of them," said Cecil as he handed Joe four envelopes. "Please thank them for me and tell them to keep up their great work," said Cecil. "I wish you could have seen the look on Paul's face when I had him write these checks guys, it was priceless," he added.

Cecil continued, "I've been sitting here talking to Becky, Connor and Benji about what's happened here at Barton in such a short period of time, and I have a question for all of you. Is what you've done here something that is sustainable?" he asked. "I mean, if I send Benji out to bring in significantly more orders, will you be able to satisfy this new demand?" asked Cecil. "The worst thing we could do is go get new orders that we can't deliver on."

"If I may, Cecil, I'd like to answer that question," said Connor.

"Go right ahead, Connor," said Cecil.

"The key to sustaining what's already been achieved is to implement the last missing element we developed on the Intermediate Objectives Map," said Connor.

"The what?" asked Cecil.

"Sorry," said Connor. "Joe, did you bring the flip chart and easel with you?" asked Connor.

"Sure, do you want me to go get it?" asked Joe.

"Yes, I think it will make more sense to Cecil if he can see it," said Connor.

Joe went and retrieved the flip chart and easel and set it up beside the table.

Connor began a brief explanation to bring Cecil up to speed. "There is a TOC thinking and strategy tool known as the Intermediate Objectives Map (IO Map), and it's used to develop strategies," said Connor. "It has three major components with the Goal at the top and Critical Success Factors (CSFs) directly underneath the Goal, and then Necessary Conditions (NCs) directly beneath them," he said. "It is read from the top down as follows using necessity-based logic—in order to have the Goal, I must have all of the CSFs, and in order to have the CSFs, I must have the NCs."

"With the help of everyone on the shop floor, Sam and Joe have satisfied the first three CSFs, but we still have one left that said that the tanks must be scheduled to meet demand," said Connor. "Today we were going to meet to discuss a TOC- based scheduling system called Drum-Buffer-Rope (DBR)," he said. "It's a simple system that is effectively a TOC-based pull system that will be used to schedule the plant."

"Where in the world did it get its name from?" asked Cecil.

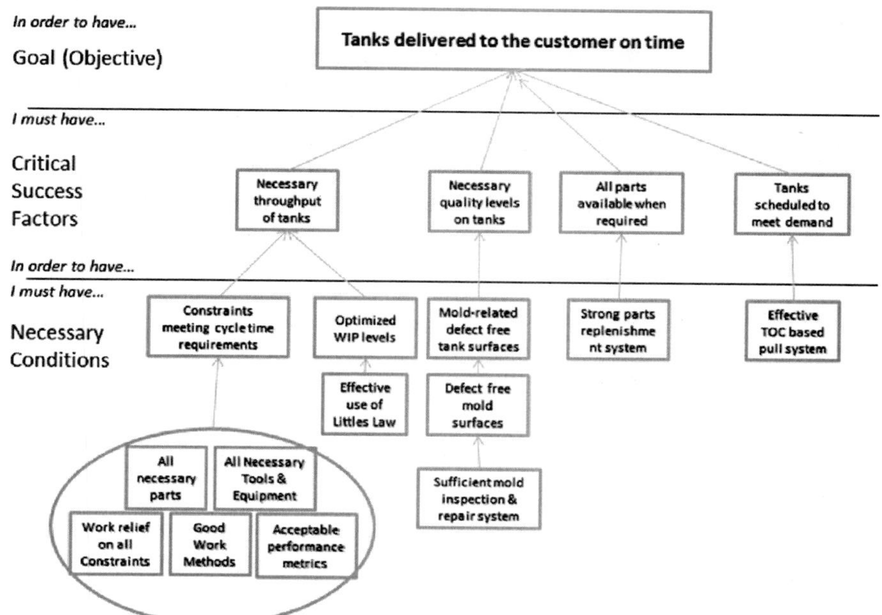

"It came out of a book called, The Goal written by Eli Goldratt, the man who invented the Theory of Constraints," said Connor. "Joe, do you have any extra copies for Cecil and Benji?" asked Connor.

"I sure do, Connor, a copy for both of you," Joe said as he handed them a copy.

"I have a question for you," said Cecil. "You just said that this will be used to schedule the plant. Are you telling me that this DBR system can be used to schedule this entire plant?" he asked.

"Yes," replied Connor.

"And how much is this going to cost me?" asked Cecil.

"Cost? Who said anything about costing anything, Cecil?" asked Connor.

"Nothing?" asked Cecil.

"Nope, we may have to put together an Excel spreadsheet, but we can do that for you," said Connor.

"Oh shit," exclaimed Cecil. "I have a contract for an SAP implementation sitting on my desk, waiting to be signed, that has a price tag of $50 million over the next four years, and here you are telling me I don't have to spend this money . . . you're sure this DBR will fill the needs for Barton in terms of scheduling?" he asked.

"Absolutely!" replied Connor. "I've done this fifty times for a lot more complicated processes than building tanks."

"Cha-ching, you just saved me a bundle of money, Connor," said an ecstatic Cecil. "I'm going back to New York to put that contract on hold and talk to my local "experts," so you guys should probably expect a few phone calls." He added, "I'm going to have to leave soon to catch my flight, but I would like to stay and hear at least the first part of your discussion on DBR."

"Let me start by saying that the standard logistical systems you're familiar with attempt to plan and control the product flow, and they do have some strengths and weaknesses," said Connor. "For systems like MRP, MRP II and SAP—the one Cecil was thinking about buying—the implementation is typically very long and as Cecil just told us, very costly," Connor explained. "Plus, the data requirements needed to maintain these type systems are enormous.

"Many times the end result is an inaccurate schedule, much longer lead times and basically unsynchronized systems," Connor continued. "The general weakness of all of these systems is that they assume infinite capacity, and they fail to recognize and manage the constraints that exist within every system," he said. "By that I mean that the constraints are not typically identified and included into the planning process. This, of course, limits the ability of these systems to generate higher levels of throughput while minimizing inventory and operating expense," said Connor. "In fact, inventory levels in these type systems are always much higher than what you'll see in a DBR system," said Connor.

"The Drum-Buffer-Rope system, on the other hand, incorporates the strengths of those other systems while overcoming their weaknesses," said Connor. "When you read The Goal, which Joe just gave you, you'll read about the Drum, the Buffer and the Rope," he said. "I'll explain each of these in more detail, but for now, let me say that the purpose of the drum is to set the pace for the entire system because it's the constraint. The buffer is intended to protect the system from things that disrupt the process, and the rope's function is to synchronize all of the resources to the drum," said Connor. "A manufacturing manager's objective is to effectively manage his machines, his workers and production materials in such a way that due dates are always met while minimizing associated costs."

"Is everyone with me so far?" Connor asked.

Everyone except Benji nodded their heads that they understood.

"This is all so new to me Connor," said Benji. "Is there another way you can say what you've just said?" he asked.

"I think it might help if I draw a simple sketch of a process so you can visualize what I've said so far."

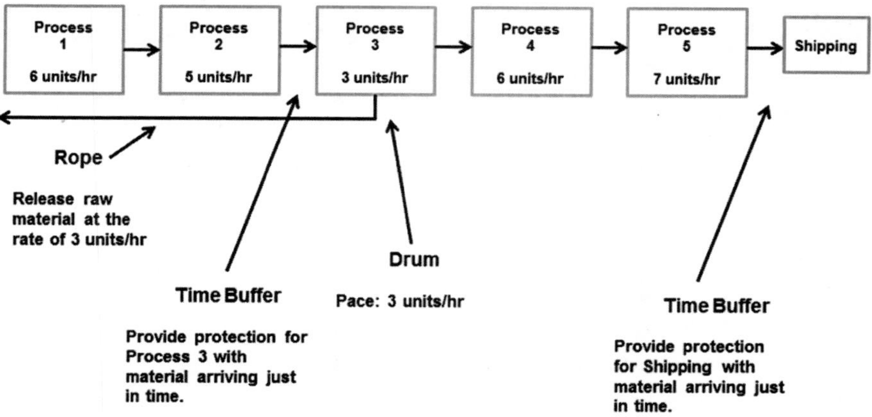

"This is a simple production line, not unlike the one we use to build tanks at Barton, with five processing steps and the capacity for each one" said Connor. Let's assume that demand for the product from this production line is unlimited, meaning that we can sell everything we make," he said. "It should be apparent that process number three, with the smallest capacity of 3 units/hour, is the system constraint and is therefore, the drum," said Connor. "In MRP II language the drum is referred to as the master production schedule." He continued. "The rope is a mechanism designed to control the release of materials into this system, and it's synchronized exactly with the pace of the constraint," he said. "By controlling and synchronizing the release of materials in this way, we automatically prevent the buildup of excess inventory into the system like we had at Barton," explained Connor.

"Still with me everyone?" asked Connor. Everyone including Benji nodded yes, so he continued.

"In order to ensure that the constraint is protected from the inevitable disruptions that always seem to occur at the worst time, we place a buffer directly in front of the constraint," Connor said. "The buffer we use is based upon time rather than inventory. By time, I mean starting material through the process just in time to reach the constraint before it runs out of materials," said Connor. "As I mentioned, the drum is a detailed master production schedule that is developed by matching customer demand to the rate of the system constraint," said Connor. "This schedule is intended to assure on-time delivery of products to the customer and reduce the general confusion on the shop floor," Connor explained. "As such, the drum determines the pace for the entire production line."

Connor pointed to the sketch. "So in this example, all process steps should be running at a rate of three parts per hour. The rope is a mechanism that provides synchronization of every step without having to control each step individually, as a kanban system requires," said Connor. "Excuse me Connor, but what is a kanban system?"asked Benji. "Sorry Benji, a kanban is a materials requirement planning system developed by Toyota Corporation as part of their just-in-time inventory system in which work centers signal with a card when they want to withdraw parts from feeding operations or even in supply bins. In Japanese, kanban just means a visible record like a card or label," Connor explained. "OK, I get it, thanks Connor," said Benji.

"The buffer is the planned lead time when all of the run times are added together, plus a safety factor of time," he explained. "Sorry Connor, could you explain what you mean by each of these times?" asked Benji. "Certainly, the planned lead time is the total length of time we think it will take to run a tank through the entire process. The run times are the actual individual times through each process step, and the safety factor time is the time we add to guard against Murphy's uncertainly," Connor explained. "Thanks Connor, sorry for all of the questions, but I just wan to understand," said Benji.

"Keep asking them Benji, I want you to understand and the only way you will is to ask questions," Connor replied.

"I do have another question for you Connor," said Benji.

"Ask away," Connor replied. "You explained the time buffer that's placed in front of the constraint, are there any other buffers?" asked Benji.

"Actually there are Benji, can you guess where they might be?" Connor asked. "I'm thinking that maybe there's one in front of shipping in case the constraint has down time? asked Benji.

Connor continued, "Benji's right, in addition to placing a time buffer in front of the constraint, many times we also place a time buffer in front of shipping to protect it from starvation and assure on-time delivery. In Barton's tank-building process we see that it is a simple linear flow, so by adding a protective buffer in front of the constraint and shipping we will protect the throughput of the entire system," said Connor.

"There's more to DBR than I have explained today, but this is the essence of what it is," said Connor. "To summarize: First we develop the drum (master production schedule) to assure it is consistent with the constraint. Next we protect the throughput of our system from disruptions by placing one time buffer in front of our constraint and another one in front of shipping. And finally we tie each process step to the pace of the constraint by limiting the release of raw materials into the system," said Connor.

"Because the key to increasing throughput is keeping the constraint busy at all times, we must never let the constraint be starved," said Connor. "It is important to remember that any time lost at the constraint is time lost forever and can never be retrieved. He paused. Are there any questions?" asked Connor.

Becky raised her hand and asked, "So Connor, how do you know how large or small to make these buffers?"

"Great question, Becky," replied Connor. "It's actually very simple. I have found that the simplest way to calculate the size of the buffer is to take one and one half times the constraint capacity—for example, if the constraint can do ten units a day, the buffer should be fifteen units." he explained. "It isn't a perfect number, but it's a simple way to get started. Based upon the performance of the system, the buffers can then be adjusted up or down accordingly," he added.

"I have a question," said Sam. "Does DBR have a positive influence on the quality of our tanks?"

"Another very good question," said Connor. "In addition to maximizing the throughput of the system, the use of buffers serves several other very useful purposes," he explained. "Because the flow of product is synchronized much better, you reduce the need for expediting—and from my experience this typically results in a better quality product," said Connor.

"Sometimes we do have what I call buffer penetration, which simply means that we've eaten up some or all of our buffer. What I always recommend is that we divide the buffer into three equal zones that relate to the amount of buffer being consumed. The three zones are the safety zone, the tracking zone, and the expedite zone." Connor continued, "These zones are intended to provide a signal to managers and operators that an intervention may be required, and as such I always color-code them as green, yellow and red respectively," he added. "By tracking the actual magnitude and cause of these buffer penetrations, we can identify chronic sources of disruptions and put improvement plans in place to correct them. For example, if one of the causes was a repeating quality problem, we can put an improvement team in place to find and eliminate the root cause of the problem," explained Connor. "When we eliminate the causes of the disruptions, one of the immediate benefits is that we have the opportunity to reduce the size of the buffer," said Connor.

"Great questions everyone. Are there any more?" asked Connor.

Benji raised his hand. "Yes Benji?" asked Connor.

"Since I'm going to be out looking for more business," said Benji, "can you estimate how much of an increase in throughput we might get from Drum-Buffer-Rope? I mean I don't want to oversell the capacity of the plant," he added.

"You guys are asking all of the right questions," said Connor. "Based upon my experience—and please Sam and Joe if you don't agree with my estimate, say something . . . as I was saying, based upon my experience, I would plan on a 30 to 40 percent increase as a start," he said. "Joe? Sam? any disagreement?" asked Connor.

"I agree in principle, but it will depend upon whether or not we solve our parts availability problem," said Sam.

"Sam's right," said Joe. "We know what we're capable of, but the parts problem is out of our hands."

Cecil spoke up and said, "Sam, here's my private phone number, and if you run into any resistance at all from Paul and Jerry, I want a call from you."

“Thank you, sir,” said Sam.

“Please Sam, call me Cecil.”

“I have a question for you, Cecil,” said Sam.

“Go ahead Sam.”

“One of the things that Joe taught me very well is the importance of selecting the right performance metrics,” said Sam. “Joe also taught me that the primary function of performance metrics is to motivate the right behaviors.”

“I totally agree with Joe,” said Cecil.

“One of the performance metrics for my manufacturing operation is manpower efficiency,” said Sam. “If you think about the behaviors that this metric motivates, it becomes clear that the only way to increase it is to either overproduce on nonconstraints or produce parts that haven’t been ordered. So Cecil, my question to you is—are you going to continue using efficiency to measure how well my operation is performing?” asked Sam.

“You know, Sam, in all my years in manufacturing, nobody has ever asked me that question, and quite frankly, I’m not sure I know how to answer it,” said Cecil.

“Perhaps I can help you with an answer,” said Becky.

“Please do, because I’m stumped,” said Cecil.

“One of the things that I have learned since I arrived here” said Becky, “is that every business I have ever looked at uses standard cost-accounting rules and metrics. And Cecil, the rules are absolutely wrong!.

“Take efficiency, for example,” said Becky. “By attempting to drive it higher and higher, all we are doing is driving up work-in-process and finished goods inventory and tying up our cash,” she continued. “So my answer is that the only place that efficiency makes any sense at all is in the constraint. I can see now that the constraint dictates, or at least it should dictate, how profitable we are, and that it must be treated like gold,” she said. “There are other cost-accounting metrics that get in our way too—like purchase price variance,” she continued. “In my opinion, we should re-think how we’re measuring everything, and maybe use Sam’s operations as a test bed.”

“I think you’re right, Becky,” said Cecil. “I’d like to send a team down here from headquarters in the next two weeks to help set up a new performance metrics system,” he said. “Joe, Sam, would you two be available to work with this team, if I send them?" asked Cecil.

"We'll make ourselves available," said Sam.

"How about Connor? Would you be available?" asked Cecil.

"No, but I know just the place where they could meet Cecil," said Connor.

"I wouldn't have them come to any other place," said Cecil.

"Oh my gosh, look at the time!" exclaimed Cecil, "I've got to run or I'll miss my flight. I want to thank all of you for a very enlightening experience, and Sam, you call me directly if you have any problems," he said. "And Connor, think about what we talked about earlier," he said as he ran out the door.

"Well, Sam, looks like you've got a new best friend," said Becky. "He's very serious about you calling him with any parts problems," she said.

"I'd like to propose a toast," said Sam, "to Cecil, my new best friend."

Chapter 12
The Parts Issue

"Good morning, Sam," said Joe.

"Hey Joe, how's everything this morning?" replied Sam.

"Going well. What did you think about everything that happened yesterday?" asked Joe.

"Yesterday was such an amazing day for me, Joe," replied Sam. "I mean, to see Paul squirm like he did was worth all of the times he's thrown me under the bus," he added.

"You know Paul much better than I do, Sam. Do you really think he will listen to Cecil and do what he's told to do about the parts issue?" asked Joe.

"I'm not sure, Joe. He's well connected within the company, and I find it hard to believe that he will just roll over and do what Cecil says," replied Sam. "Paul is very political and very good friends with Gregory Daniels III, our CEO."

"Regardless of what Becky said about Mr. Daniels, he is clearly "old school" when it comes to manufacturing, so my bet is that Paul has already connected with him about yesterday," said Sam.

"Where has Mr. Daniels been, by the way?" asked Joe.

"He's been on vacation in Europe as far as I know, but he's due back any day now," said Sam.

"How's the process running this morning, Sam?" asked Joe.

"It's going really well, except that we need more orders," Sam replied.

"Do you think Benji will deliver on them, Sam?" asked Joe.

"Benji is the best salesperson I've ever met, and if he says he can get a 30 percent increase, trust me, he will," replied Sam. "It wouldn't surprise me if Benji gets us new orders this week."

"If that's the case, then we've got to have the parts issue resolved right away," said Joe. "I think we need to meet with Jerry today to iron out the details of the new parts replenishment model. Do you know what time Becky is coming in today?" he asked.

"She should be here any time now," said Sam. "She had quite a bit to drink last night," he added.

"I'd like her to be in the meeting with Jerry, is why I'm asking," said Joe.

"Have you thought about this performance metrics team Cecil talked about last night, Joe?" asked Sam. "Or maybe I should ask, have you thought about what our performance metrics should be?"

"Actually, I haven't, but we should talk about it," replied Joe.

"I'm thinking that one of our metrics needs to be on-time delivery," said Sam.

"I agree Sam, but that's a results metric, and it won't help our guys with their daily decisions," said Joe.

"How about throughput?" asked Sam.

"Yes, we need that one too, but again, that's another results metric that doesn't give the production people a real-time order status," said Joe. "Throughput is a measure of how the system is performing for sure, but I'm thinking more along the lines of how we're managing the buffers," he said. "For example, remember how Connor told us about the green, yellow and red zones?"

"Yes," replied Sam.

"What if we came up with a way of monitoring how often we penetrate each zone?" asked Joe. "We both know that because of uncertainty, there are going to be times when we penetrate the yellow and red zones. The question becomes, how many times is too often and what happens when we do?" he said.

"I see your point," said Sam.

"By the same token, how many times should we fall into the yellow and green zones," said Joe.

"I'm sure there must be rules governing those," said Sam.

"And what about metrics for the nonconstraints?" asked Joe.

"And what about Supply? How will we measure their performance?" replied Sam.

"I think we'll probably have to have another meeting with Connor pretty soon," said Joe.

"I have an idea, Sam," said Joe. "Let's walk through what we know about the process and see if we can logically come up with some performance metrics. I'll make a list of what we come up with, and we can cover it with Connor when we see him again," Joe said. "We know from our conversations that the key to improving throughput is to maximize the product through the constraint, right?" asked Joe.

"So we want to make sure the efficiency is as high as possible?" asked Sam.

"Right," said Joe. "We also know that if we penetrate the yellow or red zones, then we run the risk of starving the constraint and being late on our customer deliveries," he continued. "So shouldn't one or both of these be a metric?"

"You mean like the number or percentage of times we penetrate either the yellow or red zones?" asked Sam.

"Yes, that's exactly what I mean," replied Joe. "It's like compliance to schedule."

"That makes perfect sense, Joe, put it on our list," said Sam.

"Let's see . . . what else?" pondered Joe.

"That same thinking applies to the shipping schedule too, Joe," said Sam.

"Yes, it does, Sam. Good point," said Joe, and he wrote that one down.

"What about cycle time of the constraint?" asked Sam.

"Yes," said Joe, "I'll write that one down too."

"Hi, guys," said the now soft and familiar voice of Becky.

"Good morning, Becky," said Joe.

"What are you guys doing?" asked Becky.

"Well, we know Cecil is going to send a team down here to come up with new performance metrics, so we thought we'd get a head start," said Joe.

"Great idea," said Becky. "Do you mind if I join you?" she asked.

"Not at all, Becky," said Joe, "We can always use fresh ideas, especially from someone as insightful as you."

"Thank you for the compliment, Joe. What have you come up with so far?" asked Becky.

Joe went through the list to bring her up-to-date on the metrics he and Sam had come up with. "This looks like a good start," said Becky.

"We're trying to look at this logically," said Sam.

"How about percent rejects or some quality measure on the constraint product?" asked Becky.

"Good one," said Sam.

"Let's take a look at the nonconstraints," said Joe. "I think the most important thing we can put in place here is something about meeting the schedule to begin the building of tops and bottoms," he said. "We know we don't want the process to start too soon or too late. If we start too soon, we'll create excess work-in-process inventory, and if we start too late, we could starve the constraint."

"So what you're saying is that we might want to measure our start time against the master production schedule," said Becky.

"Yes, if we're supposed to start the process on a Monday morning, and we don't start it until Tuesday afternoon, we're already eating into our buffer," said Joe.

"What about instead of on-time completions, we measure on-time starts?" asked Becky.

"I like that one, Becky," said Sam. The three of them continued to hash out different possible metrics, and in the end their list included fifteen different metrics.

"Maybe we could bounce this list off of Connor today or tomorrow and see what he thinks." said Sam.

"Sounds like a good idea," said Joe. "Let's go check on the status of our parts replenishment system."

"Good idea," said Sam, "Because if it isn't in place, we can't implement our new DBR system."

The three of them walked to the production area to check on their parts problem but when they arrived, it didn't appear on the surface that anything had changed.

"Let's go see if Jerry is working on it," said Becky.

"We also need to plan our DBR implementation," said Sam.

"We'll do that after we've met with Jerry," said Joe as they walked to purchasing.

"Is Jerry in?" Sam asked Jerry's administrative assistant.

"He's meeting with one of his stock room clerks at the moment," she said.

"That's perfect, let's see if we can join them," said Becky.

Sam knocked on Jerry's door and then opened it. "Jerry, are you talking about the TOC replenishment model?" asked Sam.

"Yes, we are, and I have some questions for you," said Jerry "Come on in. I was just trying to explain how we need to change our replenishment frequency," he said. "By the way, this is Sandy Peters, our Stockroom Lead."

"Hi, Sandy," said Sam. "You know Joe, and this is Becky Chen. She's here from Corporate to help us," said Sam.

"Nice to meet you," said Becky.

"Sam and Joe, maybe you could explain this system a little better than I could," said Jerry. Sam and Joe spent the next twenty minutes taking turns explaining the system to Sandy and then asked her if she had any questions.

She replied, "It seems simple enough. If I understand you correctly, my role will be to monitor the stock levels on key parts and then replenish what's been used on a periodic basis," she said. "We'll also hold most of the stock in the stock room instead of at the production line."

"Yes, that's basically it," replied Joe.

"How often should I replenish the parts?" asked Sandy.

"Our belief is that with the current throughput levels, once a week should be sufficient," said Joe.

"But having said that, Benji is out trying to get us more business, so that frequency could change when the new orders come in," said Sam.

"Jerry, how soon do you think you can have this new system in place?" asked Becky.

"It all depends on how soon we can get the vendors to supply us with new stock levels of parts, but we should have some of our key parts here this week or early next week", Jerry replied. "I've got a conference call set up with our tank fabric supplier this afternoon because they have had trouble with late deliveries in the past," he said.

"As far as the other vendors go, I don't think there will be any problems.

"I do have a question, Sam," said Jerry. "How much of an increase in business do you think we will see?"

"We think around 30 percent or at least that's what Benji told us last night, but it could be higher," Joe explained.

"With that much of an increase, then I'm pretty sure we will have a problem with our fabric supplier," Jerry said. "I mean if he's already had problems supplying material with our current order level, then I'm pretty sure the problem will only get worse," he said.

"Where is your fabric supplier located and who are they?" asked Joe.

"The name of the company is Fabrics-R-Us," said Jerry, "and they're located here in Waterford." He added, "Instead of a conference call, maybe I should have him come here?"

"Maybe a better idea is that we go there instead," said Sam. "That way we could get a firsthand look at their process."

"I'll get in touch with them and let you know when we can go," said Jerry.

"Sounds good, Jerry, we'll hear from you," said Sam.

"Can I ask a question?" said Sandy.

"Yes," said Sam.

"I understand what I have to do to make this new system work, but why are we implementing it?" she asked.

"Great question, Sandy," said Becky. They spent the next twenty minutes explaining the IO Map and the Interference Diagram to Sandy, and then Joe asked her if she had any questions.

"Nope, it makes all the sense in the world to me, and the way you guys explained it makes me understand just how important my role becomes to the success of our plant," she replied. "Thanks so much for taking the time to explain it," she added.

"You're very welcome," replied Sam.

"It's not fair to ask you to change your work habits without giving you a reason why," said Joe.

"Let us know if you run into any supplier problems and when we can meet with our fabric supplier," said Sam. Then the three of them went back to Sam's office to plan the DBR rollout.

On their way back to Sam's office, the three of them talked about the meeting they had just had with Jerry and Sandy.

"I'm worried about the fabric supplier guys," said Joe. "They could be a show-stopper!"

"We can't let them be that," said Sam. "OK," he continued, "let's plan our DBR implementation, since it looks like the parts issue will be going away pretty soon," said Sam.

"Where do we start?" asked Becky.

"I think the best place to start is the customer due date," said Joe. "If we start there, we can work backwards through the process until we reach the release of raw materials at the beginning of the process."

"We also have to consider the planned buffer time in shipping and at joining too," said Sam. "I remember Connor telling us to calculate based on constraint capacity, and then add half of that back to get the total buffer," he said. The three of them worked on developing a DBR schedule, and within an hour they had their prototype schedule.

Just as they finished, Sam's phone rang and it was Jerry. "Fabrics-R-Us can meet us today at 2:00 p.m., if that's OK with you guys," said Jerry.

Sam confirmed the time with Joe, Sam and Becky, and he told Jerry, "Tell them we'll be there, Jerry."

"I want to take Stan with us, too," said Joe. "Stan can be looking at the process while we're meeting with their GM," he said.

"Good idea, Joe," said Sam.

"Let me call him right now," said Joe. Joe called Stan and confirmed that he was available. Joe said, "Good, I need you to go with Sam, Becky, Jerry and me to our fabric supplier. Be at Sam's office at 1:30 and we'll all go together."

"Sam," said Joe, "better call Jerry and have him call the supplier to let him know about our plans for Stan."

The Barton contingent arrived on schedule and were met by the Fabrics-R-Us General Manager. "Good afternoon, I'm Sid Sanchez," said the GM.

"I'm Jerry Dumas and this is Sam, Joe, Becky and Stan," said Jerry.

"And this is Sally Bergland, our Continuous Improvement Engineer," said Sid.

"Nice to meet everyone," said Sally.

"Sally, why don't you show Stan our process and the rest of us will go meet in my office," said Sid. He offered the visitors from Barton some coffee or a bottle of water.

"We're fine," said Jerry. "Here's what we want to talk with you about—Sid, Joe and Sam have made incredible improvements in our process to the point where our sales force is out looking to increase our orders by at least 30 percent and maybe higher," said Jerry. "I know you've had problems in the past meeting our current levels," he continued.

"You're right Jerry, we have had trouble sometimes. How soon do you expect your orders to reach this new level?" asked Sid.

Jerry looked at Sam, Joe and Becky and said, "Guys?"

"My guess is that within the next three weeks we'll start to see an influx of new orders," said Sam.

"Three weeks?" said a startled Sid. "You've got to be kidding! I need more advanced notice than three weeks!" he replied, obviously agitated now.

"Sid, we want to help you increase your throughput—that's why we brought Stan," said Sam. "He's a take-charge guy, and he did some amazing things at Barton in less than two weeks, so we think he can help you right away."

"Three weeks?" repeated Sid, "Stan would have to be a miracle worker," he said.

"Sam and I will help you, too," said Joe. "And if we can't, we know just the person who can," said Joe.

"Who's that?" asked Sid.

"A man who owns a bar," said Sam.

"A bar?" said Sid. "How could a guy who owns a bar help a guy who makes fabric?" asked Sid.

"The same way he helped a guy who makes tanks," replied Sam.

"Can we go look at your operations?" asked Joe.

"Sure thing," replied Sid, and they all walked out onto the production floor. They started at Receiving and walked their way through the entire process to Shipping. They saw large looms and cutters with inventory stacked high in several locations.

"Well Stan, have you found it?" asked Joe.

"I sure have," said Stan.

"Found what?" asked Sid.

"Your bottleneck operation," said Joe. Joe had already anticipated this, and as he had done at Barton, he handed Sid and Sally a copy of The Goal. "This will explain basically what we did at Barton to make the rapid improvements that we were able to achieve," said Joe.

"Actually, what we'd like to do is provide you and your staff some basic training on something called the Theory of Constraints," said Sam.

"We don't have a lot of time to get you ready for this increase in orders, so as soon as you can let us begin the process, the sooner we can help you," said Joe.

"Who do you think should receive this training?" asked Sid.

"To start with, you and your staff, but eventually everyone in your facility," replied Joe.

"When we get ready for your hourly employees, I want to have some of our hourly operators do the training," said Sam.

"We can start tomorrow if you like," said Sid.

"Stan, are you OK with tomorrow?" asked Joe.

"You bet, boss. What time?" he replied.

"How about 7:00 tomorrow morning?" asked Sid.

"We'll be ready for you, Sid," said Joe.

"See you tomorrow, Sally," said Stan.

"I look forward to it," replied Sally with a big smile.

"Anyone up for a drink?" asked Becky on the way back to Barton.

"I am," said Sam.

"Me too," said Joe.

"How about you, Stan," asked Becky.

"I'd love to, but I've got dinner plans tonight," said Stan.

"Who are you going to dinner with, Stan?" asked Joe.

"Sally," said Stan as he stared out the window of the car.

"Sally Bergland?" asked Becky.

"Yes," mumbled Stan.

"That was quick, Stan," said Becky, "and that explains the nice smile you got from her."

"We're just going to talk about business," replied an embarrassed Stan.

"Sure you are, Stan," replied Becky as she winked at Stan.

"Before we go to Jonah's, let's go back and get our list of metrics we developed and show them to Connor," said Becky.

"I brought it with me," said Joe.

The three of them jumped into their cars and sped off to Jonah's.

"Hi Connor, it's so nice to see you again," said Becky

"Same here, you look gorgeous today," replied Connor.

"Connor, you say the sweetest things," replied an embarrassed Becky.

"Have a seat while I go get us all a bottle of Chianti," said Connor.

"Fine, but tonight I'm paying for this bottle, Connor. No more freebies," said Becky.

Connor laughed and went to get the wine and glasses. Just as soon as he came back with the wine and filled the glasses, the conversation about performance metrics began. As Connor examined the list, everyone could see his eyebrows rise. "So guys, you've obviously thought through this list and covered virtually every part of your process, but I think you're missing the point about the kind of metrics you need to put in place," said Connor. "There are metrics that you want to track for trending purposes, for sure, but what you really want is something that is visual for the operators and supervisors to follow," he continued. "The shop floor people, more than anything, need to know the real time status of the orders. With that said, let me show you a very simple way to do that." Connor took out a piece of paper and drew a sketch of what he was about to explain.

Green	Yellow	Red
Safety Zone **0 to 1 day**	**Tracking Zone** **1 to 2 days**	**Expedite Zone** **2 to 3 days**

"Remember when I explained about the three tracking zones in DBR?" asked Connor.

Yes, they all nodded.

"I told you that these zones are supposed to be able to tell your operators, supervisors and managers, at a glance, the status of orders," said Connor. "For example, if your total historical lead time through the entire process is twelve days, and your time from material release to the constraint is six days, then your constraint buffer time should be half of that, or three days," Connor explained. "Since we divide the buffer into three equal zones, then what you should have posted at the constraint looks something like this," he said pointing to his sketch. "Of course it would be in real time, so you would actually have dates listed under each zone," he explained.

"You would also fill in the order number for each tank type like I have listed here for the shipping buffer," said Connor. "As long as the order is in the green safety zone, no action is required and your order is actually ahead of schedule," explained Connor. "If it falls into the yellow tracking zone, your guys would need to prepare plans to expedite it if it becomes necessary," he said. "If it falls into the red zone, then you execute the plans you've put in place, because if you don't, the order is guaranteed to be late," he explained. "This is just one example of how you can track your order status, but the bottom line is to keep it simple and visual," he said.

"That's a simple and easy way to understand the system Connor," said Sam.

"Remember," said Connor, "this simple system is built around your master production schedule that you must develop based upon customer due dates."

"Now as far as other metrics go, the list you have is fine for trend analysis," said Connor, "but not for day-to-day decision making. Your people need to know where they are and how they're doing in real time, and it needs to be something simple to understand," said Connor. "As I said, if you don't like the drawing that I've shown you, make something else, but please keep it simple."

"No, I like what you've sketched Connor," said Sam. "I know my guys, and they'll like it too," he added.

"I agree with Sam," said Joe. "I also agree that the list of metrics we came up with should not be used on a day-to-day basis, but rather as you said, for developing trends over the longer haul."

"I do have one question though," said Joe, "what about monitoring the release of raw materials to schedule?"

"That's up to you guys," said Connor. "Some people develop a walk-about-type thing where they have their production control people and supervisors check on whether or not the materials were released when scheduled," he said. "But remember, you don't ever want to release product into the system before it should be," explained Connor. "One of the main purposes of DBR is to make sure that this doesn't happen, so some kind of signal to the gating process is in order," he said. "Let me say this another way," continued Connor. "The rate that the gating operation is allowed to release material into production is dictated by the rate at which the constraint is producing. Got it?"

"Yes," said Sam.

"How about you, Joe?" asked Sam.

"I'm all set, so let's have a drink," said Joe.

They spent the rest of the evening talking about their visit to Fabrics-R-Us and how best to deliver the promised training.

"Tomorrow is a very important day everyone, so I think I'm going to call it a night," said Joe.

"Me too," said Sam.

Just as they were about ready to leave, Sam's phone rang. "Oh hi, Benji," said Sam as he sat back down. "Wow, Benji, that's great," said Sam as he covered the phone to share some sales information with Benji.

"Benji said he thinks he has a huge order from Simco, one of the largest helicopter manufacturer," whispered Sam to the others as he continued listening to Benji.

"When does he want to come, Benji?" asked Sam. "Tomorrow? Is there any way we could move it out by one day? . . . It's the only day, huh?" said Sam. "OK, what time will he be here? . . . OK, tell him we'll be ready . . . What do you mean he doesn't want to talk to us?" said Sam. "Oh, OK, I understand."

Sam hung up the phone and said, "Benji has a huge sale pending, but the customer, a man named Ron Parsons, insists on coming here tomorrow to check out our operation."

"But what about our plans at Fabrics-R-Us?" asked Joe.

"Believe it or not, Ron doesn't want to talk to any of us," said Sam, "He wants to talk to everyone else but us. He apparently wants to meet with operators and supervisors to see and hear firsthand what Benji has explained to him," said Sam. "Apparently he's having trouble believing all of the changes we've put in place," said Sam. "Quite frankly, I prefer that he talks to our operators," he said. "They understand what we've done and why we've done it, and they'd be more convincing anyway, in my opinion."

"I agree, but I'll call Stan and tell him to be there to help," said Joe.

"That's a great idea," said Sam. "Alright, I'm leaving for the night, see you early tomorrow," said Sam.

"Hold on, I'm leaving too," said Joe.

"You ready to go Becky?" asked Joe.

"I think I'll stay for a little while longer if I can get Connor to take me to my hotel?" said Becky.

"Twist my arm, Becky," said Connor playfully. "I'd be happy to escort you back to your hotel."

"Good night, guys," said Becky with a smile.

Chapter 13
Fabrics-R-Us

Sam, Becky, Joe and Jerry met in Sam's office at 6:00 a.m. to make sure they had all bases covered for their trip to Fabrics-R-Us.

"I was thinking about our visit to Fabrics today, and their success is clearly the lynchpin for our success here," said Sam.

"You're right, Sam. We've got to do this right today," said Joe.

"I thought about how we might have the biggest impact on them today, and here's how I think it should roll out," said Sam. "First, I'd like to review what the state of our business was before we began this incredible change process, and we can actually share the performance metrics we had in place," said Sam. "I think they'll relate what they hear to their own business."

"I like that idea," said Joe.

"Me too," said Becky.

"I'd like to save the 'after' results until the end of our presentation so they can see what's possible," said Sam.

"I agree," said Joe, with Becky nodding in agreement.

"I thought then that you could pass out copies of The Goal to everyone," Sam continued, "and we'll ask them to read it in very short order."

"Next," said Sam,"I thought either you or Becky could give them a brief introduction to TOC using the piping diagram and the four-step process, and then have a discussion about what they heard. And I'd then like to take them on a Herbie Hunt to look for their constraint," Sam said. "Then we could come back and finish with a presentation of what we look like now."

"Sam, what's a Herbie hunt?" asked Becky.

"Remember from The Goal the really slow boy scout named Herbie?" said Sam. "Herbie was the constraint for the troop," Sam explained. "I want us to go find Fabric's herbie," said Sam.

"Ok, I understand Sam, I really love your approach!" said Becky.

"I love it, Sam!" exclaimed Joe.

"I think it's well thought out, and it should make a big impact on everyone at Fabrics," said Becky. "Great job, Sam!"

"I've got the presentation all laid out, so if you guys are OK with it, let's go to Fabrics," said Sam.

"I do have one slide I'd like to add," said Joe as he handed Sam a flash drive.

"What's on this, Joe?" asked Sam.

"It's just some key concepts that Fabrics will have to put in place to be successful," said Joe.

"I have an idea, guys," said Becky. "I think we should invite them all to come visit Barton as soon as possible to see firsthand what our new process looks like. I also think they should bring some of their hourly employees to meet with ours," she continued. "It's one thing to hear a message from management, but it's a completely different thing to hear it from another hourly employee," said Becky.

"What if we took a couple of hourly employees who are good speakers and had them put on a training session?" asked Joe.

"That could really make an impact," said Sam.

"We'd better get going if we're going to be there by 7:00," said Joe, and with that the four of them piled into Sam's car and drove to Fabrics-R-Us.

Right on schedule the Barton contingent pulled into Fabrics-R-Us and walked into a beautifully decorated lobby, which appeared to have samples of Fabrics' high-end fabric draped on the walls. Sam introduced himself to the receptionist, and she said, "Mr. Sanchez is expecting you, have a seat and I'll let him know you are here." Fifteen minutes later Sid Sanchez appeared, apologized for making them wait and welcomed them to Fabrics. They followed Sid to the company conference room that was filled with Sid's staff and others. Sam leaned over to Joe and whispered, "Did you bring enough copies of The Goal with you, Joe?" Joe nodded that he had.

"I want to formally welcome you to Fabrics-R-Us," said Sid, and then one-by-one introduced his staff. "We thought that it might be helpful for Barton if we presented our current state of the business so that you'd have a better picture of where we are from a business perspective," said Sid.

The Barton group listened intently as Sid and other members of his team discussed a series of topics, including their key performance indicators and their overall business strategy. As they talked, it became apparent that Fabrics had some issues that needed resolved if they were to become a reliable supplier for Barton. It all sounded very familiar to Sam, Becky, Joe and Jerry.

Fabrics' primary performance metrics were manpower efficiency and equipment utilization, which were both centered around 88 percent, yet their on-time delivery (OTD) averaged 65 percent over the last year. They were proud to tell Barton that their OTD to Barton was approximately 87 percent. But when questioned about the disparity between the OTD to Barton and their current average for all suppliers, Fabrics explained that the Barton numbers were due to heroic efforts on their part—as though they were proud of that. They also discussed their internal quality metric, first-pass yield and customer material return rates, which were both at unacceptable levels to suit Barton.

Sid finished his presentation by thanking Barton for selecting them as suppliers, and he said that Fabrics was ready to do whatever was necessary to satisfy Barton's needs. Then he turned the meeting over to Sam and Joe.

Sam thanked Sid for sharing their state of the business as he loaded his presentation. The first slide Sam presented was an agenda for today's meeting. "As you can see," Sam began, "we'd like to start today with a summary of what Barton Enterprises' performance was a little over two weeks ago," he said. "I say was because in a very short period of time, thanks to Joe and our operators, Barton has executed a remarkable transformation, which I'll cover at the end of our presentation."

"Our first order of business today is a gift from Joe for each of you," said Sam as he nodded for Joe to pass out copies of *The Goal* to all of the Fabrics' management team. "When Joe gave me this book, I have to tell you I was skeptical, but the message in it has completely changed my approach to manufacturing, so I encourage you all to read it and discuss it together," said Sam.

Sam's next slide was a review of Barton's performance metrics, which were remarkably similar to Fabrics'. "As you can clearly see, not unlike Fabrics, Barton was struggling to meet customer due dates with our OTD rate at roughly 60 percent," Sam explained. "Our major customers were all calling about their late orders with threats of cancellation. We were in a constant fire-fighting mode, and our overtime rate was going through the roof," said Sam. Heads were bobbing up and down indicating that the Fabrics' management team could relate to what they saw on the screen. "Our morale was terrible and our bottom line was suffering,"

Sam continued. "I was constantly being summoned to our corporate headquarters to explain our performance, and on the last trip I was given a mandate to either improve in two months or I would be out of a job. I had no idea what to change or what to do to turn things around," he said. "But everything changed when this man, Joe Pecci, came to work at Barton," said Sam. "As you listen today, keep in mind that Joe Pecci has only been here less than three weeks, but in this short time he has convinced me that there is a better way to run a railroad," said Sam.

"What we'd like to do next is have Joe present what he showed to me three weeks ago," said Sam.

"Thanks, Sam," said Joe. "Everything Sam has told you is true except for the part that I am the reason why things are better," he said. "I may have been the catalyst, but I did not make this performance change by myself, not by a long shot." Joe continued. "There are really six core elements that must be in place for a turnaround to be successful," he said as he flashed his next slide on the screen. Without these six key elements, success will simply not occur!" said Joe.

Core Elements for Success

- **Total commitment and leadership from Senior Leadership with an open mind.**
- **An effective process for managing change in an ever-changing environment**
- **Complete and total involvement of the entire workforce.**
- **A robust design for a new business process.**
- **A captive audience ready for change and a burning platform requiring change.**
- **A total management commitment to a process of on-going improvement.**

"Based upon what we heard this morning about Fabrics' performance," said Joe, "I think we have both a captive audience and a burning platform. But as you will hear, this captive audience must include your entire workforce." He continued, "No matter what you tell your workforce, unless and until they not only accept change, but embrace it, nothing will happen. They must not just be involved, they must be actively involved in designing your processes of the future," said Joe. "You, the leadership team, must be willing to give up the total control you now have—and I have to be honest—some of you won't be able to do that," he said. "Those of you who can let go will grow and flourish, but those of you who won't, will not," Joe said. "It all boils down to can't versus won't, my friends—it's that simple."

Sam leaned over and whispered in Becky's ear, "He's good isn't he?"

She whispered back, "I've got goose bumps just listening to him, and look at the absolute focus on their faces." Becky was right, Joe had this team focused on his every word.

Joe then presented his now infamous piping diagram and the four-step process to introduce the concept of constraints. Everyone in the room showed interest in everything Joe had to say. They answered each of Joe's questions with enthusiasm and fervor. Sam and Becky could see the transformation in thinking taking place before their eyes.

Joe then presented the concept of Throughput Accounting, and he showed why cost-accounting-based metrics like efficiency and utilization only served to lengthen cycle times, grow inventory and cause missed customer due dates. "This is why you have to be willing to abandon these two metrics," said Joe.

"But our performance as a plant is measured by these metrics," said Sid. "Our corporate office will never go along with abandoning them," he exclaimed.

"Sid, it all comes down to answering this one question," Joe replied. "Do you want high efficiencies and utilizations, or do you want high levels of on-time delivery and customer satisfaction? You can't have both, Sid!" Joe continued, "We at Barton faced the same conflict you are facing, and we decided that to turn ourselves around, we had to be bold and courageous and had to take a stand. If you aren't willing to do the same thing, then we're wasting our time here today—it's that simple," Joe said. "So what do you think, Sid?"

"I think you've convinced me," replied Sid.

"OK, then let's begin your transformation," said Joe.

Sam ended the first part of the presentation with Barton's current performance metrics—the most obvious being on-time delivery, which now stood at 97 percent.

"Sam, let's show them what we have in mind," said Joe.

"OK, Joe," said Sam, "one of the first things we'd like to do is have you come to Barton and see what we're doing. We'd like you to bring a group from Fabrics that includes some of your hourly employees and have them all meet their counterparts at Barton," continued Sam. "In fact, we were thinking that some of our more polished hourly employees would actually teach your hourly employees."

"I really like that idea, Sam," said Sid as he scanned his team for support.

Sam continued. "You met Stan Wilson, one of Joe's black belts, the other day, and we're thinking that he would lead this effort," said Sam. "He and Sally could be the team leaders and actually lead your transition team,"

"I had the same idea Sam," said Sid. "How soon do you think we could get started?" he asked.

"Whenever you are ready, we'll be ready to assist," replied Sam. Then Sam said, "Look, we've been going on for over four hours, so I'd like to suggest that we take a break."

"I agree, Sam," said Sid. "I need to make a couple of phone calls anyway."

"Sam, I'm going to step outside and call Stan and Benji to see how things are going with Simco," said Joe.

"Good idea, Joe," replied Sam.

Joe stepped outside and made his call to Stan. "Hey Stan, how is the visit going?" asked Joe.

"I really couldn't tell you, Joe, since Ron Parsons doesn't allow Benji and me out on the floor with him," replied Stan.

"Well, how does it look like it's going?" asked Joe.

"The only thing I can tell you is that one of our operators came in and borrowed our flip chart and took it to the floor to show Ron," said Stan. "I could see that he drew the piping system and looked like he was explaining the concept of the constraint. He then drew the four-step process and apparently asked Ron to come and locate the constraint on the drawing," said Stan. "Then they walked over to the joining operation and I lost all contact with them.

"Ron did ask what time you, Becky and Sam would be back, and I told him I wasn't sure," said Stan. "He apparently wants to meet with you later today to give you a debrief. Why don't you call me in a couple of hours and maybe by then I'll be able to tell you something," said Stan. "Oh, hey, I just saw them walking to supply."

"OK, Stan, I'll call you later," said Joe.

Joe went back inside and told Sam about what one of his hourly employees had done, and Sam's smile went from ear to ear. "We need to find out which of my operators did this and do something special for him," said Sam.

"I agree," said Joe.

"I hope everything went well with Simco today, but I guess we'll find out soon enough," said Sam.

The rest of the afternoon was spent laying out the Fabrics improvement plan and the key learning points, and scheduling Fabrics' visit to Barton.

As the Barton people wrapped things up and prepared to leave, Sid said, "I want to thank everyone for such an enlightening day. We want to be Barton's supplier of choice, and we look forward to our new journey." And Sid shook hands with everyone in attendance.

"I guess we'll see you guys tomorrow," said Sam.

"Count on it," said Sid. And with that, the Barton contingent left to return to their manufacturing facility to meet with Ron Parsons, the Simco sales rep that led the visit to Barton.

When they arrived at Sam's office, Stan and Benji were discussing Ron's visit.

"Hey guys, where's Ron?" asked Sam.

"He's gone," said Stan.

"Gone?" said Joe and Sam together. "Where did he go?" asked Sam.

"He went back to his hotel to change clothes," said Benji.

"What did he say? How did the visit go?" asked Joe.

"We don't know," replied Benji.

"But he does want to meet with all of us," said Stan.

"Is he coming back here?" asked Sam.

"No, he asked me where a good place away from Barton would be to just relax, sit and talk about what he saw today, so I told him Jonah's," said Benji.

"Did you tell him that Jonah's is a bar and only serves sandwiches?" asked Sam.

"I sure did," said Benji.

"And he was OK with that?" asked Joe.

"Yes, he was. In fact all he said was, 'Perfect,' " said Benji.

"What time are we meeting him there?" asked Sam.

"In about forty-five minutes," said Benji.

"Did he give you any indication at all about his feelings about Barton?" asked Sam.

"Nope, none at all," said Benji.

"Which operator was he talking to?" asked Sam.

"Timmie," said Stan.

"Let's go talk to Timmie before we go to Jonah's," said Sam.

"Hi, Timmie," said Sam, "How did it go today with Ron Parsons?" asked Sam.

"I'm not sure," said Timmie. "He's a hard man to read. I did my best to explain what we're doing here, and he asked some really good questions," Timmie said.

"Like what?" asked Sam.

"Well, for one, he wanted to know if I thought we could sustain what we're doing here," said Timmie.

"What did you tell him?" asked Sam.

"I said, of course we can," said Timmie. "I told him that because it was our process, we don't allow anyone to change it."

"Who else did he talk to, Timmie?" asked Joe.

I think he talked to almost everyone on the floor, and the people in the stock room," replied Timmie.

"How do you think that went?" asked Becky.

"I think Sandy did a real good job of explaining how we are not going to run out of any parts anymore," said Timmie.

"We need to go, Sam," said Joe.

"Timmie, I want to thank you for what you did today, and please thank everyone else for me," said Sam.

"Did we get more business Sam?" asked Timmie.

"We're going to go find out," said Sam. "And thanks again."

Sam, Becky and Joe jumped into Sam's car and headed for Jonah's. They talked about what they thought they were going to hear from Ron Parsons.

"Do you think he'll have positive things to say about Barton?" asked Becky.

"I really don't know what he's going to say," said Sam. "All I know is that my guys did the best they could, and that's good enough for me,"

"I've never seen a customer come in and only talk to the workers before," said Joe.

"Me either, but when you stop and think about it, it's a good way of finding out if a company is actually living their values and principles," said Sam.

As they pulled into Jonah's, they noticed an empty parking lot, which was strange for Jonah's. Once again, there was a sign on the front door that said CLOSED, and for a brief moment everyone panicked until Connor met them at the door.

"Hi Connor," said Becky.

Sam said, "We were worried that you were closed, and we have a major customer coming here."

"Yes, I know," said Connor. "Stan called me and told me all about it, so I decided to give you guys some privacy. I know how important this meeting is for Barton," Connor said.

"You really didn't have to do that," said Sam.

"It's no big deal," said Connor.

Just then a car pulled into the parking lot, and a very tall, handsome, and muscular man got out and waved to Benji.

"Hey, Ron," said Benji. "That's Ron Parsons," said Benji to the group as he waved back.

"How tall is he?" asked Becky.

"I'd say around six foot seven in his stocking feet," said Benji.

Everyone introduced themselves to Ron and went into Jonah's and sat down at two tables Connor had set up for them. Ron spoke first, saying, "I want to thank you for allowing me to come to Barton and meet with your people."

"It was our pleasure," said Sam.

"Do you always go to suppliers and meet with only the shop floor people?" asked Joe.

"Yes, I do," said Ron, "It's the only way I have found to determine whether or not the sales people like Benji are bull shitting me about their companies," explained Ron. "I have been burned in the past, so about three years ago I tried this technique, and it worked so well that I do it with every supplier," he said.

"So Ron, can I ask how we did today?" said Sam.

"Can we get a drink first?" said Ron, "I'm really thirsty."

"Yes, of course," said Sam as he signaled to Connor. Sam thought to himself, "Since he wants a drink first, it must not be very good news." Sam introduced Connor to Ron and gave Ron some background information on how Connor had helped Barton with their turnaround.

When everyone was served, Ron began. "I really didn't know what to expect before I got here. Benji and I had discussions about how you were able to go from chronically late on orders to being totally on time in only two weeks. After listening to Benji's stories, I must say I was very skeptical," Ron said. "I personally had never experienced such a rapid turnaround in supplier performance before, so a trip here was compulsory for me."

Ron went on, "The most important thing I use to judge a potential supplier is whether or not the people building our products actually know and understand the system they are working in," he said. "I look for intangible things like pride in their work, confidence and knowledge of their customers and the products they're producing." Ron continued, "I met with almost every operator on the floor, and I have to tell you that they all impressed me with these intangibles I just mentioned."

"Then," Ron said, "I try to understand the system that the operators are working in. I look at things like the order entry and scheduling process, the parts supply system, the quality system, the performance metrics that are being used—you know, system things," he continued. "By looking at these factors, I get an overall impression of how things might work in the future if more orders are added," said Ron.

Sam thought to himself impatiently, "Please get to the point Ron. Did we get the orders or not?"

Ron continued, "I picked out one of your operators, Timmie, and he walked me through the entire process from beginning to end. As we walked through it, I stopped and talked to every operator just to make sure they all understood the system at Barton's in which they worked," said Ron.

"At one point Timmie asked me if it would be alright for him to get a flip chart so that I could see the process from the operator's perspective, and of course, I agreed," he said. "Timmie started out by sketching, of all things, a piping system. At the time, I thought to myself, what the hell does a piping system have to do with fuel tanks? But in very short order, Timmie made me see its relevance." Ron paused. "I was not at all familiar with the Theory of Constraints before I came to Barton," said Ron. "But I have to tell you, Timmie taught me well."

"Can I get a refill Connor?" asked Ron. "This is really good wine. I've never had Chianti before and I love it."

"It's become our drink of choice here at Jonah's," said Becky.

"By the way, Connor, how did you come up with the name 'Jonah's?" asked Ron.

Joe reached into his briefcase and handed Ron a copy of *The Goal*. "The answer to that question is in here."

"Thank you, I'll read some of it tonight," said Ron.

"You might want to wait a day or two because it's the type of book that you don't want to put down," said Joe.

"As I was saying, I had never heard of TOC before, but I plan to learn all I can about it," said Ron. "Timmie went on to explain how your orders were always late, and that with a few simple changes—simple according to Timmie anyway,—Barton went from always late to always on time," he said. "And according to Timmie, the change was immediate.

"But after talking to everyone on the shop floor, here's the thing that impressed me the most," said Ron. "The operators do own their process! And what's more, management trusts them to own it," said Ron. "Timmie explained that you allowed the operators to design their new process, and Timmie saw that as the breakthrough here at Barton," he said. "Benji and I had talked about a potential for up to a 30 percent increase in orders if I liked what I saw," said Ron.

"So after taking into account all of what I've seen and heard today, I'm afraid I cannot offer to buy 30 percent more products from Barton," he explained as the faces around the table turned from smiles to frowns. "I'm actually thinking it will be closer to 40 percent!"

Everyone looked at each other, and spontaneous high fives erupted.

"We'll work out the details of the order ramp-up tomorrow, but for now please know that I have never been more impressed with a supplier than I am with Barton, and I don't pass out compliments lightheartedly," said Ron. "I have never met a workforce before that was so engaged and so in touch with their company," he said.

"One thing I didn't mention was my conversation with Miss Peters about your parts supply system," said Ron. "It's ingeniously simple, and something I'd like our parts supply people to come study and learn," he said. "We've had a chronic parts supply problem, and I'd like our supply people to mimic what you have in place here at Barton."

"I also am very impressed with your Drum-Buffer-Rope scheduling system," said Ron. "I have never heard of this type system before, and I wanted to ask you if you think that's something we could copy and use at Simco?" asked Ron.

Connor spoke up and said, "Ron, I don't know much about your business. What all do you do at Simco?" asked Connor.

Ron replied, "Our primary business is building rotary-wing aircraft for a wide range of customers. Some are commercial, but most are for the military," explained Ron. "I was thinking that since we are typically late with our orders to customers, that your DBR system might work well for us," he said.

"It might," said Connor, "but I think what might work better is something called Critical Chain Project Management, or CCPM for short," said Connor. "Critical what?" asked Becky, "What is that and how does it work?" she asked.

"Yes, I would definitely be interested in hearing about that," said a very interested Ron.

"It's another type scheduling system that is also TOC-based," said Connor. "But in order to you to understand CCPM, we'll need a little more time than we have tonight," said Connor. "Any chance you could come back tomorrow Ron?" asked Connor. "Yes, I could do that because I really don't have to be back to work until Monday," replied Ron.

Sam asked, "Connor, do you want to come to Barton and explain it?"

Ron objected, "Could we do it here instead? I really like this place, and the Chianti is great."

"We sure can," said Connor.

"But don't close the bar again, Connor, you do have a revenue stream to protect," said Ron.

"How about 5:00 p.m. tomorrow? Will that time work for everyone?" asked Connor. Everyone nodded affirmatively. "OK then, I'll see you all tomorrow around 5:00 p.m.," said Connor.

So the new deal had been sealed with a handshake, once again at their favorite watering hole. "It's getting late and we've got a lot to do tomorrow, so I think I'm going to call it a night," said Ron.

"I'll walk you to your car Ron," said Sam, "I need a cigarette anyway."

"Me too, Sam, wait for me," said Joe. Joe and Sam puffed on their cigarettes as though they were victory cigars until Sam said, "It's going to be a fun time, Joe."

"Yes it is," said Joe.

"Becky, are you ready to leave?" asked Joe.

"No, you go ahead. I'll have my driver take me to my hotel," said Becky, smiling and pointing to Connor.

Chapter 14
Training Fabrics and Greg

Right on schedule, the first wave of employees from Fabrics-R-Us arrived at 7:00 a.m. sharp. As a show of support for the event, Sid Sanchez, Fabrics General Manager, had rented an oversized van and designated himself as the driver. Stan Wilson had worked very hard to set up Barton's training room with several flip charts in place and his PowerPoint presentation loaded and ready to go. The first to arrive at the training room was Sally Bergland, Fabrics' Continuous Improvement Engineer, who was to be the coleader with Stan of the improvement effort at Fabrics. Both Stan and Sally were happy to see each other and gave each other a hug. Little did anyone know that Stan and Sally had been dating since they first met at Fabrics.

One by one, the Fabrics' employees entered the training room, and when everyone was seated, Sid kicked off the training session. Sid was an excellent speaker and his message to his employees was both passionate and motivating for everyone. He spoke of forging a new partnership with Barton—a new supplier-customer relationship based on mutual trust and sharing of ideas and information.

Sam was next to speak and welcomed everyone to Barton. He also spoke of a new relationship and encouraged everyone to relax, have an open mind and enjoy themselves. Sam then turned the proceedings over to Stan and Sally. Both Sam and Sid sat in the back of the room for a short while and then excused themselves and quietly left. Sid had business back at Fabrics, and Sam was expecting Ron and Benji to come in and discuss the new business coming Barton's way. This day was to be a turning point for Barton's storied history, and Sam was excited.

It was nearly 9:00 a.m. before Benji and Ron arrived at Barton, and neither one of them seemed very energetic. "Good morning guys, battery running low this morning?" asked Sam.

"Uh yeah, just a bit," said Ron.

"How's Becky feeling this morning?" asked Benji.

"I haven't seen her yet this morning," said Sam.

"Based on how much she had to drink last night, she may not be in until this afternoon," said Ron.

"What did you guys do after Joe and I left?" asked Sam. "I thought you were going back to your hotel, Ron."

"I was, but I decided to come back for one last glass of Chianti, and since Becky and Benji were still there, we decided to get a bottle . . . and then one turned into two and well, the rest is history," said Ron. "Let's just say we probably drank our fill for the week," said Ron.

"Ron wants to go to the floor this morning and say hello to the troops," said Benji. "He especially wants to thank Timmie for his tour yesterday."

"How are things running today?" asked Ron.

"I'll be honest with you Ron, I've been working on my weekly report and haven't been out there yet," replied Sam.

"We'll get out of your hair then so you can finish your report," said Benji.

"I'll catch up with you guys in a little while," said Sam.

Sam went back to put the finishing touches on his report and marveled at the new numbers. Overall plant efficiency was down for the third straight week at 63.6 percent, but the constraint efficiency now stood at 95.7 percent. Barton's on-time delivery was up to 98.8 percent, and because the backlog of tanks on the J40, J50 and J60 lines had been reduced from an average of six tops and six bottoms, Barton's revenue increased by well over $150,000 for the week. Plant overtime was down to nearly zero, but because of the bump in hourly pay that Cecil authorized, nobody was complaining about the lack of overtime. Net profit during the same time frame appeared to have increased from its normal 6 percent to roughly 15.9 percent. The results amazed Sam.

Just as Sam was putting the finishing touches on his report, Benji came to his office and said, "Sam, I think you need to come out to the floor right away—we have a big problem."

"What's wrong, Benji?" asked Sam.

"I think you need to hear it for yourself," said Benji.

Sam jumped out of his chair and rushed to the shop floor. "Go ahead, Timmie, tell Sam what you told us," said Benji.

"Well sir, after you all left last night, Mr. Daniels came out onto the shop floor with Mr. Johnson," said Timmie.

Ron asked, "Who are these guys?"

Benji replied, "Timmie is talking about Gregory Daniels, Barton's President and CEO and Paul Johnson, our Director of Finance."

"Go ahead, Timmie, what happened?" asked Sam.

"Well, as I said, Mr. Daniels and Mr. Johnson came to the floor and started yelling at us for not working hard enough," said Timmie. "Mr. Daniels kept telling us that our efficiencies looked terrible and that heads were going to roll if we didn't fix it right away," Timmie said. "I tried my best to explain our new system, but he told me he didn't want to hear any bullshit excuses! Those were his exact words," said Timmie. He even made us start three new tanks even though our DBR system said that we shouldn't."

"I'm really sorry that happened, Timmie, and I promise you I will go see him right away," said Sam. "In the meantime, I'll stop the new tanks from being made."

"Sam, this is really serious and until it's resolved, I'm afraid I can't increase my orders for more tanks," said Ron. "I need reliable suppliers, and if your CEO isn't buying into what you're doing, well . . ."

"I'm sure it's just a misunderstanding on Greg's part," Sam continued. "He's been in Europe for the past three weeks on vacation, so he hasn't been the beneficiary of all of this."

"Well, all I know is that I can't approve the new orders until he's on board," said Ron.

"I'll take care of this right away," said Sam. He got on his cell phone and found Joe. "Joe, we have a major problem and I need your help," said Sam.

"What's the problem, Sam?" asked Joe. "Where are you Joe?" asked Sam. "I'm in my office," replied Joe. "I'll be there in five minutes, so stay put," said Sam.

"Joe, we have a huge problem," said Sam with a very worried look on his face.

"Have a seat, Sam, and tell me what's going on," said Joe.

Sam explained what had happened to Timmie after they left for Jonah's yesterday, and Joe could feel the panic in Sam's voice.

"What's bad is, Ron is now questioning whether he should give us the new orders," said Sam. "In fact, he's not going to authorize them until Mr. Daniels is on board!"

"This is serious," said Joe. "What started all of this?"

"All I know is that Mr. Daniels and Paul were both in my shop last night and—"

"Paul?" Joe interrupted, "that explains everything." said Joe.

"Apparently before Mr. Daniels left for vacation, Paul told him that our efficiency was down to 63 percent from the mid-80s, and Mr. Daniels lost it," Sam explained.

"We need to go meet with Mr. Daniels right away, or we're going to lose the workforce and our new orders," said Joe.

Sam's phone rang and he answered it. " Hi, Becky, where are you?" he said.

"I'm in my hotel room," said Becky. "I have to catch a plane in two hours."

"Where are you going, Becky?" asked Sam.

"Back to corporate. Cecil has called a meeting with the rest of the board and he wants me there to talk about Barton's accomplishments," she explained. "It's all part of the reconfiguration of the performance metrics team that Cecil told us about."

Sam proceeded to tell Becky about what had happened in the plant yesterday afternoon, and about how Ron was going to withhold his new orders until it was all resolved. Needless to say, Becky was as upset as Sam was.

"Joe and I are going to go meet with Mr. Daniels this morning, and I'd really like you to come with us, if you can," said Sam.

"Let me see if I can get in touch with Cecil, and I'll get back to you," said Becky.

"Alright Becky, but call me back as soon as you can. I'm here with Joe," said Sam.

Five minutes later Becky called Sam and said that she had to go to Corporate, but that he should call her as soon as the meeting with the CEO was finished.

"Let's go, Joe, we've got to nip this in the bud right away," said Sam.

Sam and Joe headed directly for the CEO's office, and fortunately he was in talking with Paul. Sam told Mr. Daniels' executive secretary that he had to meet with him right away, but she told Sam to have a seat and she would let Mr. Daniels know that Sam and Joe were there.

She returned and said, "He says he can't meet with you right now."

Sam lost it for a moment and opened the CEO's door anyway. "Sir, we need to meet with you right now!" he said.

"You're in enough trouble, Sam, and you don't need to make matters worse by forcing yourself in here unannounced," said Mr. Daniels. "You can get on my schedule just like everyone else, and close the damn door on your way out!" he commanded.

"But sir, this is really important!" said Sam.

"Get on my schedule, Sam, and I don't want to tell you again!" he replied, obviously irritated.

Sam could see Paul smirking at him, which infuriated him even more.

"And Sam, don't you ever intrude on my time again. I am the CEO of this company!" said Mr. Daniels in a very condescending voice.

"Get me on his schedule right away," said Sam to Mr. Daniels' assistant.

"He can see you this afternoon at 3:00 p.m.," she said.

"That's four hours from now, can't you work us in any sooner than that?" asked Sam in a panic.

"Let's see," she said. "He has a meeting with the Kiwanis club president at 1:00 . . . how much time do you need?" she asked.

"At least an hour," replied Sam.

"No, I'm afraid that the only block of time he has is at 3:00. Should I pencil you in for that time?" she asked.

"Yes!" exclaimed Sam.

Sam called Becky back and let her know that they wouldn't be meeting with Mr. Daniels until 3:00, but that he would call her immediately after the meeting.

"Do you want me to let Cecil know what's going on down here, or do you want me to wait until you call me, Sam?" asked Becky.

"Let's wait," said Sam.

"Alright, I'm leaving for the airport now. Call me when you know more, Sam," she said.

"I will, and have a safe trip, Becky," he replied.

"Let's go and meet with Ron and Benji and see if we can salvage what we gained last night," said Sam. Off the two of them went.

It was obvious to both Sam and Joe that shop-floor morale had taken a hit because of the antics of Paul and Mr. Daniel's yesterday, so they had to get into a damage- control mode right away. Sam and Joe walked the shop floor and talked to as many operators as they could, but it was clearly evident that significant damage had been done. The familiar zest and zeal of the work force was missing today, and Sam was worried. No matter what he said to the operators, leads and supervisors, it seemed to lack impact. The mood had clearly changed, and Sam didn't know what he could do to fix it, at least in the short term.

"Joe, I'm prepared to put my career on the line for these guys, so at three o'clock I'm going to be honest and frank with Mr. Daniels," said Sam.

"I'll be right beside you Sam, every step and every word of the way," replied Joe.

The day dragged on, and nothing that Sam or Joe said would change Ron's mind about putting a hold on the increase in orders. Clearly Ron was disappointed with the events that had taken place yesterday afternoon. He said, "Guys, I'm going back to my hotel and think things through, and if something changes, give me a call."

"I'm sorry about all of this Ron, but I'm confident that we'll have a positive meeting with Mr. Daniels," said Sam.

"I certainly hope so," said Ron. "I would still like to meet with Connor about CCPM tonight, if that's OK with you guys."

"That's fine with us, Ron," said Sam.

"Alright, see you at Jonah's around 5:00," said Ron as he left.

Three o'clock finally arrived, and Sam and Joe were right on-time. "He'll see you now gentlemen," said Mr. Daniels' assistant. As they entered his office Mr. Daniels told them to close the door and have a seat.

"I don't know who you think you are, Sam, but you're not in a position to make the kind of wholesale changes you've made to my company!" said Mr. Daniels. "I've invited Paul to be here so that we can discuss your performance over the last three weeks," he said. "An efficiency of 63 percent is totally unacceptable, and I want it fixed immediately or I swear I will fire your ass, Sam!"

Mr. Daniels went on. "Paul also told me about this new financial math bullshit called Throughput Accounting," he said.

Sam couldn't control himself, and he said, "Well, Paul is an asshole and wouldn't know how to make money if his life depended on it!" Sam was upset and he did not hold back.

"How dare you use that tone of voice with me, Sam," said Paul.

"I only speak the truth, Paul!" replied Sam.

"Sir, if we could just have your attention and if you'll allow us to explain, I think you'll see why it's a better way to make decisions," said Joe in a very calm voice.

"You're the new CI man, aren't you?" asked Mr. Daniels. "Paul has told me all about you, how you came in here and filled everyone's head with all these new theories. I've been in manufacturing for thirty years, and I know how to run a business," said the CEO.

"But if you'll just listen for a minute, it will all make sense," said Joe.

"I don't have time for your theories and bullshit, I have a company to run!" Mr. Daniels replied. "This meeting is over, and Sam, you have three days to get Barton back on track, or you can clean out your desk and leave," said the CEO.

"Have you even looked at the latest financial results and on-time deliveries to our customers?" asked Sam.

"I said this meeting is over!" said Mr. Daniels.

Sam and Joe left the CEO's office and headed directly for the shop floor. Sam called a meeting of everyone on the floor including all operators, leads and supervisors. When everyone was in place, Sam spoke, "First, I want to apologize for what happened yesterday. There was no excuse for it. What you guys have to do is get back to where you were before yesterday," he said. "I will be honest with you, I am not prepared to lie down and let Mr. Daniels change what we have put in place!" Sam spoke in a passionate voice. "I need you to continue on with me until my last breath!" he said. "Will you do that?"

"Yes!" said everyone.

He exhorted them. "Are you with me?"

"Yes, we are!" was the reply.

"Now go make us some money!" he yelled. It was clear that Sam's passionate plea had worked. The workers left full of energy and enthusiasm, recapturing their familiar gait as they walked back to their jobs. Now, Sam had to figure out how he was going to back his words with actions. He decided to call Becky and let her know the outcome of the meeting with the CEO and Paul.

"Hi Becky, its Sam," he said.

"Hi Sam, how did your meeting go with Greg Daniels?" she asked.

"Oh just peachy, if you consider that he's given me until Friday to get the efficiencies back up over 80%," said Sam.

"But Sam, you know you can't do that," she replied. "What did he say when you went through your TOC presentation?" she asked.

"He didn't let us make that presentation, Becky," replied Sam. "He was too interested in dressing me down for letting things get out of hand," Sam continued. "And Paul gave us absolutely no support."

"Paul was in the meeting too, and he didn't support what you're doing?" she asked.

"No, as a matter of fact, I'm pretty sure he was the instigator in all of this," said Sam.

"Has Greg seen the new profit numbers and on-time delivery?" she asked.

"I have no idea," replied Sam. "And what about the new orders from Simco?" she asked.

"They're completely on hold until everything is resolved," replied Sam. "Ron wants to give us the increase in orders, but he says he just can't if things go back to where they were."

"I need to go meet with Cecil right away," said Becky. "Goodbye, Sam.

"Call me later," said Sam.

"So Joe, what do you think we should do about Daniels and Johnson?" asked Sam.

Joe thought for a minute and then said, "Sam we both know what we have to do. We owe it to the men and women on the line who moved outside their comfort zone and turned Barton into a potential world-class company," he said. "We must take a stand Sam, even if it means losing our jobs!"

"I couldn't agree with you more," said Sam. "Let's take a walk and see our heroes, just to reinforce the conviction that nothing is going to change."

Sam and Joe spent the next hour and a half on their production line providing reassurance to all the workers. They made sure that everyone was still conforming to the rules of DBR and buffer management, and not surprisingly, they all were.

On their way back to his office, Sam received a text message from Becky that said, "Cecil and I will be there tomorrow morning. Don't tell anyone we're coming—explain later." Clearly Becky and Cecil intended this to be a surprise visit.

Sam showed Joe the text.

Joe asked, "What do you think is going to happen tomorrow?"

"I don't know, Joe," said Sam. "But you can bet it will be in the best interests of Barton," he added.

Just then, Sam received another text message from Becky that read, "Had conference call with Ron Parsons, order increase is back on."

"Look at this text from Becky," said Sam. "What in the world do you think happened?" said a mystified Sam.

"I don't know, but I like the sound of it," said Joe.

As if two text messages weren't enough, Becky sent one more which read as follows: "Spoke with Connor and Ron about delaying the discussion on CCPM until tomorrow evening, and they're OK with the change."

"Gosh, with everything else going on, I had completely forgotten about meeting with Connor on CCPM," said Sam as he showed Joe the latest text.

"I think tomorrow evening will be better," said Joe. "I'm glad Becky has a clear head for details and remembered our meeting with Connor."

"She's just one amazing human being, Joe, and I'm glad I had a chance to meet and work with her," said Sam. "I think I'm going to go home and get a decent night's sleep for a change, Joe, and I think you should too."

"You're right, Sam, tomorrow we're going to need to be sharp," replied Joe

Although Sam and Joe had great intentions of getting a good night's sleep, neither one of them did. Both had trouble falling and staying asleep, so both of them arrived at Barton just after 5:00 a.m..

"Didn't expect to see you here this early, Joe," said Sam.

"You too Sam," replied Joe.

"I just couldn't sleep—kept thinking about what might happen today," said Sam.

"Me too," said Joe. "I'm going to my office and catch up on some paperwork."

"Wait, Joe," said Sam, "I got a call from Becky last night and she and Cecil will be here around 8:00 this morning. They actually flew in last night on Cecil's private jet," he said.

"Did she say anything else?" asked Joe.

"She said there should be some fireworks today because Cecil is not a happy camper," said Sam.

At 8:00 a.m. Sam's phone rang and it was Becky. "Cecil and I are outside. Don't you and Joe need a smoke?" she asked.

"I'll call Joe and we'll come meet you. Where are you?" he asked.

"We're in the main parking lot. See you in a few minutes," she replied.

"Becky and Cecil are out in the main parking lot and want us to join them," Sam said to Joe.

"I'll be right there," said Joe.

Joe and Sam hurried to meet Becky and Cecil, both wondering what was going to happen.

"Hey guys, so nice to see you again," said Cecil as he shook their hands. "I wanted to talk to both of you before we meet with Greg and Paul," Cecil said. "I've looked at the numbers very carefully and I have to tell you that I am really impressed with them and the job you guys have done to get them there," he said. "And let me tell you up front, that your improvements will stay in place, no matter what," continued Cecil. "We'd like you two to join us in our meeting, but I'd like to start it without you, is that OK with you?"

"Yes, of course it's OK with us," replied Sam.

"Just be outside Greg's office and when I tell you to, come on in," Cecil said.

"Give us about fifteen minutes before you come to Greg's office," said Cecil. "And bring your PowerPoint slides or at least your flip chart," Cecil added.

And so the meeting started with Greg welcoming Cecil and Becky. "Cecil, I wish I would have known you were coming, I would have had breakfast for you," said Greg.

"We already ate, Greg," said Cecil. "Greg, I'm here to talk about your numbers. What do you have to say for yourself?" asked Cecil.

"I know, the efficiencies look terrible and I want to explain," said Greg.

"Yes, please do," said Cecil.

"Well, as you know I've been vacationing in Europe for the past three plus weeks, and I made the mistake of leaving Sam in charge while I was gone," said Greg. "Actually, I'm really glad you're here because I was going to call you about replacing Sam," he added. "Well as I was saying, Sam has changed everything in the production area including the parts supply process, and the net effect of his actions is why you are seeing such low efficiencies," he explained. "When I left for vacation, the plant efficiency was close to 83 percent, and now you can see that it's close to 60 percent," said Greg.

"And what was your on-time delivery when you left for vacation, Greg?" asked Cecil.

"Uh, well, uh, it was around 62 percent, I think," stammered Greg.

"And what is it now, Greg?" asked Cecil.

"Let me get Paul in here," said Greg as he messaged Paul to come to his office.

"Cecil, you know Paul, right?" asked Greg.

"Yes I do. How's the parts availability, Paul?" asked Cecil.

"It's very good, we haven't had a stock-out in over a week, and the overall parts inventory is coming down," replied Paul.

"Paul, Cecil just asked me what our latest on-time delivery was. Could you please tell him?" asked Greg.

"Let's see, it's—wait, this has to be a misprint," said Paul. "Let me go check this number."

"Don't bother, Paul, I've already called the major customers to validate the 98.8 percent number," said Cecil.

"What is it again?" asked Greg.

"It is 98.8 percent and the customers are very happy," said Cecil. "So how were you able to manage such a high level of on-time delivery when your efficiency is so low?" asked Cecil.

"I—I—don't know," said Greg.

"Would you like to know how it's possible to have low overall efficiencies with extremely good on-time deliveries?" asked Cecil. "I'm sure Sam and Joe must have explained it all to you, Greg—didn't they?" he asked. "I mean you did ask them why the results had changed so dramatically didn't you, Greg?"

"No sir, I never gave them a chance," replied Greg.

"Paul, since you were here and heard all of this while Greg was gone," said Cecil, "I'm surprised you didn't fill Greg in when he got back."

"You knew about all of this and you didn't tell me?" asked Greg, obviously upset.

"Let's get Sam and Joe in here and have them explain how these new positive results happened so quickly—shall we?" asked Cecil. "Becky, why don't you go get them for us, and let's move to the conference room," said Cecil.

For the next two hours Sam and Joe took turns presenting the tools they had used when Cecil was last here. They started with the piping and process diagrams to present the basics of TOC and then discussed the Intermediate Objectives Map. They then presented the Interference Diagram, which clearly demonstrated why on-time delivery was so low. Joe presented the TOC replenishment model to show how they could eliminate stock-outs of parts while simultaneously reducing the total cost of parts inventory. They then presented a short piece on Drum-Buffer-Rope, and they finished the presentation with an in-depth discussion of performance metrics and Throughput Accounting. All the while Greg was attentive and asked good questions. Every once in a while, he glared at Paul as if to say, "Why didn't you explain this to me instead of bashing Sam for his low efficiencies?"

"Great job, you guys," said Cecil. "So what do you think now, Greg?" Cecil asked.

"I think I owe these guys a huge apology," said Greg. "I'm sorry Sam and Joe," he said, "I was wrong for not asking you what you had done and then taking the time to listen."

"It's not us that needs an apology, Mr. Daniels, it's the men and women on the shop floor that need to hear it," said Sam. "My people worked their asses off to turn Barton into a potential gold mine!" he said.

"I agree, and when we're finished here, I'll go speak with everyone," said Greg.

"One more thing, Mr. Daniels," said Joe. "I'd like to give you a book that will give you the reasons behind all of the changes we've made," and he handed Greg a copy of *The Goal.*

"Greg, before we leave, there's one more bit of good news that you need to hear," said Cecil. "Sam, tell Greg what's going on with Simco," he added.

"Well sir," said Sam, "Ron Parsons from Simco has spent the last two days here with us, meeting with the shop-floor employees and supply people." Sam went on. "Benji had described to him all of the changes that had taken place, and Ron wanted to come to Barton to see it and hear it from our operators just to make sure it wasn't just another hollow sales pitch," explained Sam. "Based upon what he's seen and the focused, one-on-one conversations he had with our operators, he told us yesterday that he was prepared to extend an offer for 40 percent more orders," said Sam. "His only condition is that we had to be able to prove that we could sustain both the changes we've made and the results we've achieved."

Joe spoke up, "Ron's biggest fear was if we had a leadership change, someone who didn't understand and support the shop-floor changes, that it might all be dismantled."

"And I almost did dismantle everything, didn't I?" asked Greg.

"Well, Ron did put the orders on hold, but I think Cecil has everything straightened out now," said Sam.

"Wow, 40 percent more orders?" said Greg. "Where will we put all of the new equipment and people to support this increase?" asked Greg.

"Based upon what we believe our new capacity is, we don't think we'll need to add any additional people," said Sam.

Greg was astounded at the notion of adding a 40 percent increase in throughput with very little increase in operating expense. "Do you realize what that will do to our margins?" asked Greg.

"I do," said Cecil, "and it makes me very, very happy," he added.

"I'm going to the shop floor to 'eat my crow' in front of everyone," said Greg.

"Before I go, do you know if Ron is still in town?" asked Greg.

"Yes, he's still here," said Becky.

"I'd like to meet with him," said Greg. "He needs to hear the sustainment piece directly from me."

"I know for certain that he will be here through tomorrow night since we're all meeting at Jonah's tomorrow evening for another lesson from Connor," said Becky.

"Jonah's? And who is this Connor?" asked Greg.

"Anyone up for a glass of Chianti?" asked Becky.

"I am," said Cecil, "And I think it's time for Greg to meet Connor," he added.

Chapter 15
Performance Metrics

Greg kept his word by canceling all of the meetings he had on his schedule, and he spent the rest of the day on the shop floor talking to the operators, leads, supervisors and supply/logistics people. He was like a kid in a candy shop, but in reality, he felt he had to understand and see everything that Ron had before he met with him in the morning. And he didn't limit it only to first shift either. Greg knew that unless he made a sincere attempt to learn from everyone, his words would be just hollow containers without meaning or substance. Greg had to prove himself and project the message that he knew who the true subject-matter experts were.

Around 4:00 p.m. Becky came looking for Greg to let him know that everyone was going to Jonah's and that Ron would be there as well, if he still wanted to talk to him.

"I absolutely do want to talk to Ron, so count me in," said Greg. "What time are you going Becky?" asked Greg.

"We said we'd meet in Sam's office around 5:00," she replied.

"Becky, I've had such a great day today," Greg said. "I have learned so much from these great people," he added. "By the way, where are Sam and Joe?"

"They're meeting with the Fabrics' team to find out how their training is going," replied Becky.

"What training?" asked Greg.

Becky spent the next fifteen minutes explaining how Sam and Joe had met with Fabrics-R-Us to help them improve their on-time delivery to Barton.

"Sam and Joe have really embraced this improvement initiative haven't they, Becky?" said Greg.

"To me, they are inspiring Greg," replied Becky.

"Before we go to Jonah's, could we go meet with the Fabric's team?" asked Greg.

"Sure, they're in the training room," replied Becky. And with that, Greg and Becky walked to the training room to see how things were going.

"Hi Greg," said Sam. "Excuse me everyone, I'd like you to meet Greg Daniels, our President and CEO," said Sam.

"Good afternoon, everyone," said Greg. "I just stopped by to see how everything was going and if you have everything you need."

Joe spoke, "Greg, you know Stan, but I want you to meet Sally Bergland from Fabrics. Sally is Fabrics' Continuous Improvement Engineer, and she and Stan are the two team leaders for this effort," "So happy to meet both of you and everyone else," said Greg.

"Sid Sanchez, Fabrics' General Manager and self-designated bus driver should be here any minute now, so you can meet him, if you have time," said Becky.

"Did I hear my name mentioned?" asked Sid as he entered the training room.

"Hi Sid, I'm Greg Daniels. Nice to meet you."

"Likewise," said Sid. "This has been a very enlightening experience for me, Greg, and I'm forever indebted to Barton for making me see the light," said Sid. "I just think that Fabrics-R-Us will be such a better company for this."

"It has been an enlightening experience for me too, Sid," said Greg. "I'm very proud of my guys, but I'm even prouder of my workforce," said Greg.

"The bus is ready to roll," said Sid.

"Are we ready to go to Jonah's?" asked Greg. "I'm anxious to meet Ron and Connor."

"Let's go," said Sam.

"I'll just follow you guys, since I've never been there before," said Greg.

One by one, the cars pulled out of Barton's parking lot, taking on the look of a caravan. As they pulled into Jonah's, it was obvious that Connor hadn't closed the bar tonight, as the lot was full.

"I started reading The Goal," Greg said. "Is it safe to assume that the bar's name was derived from the book?"

"That's a safe assumption," said Becky.

When they walked into Jonah's, just like many others before him, Greg was amazed at the décor of the bar with all of the manufacturing-related images draped on the wall. Greg smiled as he walked to their tables and said, "Now this is a manufacturing guy's dream place."

Ron and Benji were already seated with their now customary bottle of Chianti already half-empty.

"Ron," said Benji, "I'd like you to meet Barton's President and CEO, Gregory Daniels."

"Nice to finally meet you," said Greg.

"Me too, I've heard a lot about you in the past two days," replied Ron.

"Ron, do you mind if we take a few minutes away from our group so we can have a private conversation?" asked Greg.

"Not at all, there's an empty table right over there," said Ron "What are you drinking, Ron?" asked Greg.

"My new favorite drink, Chianti," replied Ron. "Would you like a glass?"

"Sure, I've never tasted it before, but if it's good enough for everyone else, it's good enough for me," replied Greg as Benji poured him a glass.

"We'll be back in about fifteen or twenty minutes," said Greg to the group as he and Ron moved to the empty table.

Greg began, "Ron, I know that you're fully aware of the stupid thing I did the other night, and I offer no excuses. It was wrong on so many levels." Greg continued, "Although I offer no excuses, I would like to try and explain why it happened."

"OK, sounds good to me," said Ron.

"I've been using efficiencies to measure the state of the business for over twenty-five years, and until now, I had always believed it was a great metric," said Greg. "When I saw how much our efficiency had dropped in the three weeks I was gone, I just lost it," he continued. "I had always been taught that low efficiencies translated directly into people not working hard enough and being just plain lazy."

"For what it's worth, I was taught the same thing Greg," said Ron.

"In retrospect, I made a complete fool of myself out on the shop floor," said Greg. "After that happened, as you probably know, Cecil Graham came down and met with me and had Sam and Joe set me straight on how my plant was actually performing. You see," said

Greg, "my finance director had only told me about the efficiency drop and neglected to tell me about the increase in on-time delivery.

"So today I canceled all of my meetings and spent my entire day out on the shop floor, learning everything I could about Barton's new direction," said Greg. "I have to tell you Ron, today I learned more from my hourly workers about how to run a business than I learned from all of my degrees and work experience combined," he spoke with passion. "I just never dreamed that all of this was possible," he said. "And the amazing thing about all of these changes is that my hourly workforce totally believes in and supports Barton's new direction."

"I think that's because Sam and Joe allowed them to design the new system themselves," Ron interjected. He continued, "Greg, I did exactly what you did. I immersed myself in your operations for a whole day. Before I could commit to such a huge increase in orders, I had to be certain that the improvement was not only real, but that it was sustainable," said Ron.

"But when I heard directly from the operators what you had done, Greg, I was both devastated and frustrated because I really wanted Barton to be our supplier of choice—our sole supplier of tanks," said Ron. "When you and Paul did what you did, I had no choice but to back away."

"I totally understand why you reacted the way you did, and quite frankly, I would have done the same thing if I were in your shoes," replied Greg.

"Ron, the only thing I can tell you is that I have been 'epiphanized' by my workforce, and that the best thing I can do is get out of their way and let them do their job," said Greg. "In fact, I plan to start my day on the shop floor just to make sure they have everything they need to be successful," he added.

"Actually, Greg, they have a six o'clock meeting every morning to review order status, so you might want to attend a couple of those," said Ron. "They essentially use that meeting to escalate any issues that they can't resolve by themselves. The other thing they have implemented is a "shift tie-in" meeting at the end of every shift so that they have a flawless shift-to-shift handoff," explained Ron. "From what I understand, this handoff has significantly reduced multitasking, because what was happening before they implemented this was, one shift didn't understand or know what the previous shift had completed, so they were actually repeating the work," said Ron.

"I am totally embarrassed and humiliated that my customer knows more about my business than I do," said Greg.

Ron laughed and said, "Don't be embarrassed Greg. I had to be, as you say, 'epiphanized' just like you were."

"I'm really glad that we had this meeting, Greg," said Ron. "I feel much better about increasing orders, and even more confident that with you behind this effort, the orders will arrive on time to Simco," he added. "Shall we go back and join the others, Greg?"

"You bet, and thanks for listening to my pathetic apology," said Greg.

Ron laughed as they walked back to their original table.

Connor had joined the group now, and Sam introduced him to Greg. "So this is the infamous Connor—so happy to finally meet the legend," said Greg.

"I'm no legend," said Connor. "Just been around the block a few times."

"Well Connor, all I can say is that I wish I would have learned twenty years ago, what I learned today," said Greg.

"So Greg, are you going to join us tomorrow night to hear about CCPM?" asked Connor.

"You bet I am, Connor. Wild horses couldn't keep me away," replied Greg.

The six of them continued talking about a variety of work-related subjects until Greg said, "I've got to go. I want to be at the second shift tie-in meeting tonight, and if I leave now, I'll have just enough time to get there."

"Mind if I tag along?" asked Ron.

"Not at all, in fact if the work force sees us together, they'd probably see that as a sign that I'm totally supportive of what they're doing," replied Greg. "Let's roll, so we won't be late," said Greg as they both left Jonah's.

Greg and Ron walked onto the shop floor together and stopped to chat with a few of the operators on the way in. They could see a group of workers at the joining operation beginning to have their shift tie-in meeting. Ron waved to Bradley Fox, the third shift supervisor and he waved back. "Hey Bradley, how's everything going?" asked Ron.

"Fine, as long as our stupid CEO doesn't mess things up again," said Bradley. It was clear that Bradley had never met Greg Daniels before.

"Bradley, I'd like you to meet your "stupid" CEO, Greg Daniels," said Ron.

A look of horror appeared on Bradley's face after the comment he had just made. "I'm so sorry sir, I didn't mean . . ." an apologetic Bradley started to say.

"No need to apologize at all, Bradley, I think your description of me was perfect," said Greg. "Stupid and uninformed is exactly what I was. Very nice to meet you, Bradley," he added.

Bradley was visibly shaken by his own remarks, but finally smiled when he heard Greg's comment.

"We'd like to sit in on your tie-in meeting, if that's OK with you," said Greg. "Ron has told me how effective this meeting is, and I'd love to see it," said Greg.

"Sure, I'd love to have you stay for it," said Bradley as he apologized one more time for his comment.

"Maybe after the meeting, you could take me around and introduce me to your guys too?" asked Greg.

"I'd be happy to, and I'm sure they'd love to meet you Mr. Daniels," he replied. "Please Bradley, call me Greg."

The meeting started with the incoming and outgoing leads discussing in detail exactly where they were on the tanks in the constraint so that the incoming constraint operator would know exactly what he had to do and could pick up where the outgoing operator was on the tank build. In this way, the incoming operator would lose little, if any, time trying to figure out where he should start. Since there was a lead for each of the three major lines (the J40, J50 and J60 tanks), this same conversation took place three times.

The next step was a review of buffer status. As it turned out, on the J50 line the leads decided that since they would be finished with the tank currently in the constraint before the end of the shift, the feeder step to the constraint would need to be finished on time so the constraint wouldn't be starved. Their review indicated that the feeder step would be finished exactly as scheduled. Then they walked to the part's bins to make sure all of the necessary parts would be ready and waiting for the new constraint tank when it needed them.

At a higher level, the supervisors discussed any system-wide issues that might impact the incoming third shift. Apparently one of the third shift operators had called in sick, so the outgoing supervisor asked for volunteers for overtime. And so the meeting went on just like clockwork with no major issues to discuss and correct and if there were any Greg was confident that they would either solve them or escalate them up to someone who could.

"I'm really glad that you told me about this meeting, Ron. I was really impressed with the discipline and coordination that I witnessed," said Greg.

"They're all like this Greg, or at least all that I've been to," said Ron. "As I told you before, the purpose of this meeting is to identify any potential problems and escalate them if necessary," he said. "Of course the other purpose is to reduce the amount of duplicate work and time wasted when moving from one shift to the next," Ron added. "Greg, understand that your on-time delivery number three weeks ago was over 30 percent lower than it is today, so everything that has been done here has had a major impact on it," added Ron.

"I do understand, and I'm grateful for what has happened at Barton," replied Greg. "It took me going away for three weeks to allow it to happen," He continued. "The thing that really amazes me is the whole subject of Throughput Accounting. I mean to think I can run my whole business with just three simple measures—throughput, inventory and operating expense—is mind boggling to me," said Greg.

"That was an eye-opener for me too, but the other thing that was amazing, was the TOC-based replenishment model for parts," said Ron. "It's all so counterintuitive to think that by basically just replenishing more often, you can eliminate parts shortages and have a whole lot less inventory on hand," Ron added. "When I heard about this, I immediately thought about Simco's parts availability problems and knew it would be a good fit for us," he added.

"All of it is so counterintuitive, Ron, but it is also just common sense," said Greg.

"You're right, Greg, everything we've heard and learned, all of the concepts are just based on basic common sense," said Ron. "I can't wait to hear what Connor has to say about Critical Chain Project Management."

"As much as I am enjoying being here with my guys, I think it's time to go home and get some sleep," said Greg. "I'm just going to check my emails before I leave, and I'll see you in the morning," he added.

"OK Greg, good night," replied Ron, and he left for his hotel.

Greg scanned his emails and found one that he did not understand from Cecil Graham. It read, "Greg, the Performance Metrics Review Team will be arriving tomorrow morning. Please provide them everything that they might need to make this activity successful. —Cecil."

"Hmmm," thought Greg, "I wonder what this is all about?" He noticed that Sam, Joe and Becky were copied in as well, so he decided that he would check with them in the morning to see if they understood Cecil's cryptic message, and then he left for the day.

The next morning Greg went to Sam's office to talk about Cecil's email on performance metrics.

"Good morning Sam," said Greg, "Have you checked your emails yet this morning?" he asked.

"No, should I?" asked Sam.

"There's one in particular from Cecil regarding a Performance Metrics Review Team, and I was wondering if you knew what that's all about?" asked Greg.

"Yes, I do, Greg," replied Sam. "To make a long story short, while you were gone, we had a visit from Cecil to discuss why our efficiency had dropped off the face of the earth. When he saw the remarkable improvement in our on-time delivery, he immediately drew the conclusion that maybe we, as a company, were measuring the wrong things." Sam continued, "He told us that he was going to put a review team in place and use Barton as a sort of test bed for a new set of metrics, so I guess this is the start of this initiative," said Sam.

"Thanks for enlightening me, Sam, but when they get here today, I'm going to need you and Joe and Becky to be in the meeting with them," said Greg.

"We'll be there Greg, don't worry," replied Sam.

At 9:00 a.m. the metrics team arrived at Barton, led by a man name Sylvester Malone. He introduced the rest of his team, who were all cost accountants from different divisions within American Investors, Inc. (AII), Barton's parent company. Cecil had met with the chairman of the board of AII and convinced him that the changes that had taken place at Barton were worth looking at from a global perspective for all of AII's holdings.

Greg greeted the members of the metrics team. "Pleased to meet all of you. Let me call my team to let them know you are here."

A short while later, Sam, Joe and Becky arrived at the conference room, and after brief introductions the meeting began with Sylvester making some opening remarks.

"Ladies and gentlemen, we have been commissioned to look into your accounting practices here at Barton," he said. "From what I've been told, Barton has systematically dismantled their traditional cost-accounting metrics in favor of something I think you refer to as Throughput Accounting. Am I correct?" asked Sylvester. "By the way, shouldn't your finance director be in this meeting?" asked Sylvester.

"Yes, of course, let me go get him," replied Greg and walked next door to get Paul.

"Everyone, this is Paul Johnson, Barton's Finance Director," said Greg as everyone in the room introduced themselves.

Sylvester picked up the thread again. "As I was saying, from what I've been told, Barton has systematically dismantled its traditional cost-accounting metrics in favor of something referred to as Throughput Accounting. Am I correct?" he asked.

"Yes, you are correct," replied Paul.

"I beg to disagree," snapped Sam. "That's not at all what we've done."

"Oh really?" snapped Paul. "If you haven't dismantled everything I spent years developing, then just exactly why is this team here from the corporate office?"

It was clear to Sam, Joe and Becky that Paul viewed the new throughput- accounting system as a clear threat to his personal ownership of the status quo system of cost accounting he had developed. Sam, Joe, Becky and Greg, to a lesser extent, realized that in order for Paul to accept the new TA principles and measurements, he would need to see that his system still had relevance to a certain degree. With this point in mind, Becky spoke to the group.

"I would like to propose that we follow a simple agenda today, one that I believe is necessary for our visitors to understand not only what we have done here at Barton, but why we believe a change in performance metrics is absolutely essential to the long-term health and growth of Barton," she explained. "First, I want to emphasize that we are in no way changing the rules as it applies to GAAP reporting required by law," she said. "We understand that, by law, we must continue along the same path." She continued, "But nowhere is it written in the tax code that the same information used for GAAP must be used to make the daily operational decisions. I wanted to make that perfectly clear before we get started," she emphasized. "Are we all clear on that?" asked Becky and everyone, including Paul, nodded their heads in approval.

"What I would like to start with today," said Becky, "is to have Sam, Joe and Greg present some basic information relative to Barton's new approach to manufacturing tanks, and then have them introduce everyone to a new tool called the Intermediate Objectives Map. Sam, please start," she instructed.

Sam welcomed the group and presented the now-standard piping diagram, the four-step process diagram and Goldratt's Five Focusing Steps that had worked so well educating people on the basics of TOC. He made the familiar points about why measuring efficiencies in nonconstraints is a fruitless exercise that only serves to drive inventory in the wrong direction, extend the cycle times of products being produced and cause missed shipments. Sam also presented the past and present on-time delivery results to strengthen the case for moving to a constraints-only efficiency measurement. Sam also presented Drum-Buffer-Rope and the TOC- based parts-replenishment model, emphasizing the fact that stock-outs had been eliminated while parts inventory was reduced by approximately 40 percent. Everyone in attendance, including Paul, was attentive and asked many questions along the way. When Sam was finished, he turned it over to Joe to present Throughput Accounting.

One by one, Joe presented the three basic TA components—Throughput (T), Inventory (I) and Operating Expense (OE) and the formulas for Net Profit (NP), Return on Investment (ROI), Productivity (P), and Inventory Turns (IT). Joe emphasized the fact that this definition of throughput was based upon the sale of the product, rather than producing it for stock. He also stressed that all of these definitions and formulas were financial, so as to spin up the receptivity of the group. Joe concluded his presentation by saying, "With these three financial measurements, the ability to make daily operational decisions becomes much easier, and the decisions will be much better."

The group had been at it for two solid hours, so Sam suggested that they take a fifteen-minute break. Sam's real reason was that he wanted to talk to Becky about the IO Map, plus he needed a smoke.

"So Becky, what did you have in mind for the IO Map" asked Sam. "What purpose will it serve?" he continued.

"I see it recapitulating everything you guys have done here into a single page that will make it easier for the group to see the interconnectedness of the systems we have," replied Becky.

"Can you please translate what you just said down to my level?" asked Sam as he took a drag off of his cigarette.

"Becky laughed and replied, "I want them to see everything you guys have done here on one page. Plus," she added, "I think that once they see the individual IO Map components, the metrics that we need to use will become obvious."

"Becky, I think you are simply one brilliant woman!" said Joe. "You have turned this into such a simple task, and I respect you so much!"

"Flattery will get you everywhere, Joe," Becky said with a smile.

"Who's going to lead the IO Map part?" asked Joe.

"I certainly can if you like," said Becky, "but I think it would be better coming from one of you two."

"I have an idea," said Joe. "How about if Sam presents the one we already completed, and then I'll lead us when we complete the new one."

"I think that's a great idea, Joe," said Becky. "So now who's the brilliant one Joe?" she asked.

When the group was back in place, Sam explained the purpose of an Intermediate Objectives Map (IO Map) and how to construct one. He walked the team through the IO Map that they had already constructed, and Becky was right, everyone connected with all of the changes and improvements that had been made at Barton. They were able to see the genesis of Drum-Buffer-Rope, the TOC parts replenishment system and all of the other improvements. When Sam was finished, he turned the meeting over to Joe to lead the group in the development of this new IO Map.

Joe knew that everyone would necessarily have to agree on a goal. Knowing this group was motivated by money and financial metrics, he suggested that the goal should be read, "Make more money now and in the future," and everyone nodded in acceptance. Joe then explained the concept of the Critical Success Factors (CSFs) and Necessary Conditions (NCs) to the group. After many attempts to develop a complete IO Map, the group finally agreed on the final version. It was not perfect, but for its purpose today, perfection wasn't a prerequisite. After all, the real purpose of this team was to develop a new performance measurement system, and this diagram would facilitate that objective.

The next step for the team was to focus on what metrics would be used to evaluate Barton's overall performance in the days to come. With that in mind, Becky suggested that the group take another fifteen-minute break. She also knew that Sam and Joe were dying for a smoke.

Barton Intermediate Objectives (IO) Map

In order to have...
Goal (Objective)
Make more money now and in the future
I must have...
Critical Success Factors
Increasing throughput of tanks
Optimized Operating Expense
Optimized Inventory
Superior Tank Quality
Superior On-Time Delivery
In order to have...
I must have...
Necessary Conditions
All parts delivered on time
Maximum constraint efficiency
Effective non-constraint subordination
Optimum labor/minimum OT
Compliance with Little's Law
High Constraint First pass yield
Superior TOC based scheduling system
Effective parts replenishment system
Minimized D/T in Constraint
Superior Defect prevention system

"So how do you think it's going Becky?" asked Joe as he lit his cigarette.

"I think it's going very well," she replied. "Let's just hope that the selection of metrics will flow as easily," she added.

Just as Joe and Sam lit another cigarette, Paul came out to join them, and to their surprise, he actually complimented them on their work so far. Needless to say, they were all stunned, but they were even more stunned when Paul asked if he could lead the metrics piece. "Of course you can, Paul, and if you get stuck, we'll be here to help," said Becky. And with that, they went back into the conference room.

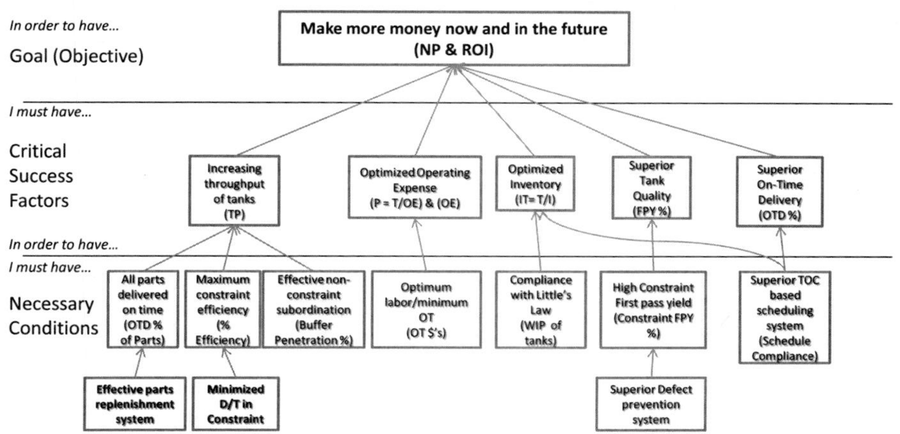

Paul was simply brilliant in his leadership of this phase of the group's activities, and the final outcome, the IO Map with metrics, was a thing of beauty—at least that was the consensus of the team. It was clear that Paul had just been epiphanized and it would not go unnoticed or unreported in Becky's mind. Paul had somehow managed to incorporate all of the Throughput Accounting metrics and formulas into a single blueprint for Barton that everyone agreed would work.

With their mission complete, the team said goodbye and thanked everyone for their help and for the new education they had received. One thing was certain, things would never be the same at Barton, and neither would Paul. When everyone had left, Joe, Becky Sam and Paul discussed the IO Map and what a great job Paul had done leading the effort.

"Paul, I was very proud of you today," said Becky. "That was one of the best facilitation performances I have ever witnessed, and you should feel really good about it," she added. "I think Cecil will be very pleased when the team reports back to him, and I will certainly back up everything the team tells him.

"Joe, is there some way you can turn this document into an electronic format?" said Becky. "I'd really like Cecil to see this before the team shows him," she added.

"I'll do that for you, Becky," said Paul. It was clear that Barton had a new member of the team with Paul's epiphany, and he would be a very valuable addition.

Chapter 16
CCPM—Part 1

"What time did we tell Connor we'd be at Jonah's tonight?" asked Becky.

"I think he said 5:00 p.m., if I'm not mistaken," said Sam.

"OK, we've got plenty of time then," replied Becky. "So what did you guys think of our meeting today?" she asked.

"I think it went really well, and I was astounded by what Paul did," said Joe.

"Yeah, what was that all about?" asked Sam.

"Do you think it was because you were there, Greg?" asked Joe.

"I really don't know what changed his mind," said Greg, "because at the beginning of the meeting he was argumentative, and then it was like someone turned on his positive switch."

"Well, whatever it was, it was a breath of fresh air as far as I'm concerned," said Sam.

"By the way, where did Paul go?" asked Sam.

"I saw him walking out with Sylvester Malone a few minutes ago," said Joe. "I wanted to tell him what a great job he did leading the development of the performance metrics."

"Yes, he did," replied Sam. "Did anyone invite him to Jonah's tonight?" asked Sam.

"No, but I think we should," said Greg.

Just then Paul walked in the door to spontaneous applause from the three of them. "Great job today, Paul," said Sam. "I didn't know you had it in you," he joked.

"To tell you the truth, today I just tried to listen with an open mind rather than looking for ways to find fault in what you were presenting, like I normally do," Paul said. "Today I just tried to make sense of what you and Joe and Becky presented," he said. "And you know what happened? You actually made sense to me"

Paul continued, "Sam, I want to apologize to you for how I have acted the past three weeks."

"I don't know what to say," said Sam.

"Just say, 'You're forgiven Paul,' " said Paul.

Sam burst out laughing and held his hand out to shake hands with his new comrade, Paul. "Listen Paul, we're all going to Jonah's tonight to hear about Critical Chain Project Management and you're definitely invited," said Sam.

"I'd love to hear it, but let me call my wife first to make sure we don't have other plans," replied Paul. Paul stepped away to call his wife and came back to tell the group that he was good to go.

"I'm ready for a glass of Chianti," said Becky. "Me too," said Greg. So off they went to Jonah's once again, to learn from the master.

As they pulled into Jonah's, it was apparent that Connor had closed the bar again. "I wish he wouldn't do that," thought Becky. "He has a business to run, and by shutting down every time we come as a group, his revenue takes a hit." One by one, the cars filled the parking spaces.

"Why did he do this again," Becky said to Sam.

"You mean closing the bar for us?" he asked.

"Yes, I'm starting to feel guilty about it," she replied.

"Becky, Connor can obviously afford to do this, and I firmly believe he actually looks forward to these sessions," Sam replied.

"Still, it makes me feel guilty," she said as they walk into the bar. What started out at Jonah's as just Joe, sitting at a table, had grown significantly to include Sam, Becky, Ron, Benji, Greg, Cecil and now Paul.

"Good evening, everyone," said Connor. "The usual?" he asked as he reached for two bottles of Chianti. It's a thumbs up from everyone except Paul.

"What's he mean, the usual?" Paul asked.

"Chianti has become somewhat of a symbol for us," said Joe.

"I'm not much of a wine drinker," said Paul.

"You have to have at least one glass to become a full member of this club," Becky said.

"OK then, pour me a glass," said Paul. He took a sip, swirled it around in his mouth and said, "This is actually quite good, Becky."

"It's really all we've been drinking for the past few weeks, and we seem to all have developed a taste for it," Becky replied. And with that, Connor rearranged the flip chart and starts.

"Before I start, let me tell you now that we won't finish this training in one evening, so we'd better plan on this being two sessions," said Connor. "Everyone alright with that?" he asked. Everyone nodded in agreement.

"All of you are familiar by now with Drum-Buffer-Rope and how well it has done for you," said Connor. "Can someone please explain why it works so well in the production environment?" he asked.

Sam is the first to answer, "Because it buffers everything from uncertainty."

"That's true, Sam, it clearly does that," said Connor. "What else?" he asked.

"It helps keep us focused on the constraint, which helps us achieve the throughput that we need," said Joe.

"That too is a very true statement," said Connor. "But from a system perspective, why does it work so well?"

"Well, I'm not a production expert, but to me it provides the necessary synchronization throughout the manufacturing process," said Becky. "By synchronization, I'm talking about knowing when to start a new tank, what we need to work on to prevent downtime and so on." she explained.

Joe thought, "Leave it to Becky to describe exactly what is happening. She is just such a brilliant and beautiful woman."

"Exactly!" exclaimed Connor. "Think back several weeks ago—were your operations synchronized, Sam?" asked Connor.

"Not at all," Sam replied. "In fact, because we were so out-of-sync, we couldn't produce the right products and ship anything on time," said Sam.

"And now?" asked Connor.

"We know exactly where we are and what to do all of the time—we're synchronized," said Sam. "We know what our priorities are at any moment in time."

"Look at how far you've come, everyone," said Connor. "And how much money did you spend implementing everything?" he asked.

"Next to nothing," said Paul.

"Well, Ron, the same thing can happen at Simco," said Connor. "Ron, please describe what life is like at Simco."

"Well, let me paint my picture for everyone," said Ron. "Our primary purpose, the way we make money, is to design and build rotary-wing aircraft," he explained. "We do this by purchasing most of the parts we use from outside vendors, but we do fabricate some of them ourselves."

"And how do you schedule your assemblies?" asked Connor.

"Since we consider each new aircraft an individual project," said Ron, "we use traditional project management software to schedule the sequence of how the aircraft should be assembled." He went on, "When we get a new order, we usually start it as soon as we can, so that we're ahead of the game."

"So the belief is that if you start the projects sooner, they will finish sooner?" asked Connor.

"Yes, that's exactly what the message is from our leadership," Ron replied.

"And how's that working out for you Ron?" asked Connor.

"I think you know the answer to that question, Connor," replied Ron.

"Do you have parts problems Ron?" asked Connor. "And by that I mean, are the parts all there when you need them?"

"We have a major problem with parts and until recently, Barton was a real problem supplier for us," Ron replied. "But we've got a lot more 'Bartons' in our supplier base."

"So what would you say is your on-time completion rate, Ron?" asked Connor.

"Not more than half of them," Ron replied.

"On the projects that finish on time, is there a lot of overtime used?" asked Connor.

"Oh gosh, yes," said Ron. "Hell, there's a lot of overtime even on the ones that finish late," he added.

"I think what I hear you saying is that you don't have good synchronization, am I right?" asked Connor.

"Yes, I guess you could say that," Ron replied.

"OK, so does everyone agree that in projects, like manufacturing, it is important to have synchronization?" Connor asked. Everyone nodded their heads in agreement.

"OK, let's move on," said Connor.

"In your project management plans, how many individual steps would you say are included?" asked Connor.

"I have no idea, but the assembly packages are an inch thick, if not more, so I would say hundreds," Ron said.

"And does each step have an expected duration listed for it?" asked Connor.

"Yes, but why did you ask that question?" asked Ron. "Shouldn't there be estimated durations on each task?"

"I'll answer that question a little later," said Connor. "In your industry, would you say that Simco is competitive in terms of total cycle time to assemble one of these birds?"

"Yes, I think we are," Ron replied.

"So if there was a way to significantly reduce your cycle times, then that would be a clear competitive edge for Simco?" asked Connor.

"Yes, of course it would," Ron replied.

"Ron, have you ever asked the project managers why their projects come in late?" asked Connor?

"Yes, we always have project reviews for every project," Ron replied.

"And what would you say is the most common reason given for these projects being late?" Connor asked.

"Most of the time everything is blamed on things the project managers have no control over," Ron said.

"So would you say that most project delays are blamed on uncertainty?" Connor asked.

"Yes, you could say that," Ron replied. "You know, for example, if a part comes in later than planned, things like that," said Ron.

"But don't you plan for uncertainty, Ron?" asked Connor.

"I guess we do," he replied.

"Have you ever asked your project managers how they come up with their duration estimates?" Connor asked.

"No, I never have," Ron replied. "Connor, when are you going to start the training?" asked Ron.

"Shortly, Ron," said Connor. "I just need to fully understand what Simco's environment looks like. Be patient."

"So here's what we know about Simco so far," said Connor. "At least 50 percent of their projects, assembling helicopters, are coming in late." Connor went on. "Simco uses overtime hours to attempt to bring their projects in on time, but as we heard, they still come in late 50 percent of the time. We also know that individual durations are placed on every task," Connor added. "Finally, the biggest reason given for why the projects come in late is because of things the project managers have no control over. Uncertainty over things like parts availability. Did I miss anything?" asked Connor.

"Yes," said Paul, "Simco is lacking synchronization."

"Good catch, Paul, you were listening," said Connor as he pats Paul on the back.

"Just a few more questions, Ron," said Connor. "How does Simco measure progress on their projects?"

"We have weekly reviews on the status of each project, and we monitor the percentage of work completed," said Ron.

"Do you mean that you measure the number of tasks completed compared to the total number of tasks required and convert that to a percentage?" asked Connor.

"Yes, that's exactly what we do," replied Ron.

"So let me guess," said Connor, "in the early part of a new project the rate of completion of tasks is very high, so that is interpreted to indicate that the project is either on or ahead of schedule, correct?"

"Yes, that seems to be the pattern," replied Ron.

"As a result, getting to 90 percent complete, there are very few hiccups," said Connor, " but that last 10 percent seems to drag on forever."

"That's exactly what happens at Simco . . . how did you know that?" Ron asked.

"You'll be able to answer that question yourself, Ron," Connor replied. "The bottom line is that a company can make this measurement look good by ignoring problems and moving onto different tasks," said Connor. "It's sort of like ignoring the constraints at Barton."

Connor continued, "Ninety percent of the project managers around the world are using the same method Simco is using, Critical Path Project Management (CPPM). If you ask a typical project manager about the factors that delayed a project, most will tell you that something they didn't expect, or had no control over cropped up in some of the tasks and caused a delay. In other words, uncertainty or the Murphy bug bit them," said Connor.

"Every project from virtually every environment has uncertainty associated with it," said Connor, "and how this uncertainty is dealt with determines the ultimate success or failure of the project," he explained. "So in order for a project to be successful, there must be a way to protect it from uncertainty."

"Just like our DBR system at Barton, right?" asked Becky.

"Yes, exactly like that," replied Connor. "So let's take a look at how traditional project management, or Critical Path, attempts to protect a project from uncertainty," said Connor.

"Why is it called 'Critical Path'?" asked Paul.

"Good question, Paul," Connor replied, "and I promise I'll get to the answer later, OK?"

Connor went on, "Critical Path uses a fudge factor to protect projects from inevitable uncertainty. Like you're doing at Simco when you develop the project plan, durations for each individual task are estimated by the resources that are responsible for executing them," said Connor. "But then a safety factor is added to each task by the person responsible for completing it. For example, suppose a realistic estimate of time for an individual task is one week," said Connor. "Is one week the amount of time he actually tells the project manager? No, typically, the resource will add in his own personal safety factor to guard against "things" that might happen that would delay completion of the task," Connor explained. "So it's not unusual for one week to be quoted as two weeks. Resources react this way because they know from experience that as soon as they give the project manager an estimate, it automatically becomes a commitment!" he exclaimed.

"Can anybody guess what happens next?" asked Connor.

Becky said, "The project manager adds his or her own fudge factor?"

"Exactly," said Connor. "The project manager adds up all of the individual, inflated time estimates, and then adds his or her own safety factor."

"So if this is what happens," Ron asked, "then why with all of this extra safety imbedded are the projects still coming in late?"

"Great question, Ron, and I promise I will answer that question too shortly," replied Connor.

"Can anyone tell me why resources and project managers add all of this safety to their tasks and projects, besides it becoming an automatic commitment?" asked Connor.

When nobody answered, Connor said, "Project managers know that at some point in the project Murphy will strike, and some of the tasks will be delayed, so they add a safety factor to protect the project from being late." He continued, "Keep in mind that every resource inflates every task, so it's not uncommon for the estimated durations to be at least 50 percent greater than it actually takes to complete the tasks. So with all of this safety built into the project, theoretically the project should be completed ahead of schedule, or at least on-time . . . right?" he asked. "So it would seem . . . so it would seem," said Connor. "We'll come back to this point in a bit."

Connor went on, "Like we heard from Ron, in traditional project management projects, progress is tracked by calculating the percentage of individual tasks completed and then comparing the percentage against the due date. Sounds reasonable, but is this the right way to track progress?" asked Connor.

"Apparently it isn't, or you wouldn't have asked the question," said Ron as he and everyone else laughed.

Connor continued. "The problem with using percentage of tasks completed is that not all tasks have the same duration, so that comparing a task that has an estimated duration of one day to a task that should take one week is an invalid comparison," he explained. "Compounding this problem is the mistaken belief that the best way to ensure that a project will finish on time is to try to make every individual task finish on time," he said. "This probably sounds like a reasonable approach, but as you'll see later on, it just isn't so.

"OK, back to Ron's question about why projects are late with all of the added safety," said Connor. "This phenomenon is explained to a large degree by two common human behaviors. Think back to your old high school days. When you were given a homework assignment on Monday to write a paper by Thursday, when did you start working on it?" Connor asked.

"Wednesday," said Joe as everyone chuckled.

"Eli Goldratt coined the expression, the Student Syndrome, to explain why much of the imbedded safety gets wasted," Connor said. "Because the person responsible for completing the tasks knows the safety is there, he or she procrastinates on starting the task. And then when Murphy strikes," said Connor, "the task becomes late.

"The other human behavior that lengthens projects is referred to as Parkinson's Law," said Connor "Resources intuitively know that if they finish a task in less time than the estimate they gave, then the next time they have the same or similar task to complete, they will be expected to finish it early again," he explained. "So instead of notifying the project manager when they do finish a task early, they wait until the due date to do so. Parkinson's Law states that work expands to fill the available time," said Connor. "We're talking about the personal credibility of the resources that provided the task-time estimate here, so to protect it, early finishes are not reported," Connor explained. "So the impact of these two behaviors on project completions is that delays are passed on, but early finishes are not," said Connor. "So is it any wonder that projects are late?"

"Wow, the reason is behavioral," said Ron.

"Yes, but there are other reasons why projects are typically late," said Connor.

"Would anyone like a refill before I go on?" asked Connor. Everyone did, so Connor signaled to his server to bring another bottle.

"Ron, let me ask you another question," said Connor. "Do you have multiple projects going on simultaneously?"

"Yes, of course we do," replied Ron.

"And do these projects share resources?"

"Yes, they do, Connor," Ron replied.

"Many organizations have multiple projects, and there is competition for these shared resources," explained Connor. "In fact, it's not uncommon for project managers to 'fight' over these shared resources because leadership holds them accountable for completion according to schedule."

"You just described Simco's work environment," said Ron.

"Leadership in these environments initiates projects without considering the capacity of the organization to complete the work," said Connor. "They also mistakenly assume that the sooner a project is initiated, the sooner it will be completed, so they push more projects into the mix. After all, everyone knows that the sooner you start a project, the sooner it will be completed . . . right?" asked Connor. "As a result of these actions, the most devastating problem of all associated with project completions occur—multi-tasking!"

"But I thought being able to multitask was a good thing." said Paul.

"Au contraire," replied Connor. "So far, we've discussed behavioral problems associated with project completions," he said. "Now let's look at multitasking in a little more depth. Multitasking happens when resources are forced to work on multiple project activities at the same time," said Connor. "Many people believe that multitasking is a good thing because it increases efficiency since resources are "busy" all of the time."

"There's that metric efficiency rearing its ugly head again," said Greg.

"Yes, Greg, as you learned at Barton, it's not a good way to measure performance except at the constraint," Connor replied. "If you remember in The Goal," he reminded everyone, "Goldratt used his robot example, where running the robots continuously did increase efficiency, but only served to create lots of excess inventory. The negative impact of multitasking in a project environment is much, much worse, as you will see shortly," said Connor.

"I think it's time for an example, so you can see the impact of multitasking," said Connor as he turned to the flip chart and sketched three hypothetical projects. "Suppose you have three projects that are assigned to move through your system, and each project has a time estimate of nine days," Connor said. "Each project manager has developed his or her own schedule in isolation of the other two, and each project has the same, or a similar, start date, so each project manager will assume their project only takes nine days to complete," said Connor. "But each of these projects must use the same resources to reach completion, and all three can't begin on the same day because there just isn't enough capacity," Connor explained. "If there is pressure from all three project managers to show some progress on their project, what do the people on the line do?" Connor asked, making a drawing for the group on the flipchart.

Project 1 Time estimate 9 days	Project 2 Time estimate 9 days	Project 3 Time estimate 9 days

"Well," said Ron, "Since you want to satisfy all three project managers, you probably end up splitting your time between the three projects."

"That's exactly what would happen in this type of environment," said Connor as he turned to the flip chart to sketch another drawing.

Project 1 3 days D 1,2,3	Project 2 3 days D 4,5,6	Project 3 3 days D 7,8,9	Project 1 3 days D10,11,12	Project 2 3 days D13,14,15	Project 3 3 days D16,17,18	Project 1 3 days D19,20,21	Project 2 3 days D22,23,24	Project 3 3 days D25,26,27

"Just as Ron suggested, the shared resource splits time between the three projects," said Connor. "He or she first works on Project 1 for three days, then works on Project 2 for three days, and then Project 3 for three days," he said. "Then, its back to Project 1 for three days and so on."

"Good grief, that's exactly what happens at Simco!" said Ron.

"I know, and it's not only at Simco," said Connor, who always seemed to know the obvious before anyone else. "By multitasking, look what's happened to the time line to complete each individual project," he pointed out. "Each project manager planned their project to take only nine days, even with the safety factor added to the tasks. And without multitasking, each project should take only nine days to complete."

"But assuming all of these projects were scheduled to begin on or near the same start date, with the multitasking rule now being enforced, Project 1 now takes twenty-one days to complete instead of nine days," said Connor. "Project 1 started on time, but eventually finishes twelve days late because of the perceived need to also work on the other two projects. Project 2 now takes twenty-four days to complete instead of the planned nine days, and Project 3 takes twenty-seven days to complete," said Connor. "One other thing that we didn't take into account was the time lost having to reacquaint yourself with each project. By that I mean, the shared resource has to review where they left off before they can start working on a project again," said Connor. "And based on my experience, this adds a significant amount of time to each project.

"So let's summarize what we've learned so far before we move on," said Connor. "We've learned that time estimates for tasks are artificially lengthened as a protective measure against Murphy and all of the negative baggage he brings to the party," said Connor. "We've learned that even though there is a huge amount of safety built in, most of it is wasted because of the Student Syndrome and Parkinson's Law," he said. "With the Student Syndrome we put off work until the last minute while with Parkinson's Law, if we're given ten days to complete a project, that's the best case scenario on how long it will take, even if it is completed earlier." Connor continued summarizing, "And finally, we learned how devastating multitasking can be to the completion dates of projects, and how if we could eliminate it, we know our on-time completion rates would improve. And although all of this is true, there are still other things that can be done to significantly reduce the time it takes to complete projects," said Connor. "Any questions so far?"

"I have a question," said Ron. "What you've explained to us tonight is a real eye-opener for me personally. And I can see that Simco will be able to significantly improve completion rates just by correcting these behavioral factors. My question is this . . . " Ron paused. "Will Critical Chain Project Management also work in a design environment?"

"Great question Ron. What does the group think?" asked Connor.

As usual, Becky was the first to answer Connor's question. "My belief is absolutely yes, it can be used there," she said. "I have been sitting here listening to your explanation, and I think I understand more clearly now why you recommended CCPM to Ron instead of Drum-Buffer-Rope," said Becky.

"Why is that Becky?" asked Connor.

"Well, I may be wrong, but it seems to me that it's simply a question of the time involved to complete the work and the complexity of the work," Becky explained. "It seems to me that DBR is well suited for an environment where less time is required to complete a set of activities, while CCPM is more suited for extended projects with more uncertainty that also require more time to complete," she said. Becky continued, "So if you are designing a new product, for example, there is a high degree of uncertainty and it consumes major amounts of time. In this case, CCPM might be better suited for it," she said.

"Becky, not only are you beautiful, you are brilliant as well," replied Connor. "Becky is right on the money folks," he said. "That was very perceptive of you, Becky."

"Any other questions?" asked Connor.

"I have one," said Ron. "Based upon your experience with CCPM, what would be your ball park estimate of how much time Simco could reduce its assembly times on helicopters?" he asked.

"Another excellent question," Connor replied. "Conservatively

Ron, you should see a 40 percent reduction on your assembly times."

"Forty percent?" exclaimed Ron. "Do you know how much of a revenue gain that would be for Simco?" he asked.

"Not really, but I'm sure your Board of Directors would be very, very happy," Connor said.

"So what time would you like to get together tomorrow?" Connor asked the group.

"This is so amazing and helpful for me, could we start earlier than we did today?" asked Ron.

"Certainly, how about two o'clock tomorrow afternoon, when my crowd thins out?" asked Connor. Everyone agreed on the time and got up to leave.

Ron approached Connor with a question, "Connor, would you consider coming to Simco and helping us implement CCPM?"

"Where is your company located, Ron?" asked Connor.

"Near Phoenix," Ron said.

"I might be able to break away for a week or so, as long as there is some time allotted for golf," replied Connor.

"I'll even be your caddie, Connor," said Ron.

Connor laughed and said, "We'll talk about this tomorrow, Ron."

"Good night everyone," said Connor.

"Good night," everyone said together.

"So what did you think, Ron?" asked Sam, who had paused to have a smoke with Joe before leaving.

"So far I can see, there are so many advantages for Simco if we switch to Critical Chain," he replied.

"The way I see it," said Sam, "We haven't really heard about Critical Chain so far," he said. "We've heard about behaviors that could have exactly the same impact on Drum-Buffer-Rope."

"I was thinking exactly the same thing, Sam," said Joe.

"I'm very excited about hearing the rest of it tomorrow," said Ron. "I'm going to go email my boss and let him know about what I learned today . . . Good night Sam and Joe."

"See you tomorrow, Ron," said Joe as they all walked to their cars.

"Becky, do you need a ride to your hotel?" asked Ron.

"No, I'm fine. I'm going to have one more drink with this man who thinks I'm beautiful and brilliant . . . I think he'll drive me back," said Becky.

Chapter 17
CCPM—Part 2

The next morning Sam and Joe pulled into the parking lot at almost the same time.

"So Sam, what did you think of Connor's presentation last night?" said Joe.

"I thought it was brilliant, as usual."

"I love the way Connor asks key questions to set up whatever his presentation is about," said Joe.

"I do too," said Sam. "And he never actually gives a direct answer to a question, but rather answers with a question of his own,"

"He's excellent," said Joe.

"But I'll tell you who impressed me the most was Becky," said Sam. "Becky thinks on a different level than I do."

"I know I've said it before, but she is one very impressive woman," said Joe.

"She is that for sure," replied Sam. "Say, what are you doing over here so early, Joe?"

"I came to check in with Stan and Sally to see how everything was going with Fabrics' training."

"By the way, Joe, I was wondering about something," said Sam, "Do Stan and Sally have a thing going on?"

"I'm not sure . . . why would you ask that?" asked Joe.

"Well, as we were leaving Jonah's last night, I noticed them sitting in Stan's car in the parking lot," Sam said. "It looked like they were kissing. And Stan's car windows were all fogged up."

"Huh, you may be right," said Joe.

"I mean it's none of my business," said Sam. "They're both single, so more power to them."

"They're both such wonderful people and very smart," said Joe.

When Joe and Sam finally arrived at the training room, Stan was up front lecturing while Sally was passing out papers of some kind.

"Good morning, everyone," said Sam. The group smiles and waves back.

"How's everything going, Stan and Sally?" asked Joe.

"Really great," said Sally. "Stan is such a talented man in so many ways, but his teaching skills are probably the best I've ever seen. I wish he had been my black belt trainer," she said.

Sally finished passing out her papers and took a seat up front. When she sat down, she rested her chin on her hands and just focused on listening to Stan, as though she were in a different world. Sam nudged Joe and motioned for him to look at Sally, and then he whispered to Joe, "Yeah, I'm pretty sure they've got something going on." Joe just smiled and motioned for Sam to follow him out of the room.

"I need to check my emails, Joe," said Sam, and they walked to Sam's office. "Joe, look at this one from Cecil Graham," said Sam. And he read it to Joe:

"Sam, I need you in our corporate offices on Monday morning. Be prepared."

"What in the world do you think this is all about?" said Sam. "The 'Be prepared' part has me worried," he said.

"Sam, our results are outstanding, so why would you be worried?" asked Joe.

"I've been around here for a long time, and when you receive a two-liner like this, it usually always spells trouble," Sam said.

Joe booted up his laptop and discovered that he also had a message from Cecil. "Guess what Sam, you've got a traveling partner," said Joe. "I got the same identical message from Cecil. Now I'm worried."

"We'll ask Becky when she gets in," said Sam.

"If anyone knows what this is all about, it would be Becky," said Joe.

So Sam and Joe had been summoned to corporate headquarters and they had no idea why. They spent the next hour and a half trying to understand why they had to go to Corporate. Was this going to be a good or a bad trip?

Sam and Joe finally saw Becky Chen's car pulling into the parking lot, and they walked out to meet her.

"Sleep in, Becky?" asked Sam.

"Heavens no, I've been working since about six o'clock this morning," she replied.

"Becky, both Sam and I have received an email instructing us to report to corporate on Monday morning," said Joe, "and we were wondering if you knew the reason why."

"I don't have a clue. What did the email say?" asked Becky.

Sam answered, "It was two sentences from Cecil. He said: 'Sam, I need you in our corporate offices on Monday morning. Be prepared.'"

"And Joe got exactly the same email," Sam said.

"That's all it said?" asked Becky. "No other explanation?"

"That's all the email said, Becky. We were hoping you'd have some inside information," said Sam.

"Sorry to disappoint you, gentlemen, but I really don't have a clue," she replied.

Sam and Joe spent the rest of the morning checking Barton's delivery status. Everything seemed to be going well.

"Its 11:30, guys, and we don't actually meet with Connor until 2:00. Why don't we go to lunch?" said Becky.

"Sounds good to me. Where would you like to go?" asked Sam.

"I have a craving for a ham sandwich," Becky laughed. "We might as well go to Jonah's now and then wait around for everyone else," she said.

"Sounds fine with me," said Sam.

"Should we ask Paul, Ron, Greg and Benji if they want to go?" asked Joe.

"Yeah, we should. I'll give them a call," said Sam. Sam tried all of their numbers, but none of them answered. "Couldn't reach any of them," said Sam, so off the three of them went to Jonah's for the world's best ham sandwich. As they pulled into the parking lot, it was immediately clear why they couldn't reach the others. They were already here at Jonah's.

It was still two hours before Connor would deliver his next training session, so everyone ordered a lunch plate and, of course, each table had a bottle of Chianti. Chianti had become their drink of choice as though it were some kind of magic potion, or at least it seemed that way. First Joe, then Sam, then Becky and the rest, including the chairman of the board, just fell into place—all die-hard fans of this Italian masterpiece. By the time Connor was ready to begin, he had a captive audience, all of whom were ready to learn the final piece of CCPM.

"Before I begin, I want you to know that I am only giving you the basics of CCPM and not the full details of how it works," said Connor. "When I'm finished tonight, I would recommend that you use a search engine to look for the many books that exist on the subject."

"As I told you last night, CPM task durations are inflated to protect against Murphy," said Connor. "What if there was a way to significantly reduce these imbedded safety buffers and still be able to provide the protection from Murphy that we need? Ron, would that be of interest to Simco?" Connor asked.

"Yes!" said Ron. "I'm all ears."

"In my example from last night, suppose we were able to reduce the estimated duration by as much as 50 fifty percent and still protect against Murphy?" asked Connor. "Does that sound like a significant reduction?" he asked.

"But if we're already late on projects with all of this built-in safety, how in the world would reducing these durations result in better project on-time completion rates?" asked Ron.

"Would you like me to show you?" asked Connor.

"I can't wait for this explanation," said Ron.

"Me too," said Becky.

"OK, so what I'm proposing is that on my other example, we said that we had three projects each with an estimated duration of nine days. So using my method, I'm suggesting that each will now take four and a half days, correct?" asked Connor as he sketched it on the flip chart. "So the total time for all three projects to be completed is theoretically thirteen and a half days, right?

Everyone in the group agreed.

Project 1 Time estimate 4.5 days	Project 2 Time estimate 4.5 days	Project 3 Time estimate 4.5 days

"How many of you believe we can reduce our safety by 50 percent and safely guard against the uncertainty introduced by Murphy?" Connor asked.

Nobody raised their hand to agree.

"Well, for all of you nonbelievers staring at me, the correct answer is, yes we can," he said. "But before I show you how, let me refresh your minds a bit on the Theory of Constraints," said Connor. "You all recall the piping diagram and the simple four-step process that Joe has presented so many times. What was the key to improving throughput in both of those drawings?" asked Connor.

Sam raised his hand and said, "We had to identify the constraint and then exploit it."

"Correct," said Connor. "And how did we prevent a WIP explosion in the process?" he asked.

Paul raised his hand and said, "By subordinating everything else to the constraint."

"Yes, Paul, very good," said Connor. "So attempting to reduce cycle times at nonconstraints is basically a fruitless exercise. The focus must be on never letting the constraint sit idle, correct?" asked Connor.

The group agreed.

"So here is a question for you," said Connor. "In a project, what is the constraint?"

After careful deliberation, Becky raised her hand and said, "I think in a project, it's not the longest task necessarily that is the constraint, it's probably the longest set of sequential tasks, where one task is dependent upon another." She went on. "This series of interconnected tasks is probably where the term critical path came from, so I'm thinking that the critical path is the constraint?" she asked.

"Becky, is this really the first time you've been exposed to project management?" asked Connor.

"Yes, why?"

"Because in all the years I've been doing this, I can count on one hand the number of people who have actually answered that question correctly. Does everyone understand what Becky just explained?" asked Connor.

Heads are bobbing up and down indicating that they do.

"Let me repeat it one more time," said Connor. "In a project management environment, the critical path is the constraint," he said. "Having said this, when we talk more about the critical chain, you will see that it too is the constraint, but it's very different than the critical path."

Connor continued, "OK, earlier I demonstrated how by simply

eliminating multitasking, significant gains could be made in project completion rates. But we still have to address the impact of both the Student Syndrome and Parkinson's Law," Connor said. "We know now that both of these behaviors work to extend the time required to complete a project," he explained. "You'll recall with CPM, planning resources estimate individual task times and then add in their own protection against disruptions caused primarily by Murphy. And then the effects of Parkinson's and the Student Syndrome waste most of the safety that has been added," said Connor. "So how does CCPM deal with these behaviors?

"While CPM relies on individual task durations as well as scheduled start and finish dates, CCPM does not," explained Connor. "The project focus is no longer on finishing individual tasks on time, but rather completing tasks as soon as possible," he said. "So I know you're wondering how this works . . . Like CPM, CCPM still gathers estimates on individual tasks and identifies its own version of the critical path. However, unlike CPM, CCPM also considers the competing resources and includes them as part of the critical path," he explained. "Let's look at an example," and Connor sketched a new figure on the flip chart.

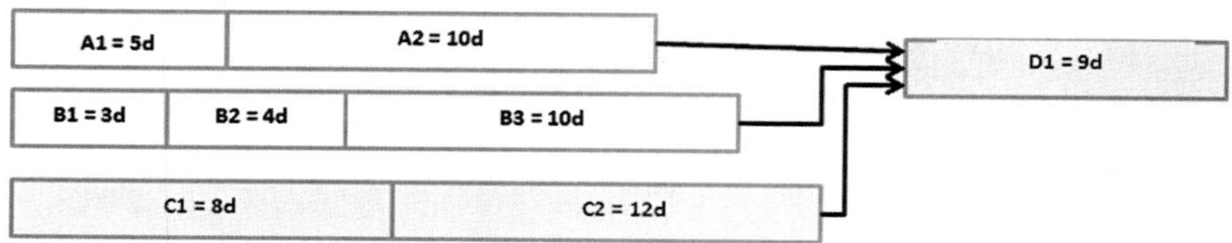

"As I explained, CPM defines the critical path as the longest path of dependent tasks within a project. That is, tasks are dependent when the completion of one task isn't possible until the completion of a preceding task," he explained. "Any delay on the critical path will delay the project correspondingly.

"Everybody with me?" asked Connor. "Paul, are you understanding this?"

"Yes, I think so," Paul replied.

"So on this drawing, I've highlighted the critical path according to the CPM method," Connor said. "Remember, CPM determines the critical path by looking at the task dependencies within the project," Connor reminded everyone.

Benji, who had been quiet, gingerly raised his hand and said, "I'm sure everyone else understands task dependencies, but could you explain that for me?"

"Certainly," Connor replied. "Looking at the sketch I've drawn, it simply means that task A2 can't be started until A1 is complete, so we say that A2 is dependent upon A1," he explained. "Likewise, for B3 and C2," he said.

Benji listened and then asked, "So D1 is dependent upon the completion of A2, B3 and C2?"

"Yes, Benji, you have it exactly right," Connor replied. "So here's a question for you," said Connor. "Using the CPM method, what is the critical path in this project, and how long would it be?"

Like a young child in school, Paul raised his hand and said, "I know, I know! The critical path would be C1-C2-D1, and the project completion estimate would be the sum of those days, or twenty-nine days."

"Very good, Paul," replied Connor. "Let's take a short break so that your instructor can use the restroom," said Connor with a smile.

While Connor took a bathroom break, the group was actively discussing what they'd heard from Connor so far.

"What do you think, Ron?" asked Greg.

"Excuse my French, but this is some good shit!" Ron exclaimed. "I can't wait to hear what he has to say next."

Connor returned from the restroom and asked, "Before we get started, does anyone need a refill?"

Paul said, "I do."

"I thought you weren't much of a wine drinker, Paul," said Becky.

"I'm not, usually, but I love this stuff," Paul replied.

"Let me emphasize again, what I'm explaining to you today is just the tip of the iceberg as far as project management goes," said Connor. "If we were actually going through a CCPM implementation, there would be lots more, and we would even be playing some dice and bead games to clarify certain points," he added.

"OK, one of the shortcomings of CPM is the failure to consider or recognize the existence of resource dependencies," Connor explained. "What if, in our example here on the flip chart, tasks A2 and B3 are performed by the same resource?" asked Connor. "Would the critical path be different?"

"Yes it would be," said Becky.

"How so, Becky?" asked Connor. "Would you care to show us on the flip chart?" he asked as he handed her the marker.

"Well," Becky said as she redrew the project steps,"since A2 and B3 are done by the same resource, they can't both be done at the same time," she explained. "Because of this dependency, we have to move B3 to begin after the same resource completed A2," she said. "So by my thinking, the new critical path would be A1-A2-B3-D1," she explained. "And if I'm correct, the new project estimate increases from the original twenty-nine days to thirty-four days," said Becky. "Am I right?" asked Becky as she handed the marker back to Connor and sat down.

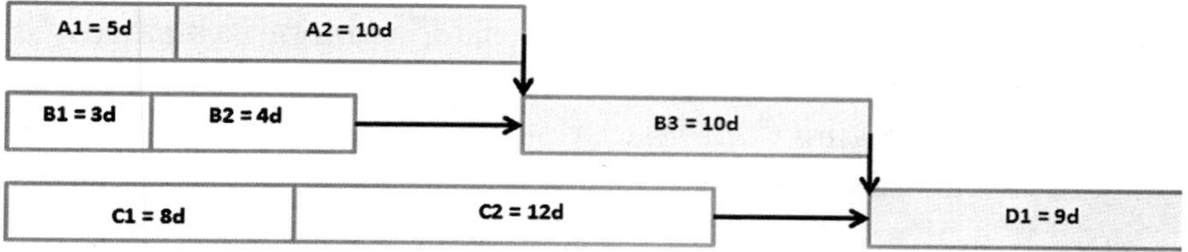

"What does everyone think?" asked Connor. "Is Becky right?"

"Yes, I totally agree with her thought process," said Joe.

"And what does the recognition of resource dependencies do to the on-time completion of this project?" asked Connor.

Ron explained, "It means that without considering resource dependencies, using CPM, the project is guaranteed to be late!"

"Yes, that is absolutely correct, Ron!" Connor exclaimed.

"Nice job, Becky," said Sam.

Connor continued, "This simple consequence of incorrectly identifying the critical path—which we will now refer to as the critical chain—is that the project team will never be able to complete their project on time without heroic efforts, adding additional resources, overtime or a combination of all three." Connor added, "The practical implication of incorrectly identifying the real critical chain is that the focus will be on the wrong tasks."

Greg interjected, "This is really no different than focusing on nonconstraints in a production process, right?"

"Precisely," said Connor.

"Now I understand why our projects are late so often," said Ron. "I can't wait to get back to Simco." Ron took the thought process a little further. "The only problem is that when I add resource dependencies to the project, I will actually lengthen the project completion time, and that won't go over very well at Simco," said Ron. "What do I have to do to shorten the project time?" he asked.

"Great question, Ron," said Connor. "Remember earlier how we said that excessive safety is imbedded within each task as a way to guard against the uncertainties of Murphy."

Heads nodded affirmatively.

"CCPM takes a completely different approach by assuming that Murphy's uncertainty will happen in every project," said Connor. "Unlike CPM, CCPM actually removes these safeties within each task and pools them at the end of the project to protect the only date that really matters, the project completion date," Connor explained. "In other words, instead of protecting the task due dates, we shift our thinking to protecting the project due date. Do you understand the difference?" he asked.

Again, heads nodded in agreement.

"Remember I told you that tasks are over-inflated by at least 50 percent?" Connor asked.

"Yes," the group answered.

"Well here's where we take advantage of this extra time," said Connor as he drew another sketch on the flip chart.

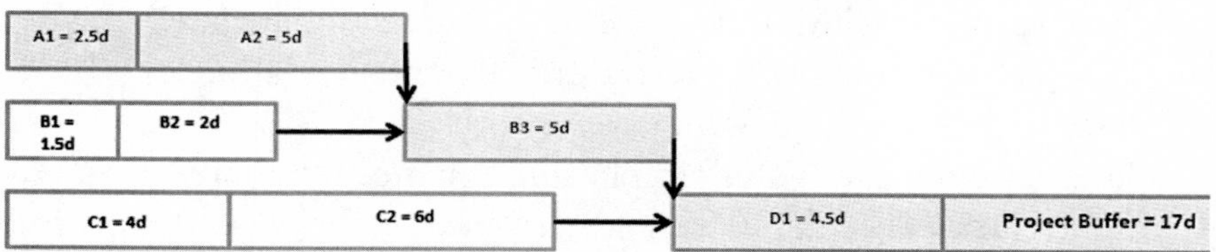

"As you can see, the new tasks times are half of the original estimates," he said. "But you can also see that we now have added a project buffer." He pointed it out on the sketch. "This isn't exactly how creating the project buffer works, but for demonstration purposes, it will suffice. In the real world, we would only add half of this number, or eight and a half days, as the project buffer," he said. "So the question I pose to you is this—How does having this project buffer improve the on-time completion of projects?" he asked as he looked directly at Becky.

But another voice answered the question. "If I understand this concept," said Greg, "the project buffer works like a bank account with deposits and withdrawals." He continued, "If a task takes longer than the estimate, you withdraw time from the project buffer. But if the tasks is finished in a shorter amount of time, you add the time back into the project buffer."

"That is a great analogy, Greg!" Connor exclaimed. "Greg is absolutely right. Remember what we said earlier," said Connor. "With CPM, delays are passed on while gains are lost. This is such a significant difference!" said Connor. "The project buffer protects us from delays, One other point, we also add feeding buffers to make sure that tasks not on the critical chain are completed on time, but I'm not going into that tonight," said Connor.

"I have a question, Connor," said Ron.

"Go ahead, Ron," said Connor.

"I haven't seen any way yet to eliminate the effects of the Student Syndrome or Parkinson's Law?" Ron said.

"Great point, Ron," Connor replied. "One of the key differences between CPM and CCPM is what happens at the task level," said Connor. "By this I mean that in traditional project management, CPM, each task has a scheduled start and finish date," he said. "CCPM completely removes the start and finish dates from the schedule so that the focus will be on passing on tasks as soon as they are completed," he explained. "By doing this, both the Student Syndrome and Parkinson's Law are pretty much neutralized. CCPM uses a relay race mentality whereby the runner completes a certain distance and then passes off the baton to the next runner who is waiting.

"Earlier I explained that in CPM we track progress of the project by calculating the percentage of individual tasks completed and then comparing that percentage against the project due date," said Connor. "The problem with this method is that it is nearly impossible to know how much time is remaining to complete the project," he explained. "If you use this method to track progress, many times you'll see 90 percent of a project completed only to see the remaining 10 percent take just as long. In fact, looking at the number or percentage of tasks completed, instead of how much of the critical path has been completed, only really serves to give a false sense of schedule conformance," he explained. "Does everyone see my point here?" asked Connor.

"I certainly do," said Ron. "Now I understand why we are normally scrambling during the last 10 percent of all of our projects."

"CCPM measures project performance in a much different way, and in so doing, allows the project to make valuable use of early finishes of tasks," said Connor. "CCPM uses something called a Fever Chart, which is simply a run chart of the percentage of the critical chain completed versus the percentage of project buffer consumed," said Connor as he passed out copies of a fever chart to everyone. "If you look at this fever chart, you'll see three different colored zones," he said. "Anyone want to take a guess as to what each zone means?" asked Connor.

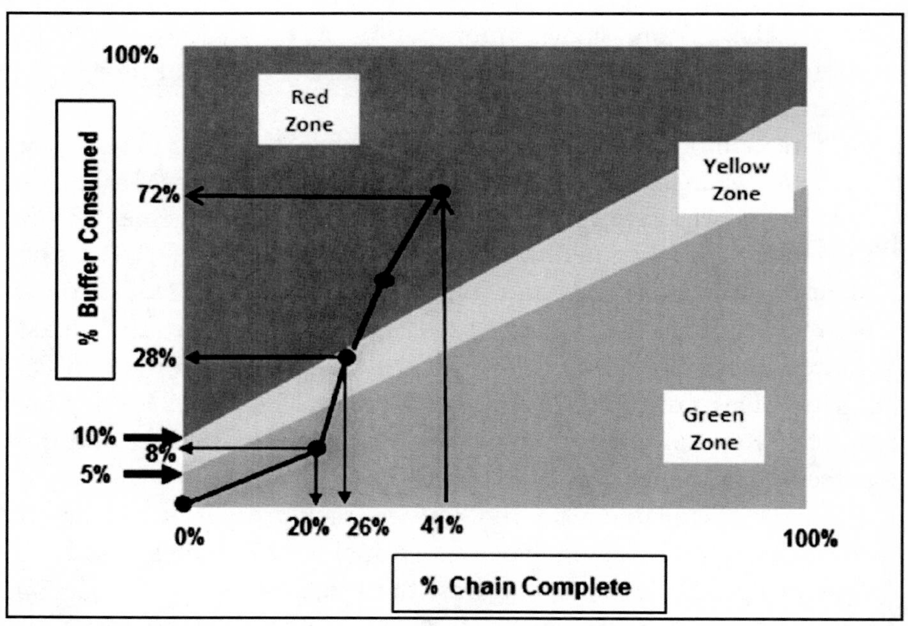

Joe said, "If I had to guess, I would say it's just like a traffic signal where green means go, yellow means proceed with caution and red means stop."

"Very good, Joe. Can you expand that just a bit to the project world?" Connor asked.

Joe responded. "My interpretation would be that as long as it is in the green zone, the project is either on or ahead of schedule," he said. "If it's in the yellow zone, the rate of buffer consumption is either ahead of the plan or at plan, but you better take a look at it and make the necessary plans if it goes into the red zone," Joe continued. "If it enters the red zone, you must take action immediately, or the project will be late because it might eat up the entire planned buffer," said Joe.

"You guys are starting to amaze me with how quickly you're picking up these concepts," said Connor with a smile on his face. "Joe is almost totally correct, so let me ask a clarifying question. Is it ever acceptable for your project to finish in the red?"

Immediately Becky said, "Yes."

"Really, Becky?" said Connor. "And under what circumstances would that be acceptable?"

"As long as the critical chain is 100 percent completed, and you haven't used more than 100 percent of your project buffer, then finishing in the red is perfectly acceptable," she explained. "In fact, if both of these variables are at the 100 percent level, the project is exactly on time."

"Now that, gentlemen, is a perfect answer," said Connor. "Look at the fever chart I gave you and tell me what you see . . . interpret it for me," Connor said.

Ron said, "This project started off ahead of schedule by completing 20 percent of the critical chain while only consuming 8 percent of the buffer. But if you look at the latest data point, only 41 percent of the chain is complete, but 72 percent of the buffer has been consumed." Ron continued, "This project is now behind schedule, and unless some kind of intervention is employed, the project will be late."

"Does this mean that the project is doomed?" asked Connor.

"Absolutely not," said Ron. "It only means that some kind of action must be taken, or the project will be late completing."

"What might be a reason at Simco that this might occur?" asked Connor.

"One example might be that the assembly failed an intermediate inspection," said Ron.

"Good job, Ron," said Connor. "The key point to remember here is that you should get excited with vertical rises because it always spells trouble if left unattended," Connor said.

"I have an observation, Connor," said Sam.

"Yes Sam, what is it?" asked Connor.

"It would seem to me that you could calculate an index to demonstrate how well the project is proceeding," Sam said.

"Go on," said Connor.

"Well," said Sam, "if you were to divide the percent of the critical chain completed into the percent of buffer consumed, this ratio could give a single number that would tell you how well you're doing." Sam continued, "So if you were above one, your rate of buffer consumption would be too high, while if the ratio is below one, everything is going well. Does that concept make sense?" asked Sam.

"It makes perfect sense, especially for us math geeks," Becky laughingly replied.

"I have an observation too," said Paul. "Well, maybe it's more of a question," he said. "To me, the CCPM concept is really based on the same principles as Drum-Buffer-Rope. The critical chain is the drum, the buffer is the buffer, and the project due date is the rope. Does that make any sense at all, Connor?"

"Yes Paul, you're dead on," Connor replied.

"That's the quasi-technical side of CCPM, said Connor. "But before you leave, I want to cover a couple more critical items that involve managing and using CCPM," he said. "There are several key things that must be done if a CCPM implementation is going to be successful. Every day there must be stand-up meetings to find out what your resources need," he said. "By that I mean, go to the resources and ask them if they have everything they need and if they have any problems. If you can't resolve their issues, then you must escalate the problem up through the various levels of management," he said. "This may sound trivial, but believe me it isn't. If you don't take this step seriously, you will never sustain your implementation," said Connor.

"I remember an MRO contractor to the Department of Defense that stopped doing this and began backsliding to the point that their cycle times deteriorated and their on-time delivery fell to unacceptable levels," said Connor. "They had new leadership who clearly hadn't bought into CCPM, and the negative results validated it," he added. "The leadership of this company was clearly not involved in the process, and it eventually failed," said Connor.

Behavioral Changes

1. **Eliminate the focus of working to task duration estimates.**
2. **Eliminate multi-tasking by insisting on one task at a time and passing on the results as soon as the task is complete.**
3. **There will be idle time in non-constraints, so don't insist on busy work.**
4. **Everyone must stay on plan and use the buffers. Buffers are meant to be used, not saved.**

Connor turned to his flip chart and wrote down four organizational behavior changes. "These four behavioral changes must take place in your organization if you are going to successfully implement CCPM," said Connor.

"That's all I have, and I hope this was helpful for you, Ron." said Connor.

Ron replied, "Not only was it helpful, it amazes me that Simco hasn't heard about this before. It's so clear to me why our projects always come in late, and I'm convinced that if we implement CCPM, it will be a turning point for Simco." Ron went on. "I can see significant increases in project throughput, significant decreases in overtime, and best of all, I can see Simco taking the market!" he exclaimed.

"Connor, I can't thank you enough for taking the time to teach us all yesterday and today," said Ron. "And what you and I discussed yesterday about helping Simco is still on the table," he added.

"Why don't you call me next week after you've had a chance to talk to your leadership Ron," said Connor. "Besides, I noticed it was going to be raining this week, and that would interfere with my golf," he joked.

As they were leaving, Joe and Sam stopped to have a smoke and chat about their meeting at Corporate on Monday morning.

"Well Sam, have you thought about what's going to happen on Monday?" asked Joe.

"I've thought a lot about it, but I decided that I'm not going to worry about it anymore," Sam replied.

"Me either Sam," said Joe.

"We have clearly turned the corner here at Barton, and I don't think we can do any more," said Sam. "Are you doing anything special this weekend?" he asked Joe.

"My wife is coming in for one more house-hunting trip, so I'll be out of touch," said Joe.

"Would you like me to pick you up Monday morning so we can ride to the airport together?" asked Sam.

"That would be great Sam. See you Monday."

Chapter 18
Joe's and Sam's Trip to Corporate

Joe spent most of his weekend looking at homes with his wife Jennifer, and to his delight found one that both he and Jennifer really liked. Joe was getting very tired of living out of a suitcase, and he wanted to be with his wife. It was Sunday already, so he and Jennifer drove to the airport to catch her flight back home. On the way to the airport they talked about Joe's trip to Corporate and what it might all mean.

"Joe, I know you haven't been at Barton very long, but from what you've told me over the phone, you've really made a significant difference here," said Jennifer.

"I think so, Jen, but I'm still worried about why we're being summoned to Corporate."

"What has you worried, Joe?"

"I'm not sure," he replied.

"For all you know, Joe, this could be something really good for you."

"You're right, Jen, but that doesn't stop me from worrying," he replied. "I really miss you and the kids, Jen, and I just know if you were here all of the time, I wouldn't worry so much."

"Now boarding Flight 742," the announcement came over the loud speaker. "That's my flight Joe," said Jennifer.

"I really enjoyed myself this weekend, honey, and I wish you could stay," said Joe.

"Me too, sweetie, but I have to get back to the kids," she replied. "Please call me Monday after your meeting Joe . . . I'll be worried until I hear from you," she added.

"I will honey," said Joe.

"Final call for Flight 742," came the announcement, and Joe kissed her goodbye. He watched her until she rounded the corner of the boarding ramp and disappeared. "Gosh, I can't wait until she's here full time," he thought. Joe waited until the plane pulled away from the gate and then left to find his car. He drove back to his hotel and spent the rest of the day just lounging around, not thinking about the trip he and Sam would be taking to Corporate on Monday.

Joe's and Sam's flight was at 6:00 a.m. At 4:30 a.m. Sam's car pulled into the hotel. "Good morning Joe, how was your weekend?" asked Sam.

"It was great, Sam. Jennifer and I finally found a house we both like," replied Joe.

"Where is it, Joe?" asked Sam.

"It's in Sunbriar Estates," replied Joe.

"Really? That's my neighborhood," said Sam, happy to have Joe as a neighbor.

"I can't wait for Jennifer to get here so she can meet my wife Peggy," said Sam.

"Me too, knowing someone will make it much easier for her when she moves here permanently," said Joe.

"Make sure you give me Jennifer's cell number, and I'll have Peggy call her," said Sam.

"Remind me later Sam, I think Jennifer would really like to meet her" said Joe.

Joe and Sam drove around the airport parking lot looking for parking spaces. They had to park near the back of the lot—a sign that the terminal was going to be busy. They both lugged their overnight bags into the terminal, and it was a madhouse. They checked in at kiosks and headed for the security line, which by now was backed up around the corner of the building.

"I hope we make our flight, Sam," said Joe.

"Come with me Joe, I'm a platinum traveler, and I'm sure I can talk them into letting you through with me," said Sam. "I've made this trip many times, Joe, and not under pleasant circumstances," he added. "Usually I've gone to Corporate to explain why the results are so bad, but thanks to you, that isn't the case this time." True to his word, Sam was able to get Joe through security on his platinum status.

Corporate had made the flight arrangements for Joe and Sam, and neither had noticed that they had first-class tickets. When they realized this, both of them felt much more at ease as to the purpose of this trip.

"We can't be in too much trouble, Joe, if they're flying us first class," said Sam.

"This is great, Sam. I can't remember the last time I flew first class," said Joe.

"Me too, Joe, I usually have to fight for an upgrade, if I get one at all," replied Sam.

The flight attendant was busy taking orders for drinks, and when she asked Sam and Joe what they wanted, both of them said they wanted just coffee.

Joe laughingly said, "I almost said 'Chianti.'"

"Just for the heck of it, I'm going to ask her if they have any, for the trip home," said Sam.

When she brought their coffee, Sam asked about Chianti, and to his and Joe's surprise, they did have some. "I know what I'm drinking on the way home," said Sam.

The flight to New York was uneventful, but when Joe and Sam exited the runway to the terminal they noticed a man in a suit and hat holding up a sign with their names on it. Sam looked at Joe, shrugged his shoulders, raised his eyebrows and let the man know who they were.

"Follow me, gentlemen," said the man.

"What is going on, Joe?" asked Sam.

"I don't know, but I like it so far," said Joe.

They walked to a black stretch limo and crawled in. "Gentlemen, Mr. Graham sends his best wishes," said the driver. As they drove down the interstate Sam couldn't help but display his wide grin, which Joe noticed.

"What are you smiling about, Sam?" asked Joe.

"All of the worrying I did all week, and then this," replied Sam.

"I know, I feel so much more relaxed," said Joe.

"I'd still like to know the purpose of this trip," said Sam.

"I guess we'll find out soon enough," said Joe.

The limo pulled into the parking garage of the offices of American Industries, and that surprised Sam.

"What's wrong, Sam?" asked Joe.

"This isn't where I usually face the firing squad," said Sam. "I normally go to Barton's offices, which are down three blocks. This is AII's headquarters, Joe, not Barton's corporate office," Sam said. "This is where the big dogs live."

Joe and Sam exited the stretch limo, and once again the driver said, "Follow me, gentlemen." They entered the elevator, and the driver pushed the button for the twenty-eighth floor, the penthouse.

"God, Joe, I hope we're not underdressed," Sam said jokingly.

The elevator door opened and there stood Cecil Graham. "Gentlemen, so nice to see you again," said Cecil. "How was your trip?"

"It's the best trip I've ever made to New York," replied Sam.

"Well come on, boys, I want you to meet someone," said Cecil.

Cecil led Sam and Joe into a spectacular office decorated with impressive paintings and various other pieces of art. A distinguished, well dressed gentleman sat facing them behind an very large, well polished desk. Cecil addressed him.

"Good morning, Thomas, I want you to meet Sam Henderson, Barton's VP of Operations, and Joe Pecci, Barton's Continuous Improvement Manager," said Cecil.

"Very nice to meet both of you. I'm Thomas Ramsey, President and CEO of American Industries," he said as they shook hands. "I have heard some wonderful things about both of you from Cecil," said Thomas.

"Nice to meet you too, sir," said Sam.

"Yes, it's a pleasure to meet you, sir," said Joe.

"No more sir, please call me Thomas," he said.

"Yes sir, Thomas," said Sam, as both Thomas and Cecil laughed.

"I want you to know how very pleased I am with Barton's performance," said Thomas. "I also know that you two are the reason behind such a magnificent turnaround.

"Thank you Thomas, but it wasn't all just the two of us," said Sam.

"Sam's right, it was the cohesive team at Barton that pulled off this turn-around in performance," Joe interjected.

"Will you be joining us, Thomas?" asked Cecil as they exited Thomas's office.

"Yes, I'll be there in a few minutes," he replied.

As Cecil walked with Joe and Sam down a carpeted hallway, Sam asked, "Cecil, may I ask why you had us come here today?"

"I wanted you to hear firsthand what the performance metrics team is going to say," replied Cecil. "This will be the first time I've heard their recommendations, and I thought it would only be fitting for you two to be here," he added.

Both Sam and Joe let out a sigh of relief when they heard that was why they had been flown here.

"Let's go to the conference room," said Cecil. "Would you like some coffee?"

"Yes, love some," said Joe.

"I'll take some too," said Sam. "What a gorgeous conference room this is," he said. Paintings of the previous CEO's and past board chairmen hung on the walls, which were adorned with exquisite tapestry. In the center of the room was an enormous, beautifully designed conference table with a large group of people seated around it.

Sam and Joe scanned the room and recognized one familiar face, Sylvester Malone, who had led the performance metrics review team at Barton. They walked over to him and shook hands.

"Nice to see you again," said Joe.

"Nice to see both of you guys too," said Sylvester. "I hope you like my presentation today, and thanks for all of your help," he added.

"We were happy to do whatever we could, Sylvester," said Sam. "Come see us anytime you'd like."

Cecil took Sam and Joe around the board room to meet each of the seated board members. Generally the comments were positive—but a few of the older members acted aloof. Now Thomas Ramsey entered the conference room and took his customary seat at the head of the massive table. It was time to hear Sylvester's presentation.

Sam and Joe didn't know what to expect from Sylvester today. Did he agree with the final metrics recommendations or not? But Sylvester surprised both Sam and Joe as he walked the board through the now familiar piping diagram and four-step process with remarkable deftness and skill as though he had known about the Theory of Constraints principles for years. His presentation on Throughput Accounting was superb, and for the most part, his audience seemed to be buying into everything he had to say. What the board members really liked was the IO Map. After answering numerous questions about the chosen metrics, he finished his presentation by thanking Joe and Sam for showing him a superior financial accounting methodology. When he finished, there was immediate applause, but what Sam and Joe didn't grasp, at least at first, was that the applause was for them. One of the board members motioned for them to stand up, and the applause grew even louder. It continued until Thomas stood up to speak.

"Sam and Joe, it is our distinct pleasure to welcome you to New York City and to extend our sincere thanks for the job you've done for Barton," said Thomas. "Not just for Barton, but for our corporation in general," he added. "On Thursday I received a phone call from the CEO of Simco who had nothing but praise for the work you two have done," said Thomas. "He told me about your new on-time delivery rates and your willingness and enthusiasm to help his sales rep learn a new way to complete project management projects. In all my years, I've never gotten a phone call quite like that from another CEO before," Thomas said. "Sam and Joe, what you have taught Sylvester and his team in such a brief amount of time is simply remarkable. In fact, I would like my operations people from some of our portfolio companies to come spend time with you guys so they can learn your new way of running an operation," he concluded.

After more applause, the meeting broke up and Cecil invited Sam and Joe to have lunch in his private room at Barton's corporate office. All three of them rode in the same black stretch limo that had picked them up at the airport. Sam had been in this office complex many times in the past year, but never under more pleasant circumstances than today. After a brief limo ride, they arrived at Barton's corporate offices.

"Sam and Joe, it would be an understatement to say I'm very proud of both of you," said Cecil. "I didn't bring you to New York just to hear Sylvester's presentation," he said. "Because of your outstanding performance, I have reached a decision. Sam, I'd like you to take over as CEO of Barton. And Joe, I'd like you to move to our corporate office, assume a vice president's position and head up our continuous improvement efforts for all of American Industries, Inc.," said Cecil.

Sam and Joe looked at each other in silence with very confused looks on their faces until Sam broke the silence. "Mr. Graham, I can't speak for Joe, but for me, I think you're making a mistake."

"A mistake?" said Cecil. "Good grief Sam, I saw the way Greg and

Paul acted when I was there the last time, and I'm convinced that it's the right move," Cecil said. "Why in the world do you think it's a mistake?"

"Well sir, for the first time in my entire career, I love my job," said Sam. "I've learned so much from Joe and Connor, and I want to stay right where I am," he affirmed. "And what you don't know is that both Greg and Paul have had their own personal epiphanies and have become an important part of the Barton improvement effort," Sam explained. "To change leadership right now, to change this team would be a serious mistake in my opinion," he added.

"Sam's right sir," said Joe, "what we have started at Barton is just the beginning, and Greg and Paul have immersed themselves in learning this new way." He stated, "I have to respectfully decline your offer to move to New York. There's just too much left to do at Barton, sir," said Joe.

"I too need to respectfully decline your offer, Cecil," said Sam. "Like Joe just said, this is only the beginning," he added.

"Well, in all my years," said Cecil, "I've never had anyone turn down promotions of this magnitude before."

"Please don't misunderstand why I am declining your offer, Cecil," said Joe. "I am totally flattered by it, and perhaps at a point in time it might be the right thing for me to do. But I think by staying at Barton, at least for now, we can develop what we've started to a much higher level, and it will benefit AII to a much larger degree for years to come," Joe added.

Sam agreed. "Joe's right, sir. To change horses right now could have a very negative impact on the future." He added, "I too am very flattered that you have this much confidence in me. But I believe that Joe and I working together with Greg and Paul can create a model that will be difficult for our competition to copy."

"I believe that in the future, if we do things right," said Joe, "we'll have the opportunity to dominate the market . . . please consider the nature of our concern Cecil," he said.

"Alright, alright, you two have convinced me—at least for now. I'll leave things as they are at Barton," Cecil responded.

"There was another reason I had you two come to New York," said Cecil. "What I'm about to tell you is extremely confidential, so I must trust you not to tell anyone about what I'm going to say . . . Joe, Sam, do I have your word on this?" asked Cecil.

"Yes, of course, Cecil," said Sam.

"Absolutely," said Joe.

Cecil went ahead, "Barton has been approached by a group of foreign investors to purchase our holdings in Waterford. At the moment I don't know much about the nature of the offer, but I can tell you it could be for a substantial amount of money," he added. "As you probably know, timing on deals of this nature is very unpredictable, so it could happen next month, or it could be next year," said Cecil. "What I need from both of you is to sustain the remarkable gains you've made and to continue improving our bottom line."

"Are you at liberty to tell us who the investment group is, Cecil?" asked Sam.

"No, I'm not, but I can tell you that it's so early in the process, I really don't even know myself," Cecil replied. "There have been some preliminary discussions at the highest level of American Industries, and that's about all I know right now," he added.

"I didn't know that we were even up for sale," said Sam.

"Well, we aren't," said Cecil. "But in the private equity world, investors typically only hold companies for relatively short periods of time and then sell for profits that far exceed the purchase price," he added. "But we always entertain offers at any time," said Cecil. "So remember, nothing is to be said about this to anyone,"

"Understood," said Sam.

"You have our word," said Joe.

"So how about a drink before I have my driver take you back to the airport?" said Cecil.

"Sounds good to me," said Sam.

"Me too," said Joe.

Cecil surprised Joe and Sam when he pulled out a bottle of Chianti Classico, their magic potion and drink of choice. "One thing I learned while I was down at Barton the last time I was there is that I love this wine," said Cecil as he poured three glasses.

Cecil raised his glass and proposed a toast, "To the future." The three glasses clinked together as Sam and Joe repeated, "To the future." They finished their drinks and Cecil called for his driver.

On the way back to the airport Sam and Joe were uncharacteristically quiet, obviously thinking about Cecil's promotion offer and the potential sale of Barton. As they exited the limo, Joe told Sam that he had to call his wife.

"Hi Jen," said Joe.

"Hi honey, how did it go?" asked Jennifer.

"Better than Sam and I ever imagined," said Joe. "We met the CEO of American Investors and the rest of the board and even got an enthusiastic round of applause for our work at Barton."

"I'm so proud of you, honey. You and Sam deserved it."

"That wasn't all, sweetheart," said Joe. "Sam and I turned down promotion offers." After an extended period of silence, Joe said, "Honey are you still there?"

"Yes, I'm here . . . why did you turn down the promotion offers?" she asked.

"Because the timing isn't right honey," said Joe.

"Why in the world would the timing not be right, Joe?" asked Jennifer in a very serious tone.

"It would have also involved moving to New York City, honey, and I don't think I'd be a good fit there," he said.

"New York City?" she replied. "Oh Joe, thank you for turning it down, I don't have any desire to move there . . .you must have been flattered by the offer though."

"I was, and so was Sam," he replied. "Sam was offered the job of CEO at Barton, and he turned it down too."

"Wow, why would he turn that job down?" asked Jennifer.

"Because we both knew that we have much more to do here at Barton," Joe replied.

"But wouldn't that make it easier for both of you if Sam was the CEO?" she asked.

"It's hard to explain, honey, but we both believe that making that kind of change in the organization right now would be a huge mistake," said Joe.

"Well, I trust you, Joe, and if you think that this change wouldn't be the right thing to do, you know best," she replied.

"I'll call you tonight, honey. Got to go now," said Joe.

"OK, honey, I love you," said Jennifer.

"Love you too, sweetheart," said Joe.

Sam interrupted Joe's serene mood. "Joe, we've got a problem back at Barton."

"What is it, Sam?" asked Joe.

"It seems that Fabrics has missed a shipment of tank fabric and we're about to shut down," said Sam in a concerned tone.

"Let me call Stan and see if he can give me some details," said Joe as he dialed Stan's cell number.

"Hello, this is Stan, how can I help you?" said Stan.

"Stan, this is Joe, what's going on with Fabrics?"

"They're late on their scheduled shipment," replied Stan. "I'm at Fabrics right now with Sally, and we're trying to find out what the problem is . . . I think Barton's cable supplier missed their delivery and without the cables Fabrics can't make their fabric so it just snowballed here," said Stan. "Sally and I may need to make a trip to their supplier, if that's OK."

"Yes, of course it's OK. Where are they located?" asked Joe.

"Somewhere in Arkansas, I think," said Stan.

"Well, do what you have to do Stan, and Sam and I will follow up with you when we land," said Joe.

"OK, will do," said Stan.

"I talked to Stan," said Joe, "and he and Sally are going to one of Barton's cable suppliers to see what the problem is."

"Overnight trip, Joe?" asked Sam. "I hope they focus on the supplier and not each other," said Sam in a joking way.

"Sam, they're both adults, but they're professionals first," said Joe.

"I know, Joe, I was only joking," said Sam.

"We better hurry or we're going to miss our flight, Sam," said Joe as they trotted to check-in.

"And what would you gentlemen like to drink?" asked the Flight Attendant.

Both Joe and Sam answered at the same time, "A glass of Chianti."

"I'll get that right away, gentlemen," she said.

"I hope Stan and Sally get to the bottom of this problem," said Sam.

"I'm confident that they'll do just that, Sam," said Joe.

As soon as the plane touched down, Joe dialed Stan's cell phone, but he had to leave a voice mail. On the way to Barton, Joe tried again, but still got no answer. As they pulled into Barton's parking lot, Joe's cell phone rang and it was Stan.

"Where have you been, Stan, I've been trying to reach you?" asked Joe.

"Er, uh, must have been a dead zone," replied Stan.

"Have you been to the plant, Stan?" asked Joe.

"Yes, we've been there," said Stan.

"And?" asked Joe. "The problem was with their primary loom," said Stan. "They had a major breakdown and didn't have the replacement part in stock."

"And do they have the part now, Stan?" asked Joe.

"Yes, they're installing it now, and the equipment will be operational around midnight if all goes well," Stan replied. "They're going to call us as soon as it's back on line."

"Where are you now, Stan?" asked Joe. "We're, er, I mean I'm in my hotel room," replied Stan nervously.

"OK, Stan, call me when you know more," said Joe.

"It looks like it was an equipment breakdown problem at Fabrics' cable supplier, and they should have it fixed by midnight," said Joe to Sam. "I asked Stan to call me when he knows more."

"Let's go in and see how things are going here, Joe," said Sam. "Hey guys, I understand that we have a problem?" Sam asked.

"Yes, boss, we only have a small amount of fabric left to start new tanks," said the supervisor on duty.

"Is it going to affect our master schedule?" asked Sam.

"It will if we don't get some by tomorrow on second shift," said the supervisor. "By the way, Fabrics' general manager, what's his name, is meeting with our supply folks right now," said the supervisor.

"You mean Sid Sanchez?" said Joe.

"Yeah, that's his name. I have trouble remembering names," said the supervisor.

"Thanks," said Sam. "Joe, lets go see what Sid has to say."

"Okay," said Joe.

"Hey Sid," said Sam.

"Hi, guys," said Sid. "I have good news for you. We just found a way to rework a roll of fabric that we had on hold. So I think we'll be OK until we get our next shipment from our cable manufacturer," said Sid. "Sally and Stan are at the supplier right now, so I'll give them a call and see what the latest news is," said Sid.

"No need to do that, Sid," said Joe. "I just spoke with Stan, and he gave me the latest scoop. Apparently their major loom broke down, and they didn't have the spare part they needed, but they have it now and should be up and running by midnight," said Joe. "When I speak with Stan, I'm going to have him and Sally set up a Failure Mode and Effects Analysis (FMEA) so that your supplier can prepare for and do a better job of anticipating any future problems," said Joe.

"Thanks, Sid, for doing what you did with that roll of fabric," said Sam.

"I'm going to go to my office and meet with my staff before I go home," said Joe.

"Well hello, stranger," said Judy Godfrey, Joe's lean assistant.

"Hi Judy, you look very pretty today," Joe said.

"Thank you. We've—or at least I've—missed you," said Judy.

"I feel like I've been neglecting you guys," said Joe.

"Well, you have, and I'm going to tell HR on you," joked Judy. "We know you've been very busy, and from what I hear, you've sort of changed the world," she said.

"Not really, Judy. It's really the shop floor workers and you guys that have done everything," said Joe.

"But someone had to show them a better way, Joe. Don't be so humble, and take my compliment because it's from my heart," said Judy.

"Well thank you, Judy, it means a lot to me," replied Joe. "Where's Bill and Manuel?" asked Joe.

"I'm not sure, Joe, do you need me to try and find them?" she asked.

"No, just wanted to say hi and find out what they're working on," said Joe.

"I can tell you that Joe—they're probably at Fabrics, or at least that's where Stan sent them," said Judy.

"Judy, I wanted to ask you a question, but before I do, you don't have to answer it if you feel uncomfortable," said Joe.

"Go ahead," said Judy.

"Are Stan and Sally . . . you know?" asked Joe.

"If you mean are they in love, yes. I haven't seen Stan like this ever," said Judy. "They make such a cute couple.

"OK, I thought maybe they were, but I was just curious," Joe said.

"Well, Judy, if you see Bill and Manuel, tell them I was asking about them," said Joe. "I'm going to my hotel to get some rest. See you soon, Judy," he added.

"Bye, boss. Nice seeing you again," said Judy.

Joe woke up early at around 3:00 in the morning and seemed a bit disoriented. He thought to himself, "Did Stan call me or not?" He finally realized that he hadn't spoken to Stan since yesterday afternoon, so he was wondering what the status of the cable supplier was. He decided not to call Stan since it was so early. Instead he decided to go directly to Fabrics. Joe showered, dressed and headed out the door for Fabrics.

Fifteen minutes later he arrived and headed for the manufacturing area, where he saw a flurry of activity. Joe spotted one of the employees that he had met during the first training session, and he walked over to talk to him.

"How's it going?" asked Joe.

"Hi, Mr. Pecci," he replied. "We've got this roll almost ready to go, so you shouldn't have to shut down."

"Great work. Have you heard from Sally by any chance?" asked Joe.

"Yes, as a matter of fact she and Stan just left the supplier and are headed back here," he said.

Joe got on his phone and called Stan.

"Hello, this is Stan, how can I help you"?

"Stan, it's me, why didn't you call me?" asked Joe.

"The fix took longer than we expected, and I didn't want to wake you up," said Stan.

"So where are you now?" asked Joe.

"We're on our way back to Fabrics," said Stan.

"I wish you had called me, Stan. I wanted you to set up an FMEA," said Joe.

"We did that, Joe, and identified several more areas of potential vulnerability," said Stan.

"You did that?" asked Joe.

"It was Sally's idea Joe, she's a remarkable woman," said Stan.

"Well, tell her thanks for me and you guys drive safely," said Joe.

"We will," said Stan, "See you in a few hours," he added.

So thanks to some heroic efforts by Fabrics and Barton, a crisis was avoided. It did, however, point out the need to take a hard look at first and second generation suppliers, but that would come later. Joe realized just how valuable Stan was becoming and probably always was, if he had just been given the chance.

Chapter 19
The Corporate Purchasing Team

Stan and Sally finally returned to Fabrics bearing some good news. On the way back to Barton, Stan had received a call from the cable supplier's continuous improvement manager and was informed that the fix they implemented was apparently working very nicely.

As Stan's car pulled into the parking lot, Joe was there to meet both Stan and Sally. "Hi guys, great job yesterday and today!" said Joe, congratulating them both. "I especially liked the way you suggested the FMEA, Sally," he added.

"Boss, Sally did a great job of facilitating the FMEA, and the results were really surprising to the supplier," said Stan. "They had never used an FMEA before, and it pointed out some key weaknesses in their quality system," said Stan.

"Well, thank you both for the compliments, but I was just doing my job," said Sally. "The difficult part will be making sure that they execute the actions from the FMEA," she added.

"Did you two schedule a return visit to verify that what they said they would do actually gets done?" asked Joe.

"Yes, we told them that we'd return, but I wanted to make sure it was OK with you first, boss," replied Stan.

"Yes, Stan, I think it's something that must be done so that we can avoid future materials interruptions from them," said Joe.

"How long do you think we should wait before we revisit them?" asked Stan.

"I would recommend that you have daily conversations with them, and when they tell you they have the fixes in place, go back and check it out," replied Joe. "Do you have confidence that they can put the fixes in place without your and Sally's help?" he asked.

"Yes, I think they're very capable," said Stan.

"OK, just keep me in the loop, Stan," said Joe.

"Will do, boss," he replied.

"Stan, Judy told me that you have Bill and Manuel working on some things at Fabrics," said Joe. "What are they working on?"

"Well, because of this problem with the cable supplier, Sally thought it would be a good idea to have them go through the delivery records for Fabrics' other suppliers just to make sure we don't have other issues," replied Stan. "She wanted to make sure that we were proactive instead of reactive."

"Sally, do you remember having had other supplier problems?" asked Joe.

"If I recall correctly," responded Sally, "we've had problems with our rubber supplier on occasion." She elaborated. "I remember one time when we had our calendar set up to run a batch of fabric, and when we extruded the rubber, there were pinholes everywhere on the surface. By the time the calendar operator detected the problem, we had used up the entire batch of rubber and had to scrap everything," said Sally. "There have been a few other quality related problems from the same supplier that I can remember," she added.

"Sounds like a potential candidate for a visit," said Joe. "I really like the idea of being proactive," he said.

"That was actually Sally's idea," said Stan.

"You two seem to make a great team," said Joe.

They looked at each other, smiled and said, "We think so too."

"Let me know what Bill and Manuel find," said Joe.

Joe headed over to Sam's office to check on how things were progressing with their tank builds. When he got there he found Sam and Jerry in the office with the door shut. Sam saw Joe and motioned for him to come in.

"Good morning, guys, how are things going this morning?" asked Joe.

"Jerry and I were just reviewing some data on the parts inventory, and it seems as though the TOC replenishment model is working really well for us," said Sam. "Do you realize that in the past six weeks, we've had zero stock-outs? In addition to zero stock-outs, just as Connor predicted, the total dollars tied up in inventory have dropped about 38 percent," said Sam.

"Wow, that's amazing," said Joe. "Great job, Jerry!"

"Thanks Joe," Jerry said, "but without you guys making me realize just how powerful the Theory of Constraints concepts are, I would never have bought into this model."

"The reason we're reviewing this," said Sam, "is because Jerry got an email from Corporate Purchasing yesterday afternoon saying they are sending a team of "experts" down here to help us with our parts issues."

"Parts issues, what parts issues?" said Joe. "You mean Barton's Central Purchasing?" he asked.

"No, American Industries' purchasing group," said Jerry. "When they get here, would you guys mind being at the meeting with me?" Jerry asked. "In case they ask questions that I can't answer."

"Well sure, Jerry, but you're the principal architect of this system, so I don't really think you need our help," said Sam.

"I'd just feel more comfortable if you guys were in the room with me," said Jerry.

"When are they coming Jerry?" asked Joe.

"Today," he replied.

"Wow, not much warning was there?" said Sam.

"Sam, let's go smoke. I want to talk to you about something," said Joe.

"Sure, Joe," said Sam. Sam refilled his coffee and they walked out to the smoking gazebo.

"What's up, Joe?" asked Sam.

"It's about this foreign investment group that might be buying Barton," said Joe. "I lay awake last night and thought about what could happen if we were purchased."

"What were you thinking, Joe?" asked Sam.

"What if these new investors don't buy into how we're doing things here?" asked Joe. "What if they're like other private equity firms I've dealt with?"

"What do you mean, Joe?" asked Sam.

"From my experience, they typically bring in their own team and start changing things at will based on their own paradigm of how things should be running," said Joe. "What if they don't know or aren't willing to hear about the power of TOC?"

"Then we'll just have to teach them," said Sam.

"Have you ever been involved in a leveraged buyout, Sam?" asked Joe.

"No, I never have," Sam replied.

"Well I have, and it's not usually a comfortable experience," said Joe.

"Do you really think that would happen after seeing the results of what we've accomplished?" asked Sam.

"Sam, we haven't been this good for very long," said Joe. "Private equity firms look at many years worth of performance data, and where we are now is just a small blip on the radar screen."

"I see your point, Joe," said Sam.

"Anyway, I just worry about them coming in and tearing apart what we've worked so hard to put in place," said Joe.

"By the way Sam, Stan and Sally really did a good job at Fabrics' cable supplier yesterday and today," said Joe. "They are quite the team."

"Yes, I know," said Sam as he winked at Joe.

"Sam, I'm serious, they put some things in place at the supplier with no direction at all from me," said Joe. "I'm thinking of promoting Stan to lead black belt," he added.

"How do you think Bill, Manuel and Judy would react to that?" asked Sam.

"Bill and Manuel seem to be taking direction from Stan already, and I think Judy would welcome it too," said Joe. "Of course, I would talk to Bill and Manuel first to get their take on it before I would make that change," said Joe.

"Joe, your guys have really stepped up to the plate and hit a home run here at Barton," said Sam. "If I were you, I'd give them all a raise."

"How do you think Paul would react to that?" said Joe.

"Go ask him," said Sam.

"I think I will," said Joe. "And thanks for the suggestion." He decided to see if Paul was in yet.

"Good morning, Paul, got a minute?" asked Joe.

"I always have a minute for you, Joe," said Paul.

"Actually, I was going to call a meeting with you and Greg and Sam this morning," said Paul.

"What about?" asked Joe.

"Well, I wanted this to be a surprise, Joe, but I'll share it with you now," said Paul. "But don't tell the others, so I can surprise them, OK?" He continued, "Joe, when you first came here, do you remember what Barton's profit margins were?"

"I think I remember them being around 6 percent?" said Joe.

"Actually Joe, they were closer to 5 percent," said Paul. "Last night I made some calculations on where we are now. Take a guess at what our margins are right now."

"Hmm . . . maybe 10 percent?" said Joe.

Paul laughed and said, "Guess again Joe."

"Nine percent?" said Joe.

Paul laughed even harder and then said, "Try 16 percent."

"You're kidding, Paul!" said Joe.

"Nope, I've checked the numbers three times and they're correct," said Paul. "And Joe, we haven't even felt the true impact of Simco's increase in orders yet!" he exclaimed. Simply amazing Joe."

"This is great news," said Joe.

"Well Joe, here's the truth," Paul said, "if you hadn't come to Barton, we would still be at 5 percent, so you and your improvement guys should really feel good about the job you've all done."

Joe saw this as his opportunity to bring up the pay raises for his people.

"So, what did you want to talk to me about, Joe?" asked Paul.

"It's ironic, Paul, that you just told me about our new profit level and the job my guys have done," said Joe. "I actually came here this morning to talk to you about giving my guys a pay increase," he said. "They have all worked very hard and have delivered some great results. They've all played such an important role in where we are now," said Joe.

"A pay raise, huh?" said Paul. "How much did you have in mind, Joe?"

"I was thinking maybe 10 percent," said Joe.

"Don't be ridiculous, Joe," said Paul. "I think a much more practical increase would be on the order of say, 15 percent! Your guys are the main reason we are where we are, and they deserve to be rewarded," said Paul.

Joe was simply bowled over with Paul's suggestion, but very happy to hear it.

"Joe, I'll have my administrative assistant type up a personal memo to each one of them this, and we'll make it retroactive to last week so that it shows up in this week's paycheck," said Paul.

"Thanks Paul, you've just made my day," said Joe.

"Well, thank you. You and your guys have made my career, Joe!" said Paul.

After meeting with Paul, Joe got on the phone with Judy. "Good morning, Judy, I need you to set up a meeting with our group for 9:00 a.m. in my office."

"Sure thing, boss, what's the subject?" she asked.

"I'll tell you in the meeting, Judy. And thanks," said Joe.

"Thanks for what, Joe?"

"For everything," said Joe. See you at 9:00," he said.

At 8:30, Joe ran by Paul's office, picked up the raise memos and thanked Paul once again. At 9:00, Stan, Manuel, Bill and Judy were already seated in his office speculating about the meeting.

"Good morning, boss, what's up?" asked Stan.

"Good morning, everyone. I just finished meeting with Paul Johnson to go over the state of the business, and I have to tell you there's been a major turnaround for the good," said Joe. "This morning I want to talk to you all about the job you've been doing for Barton,"

"W-were h-h-having f-f-fun s-s-sir," said Manuel.

"Yes, boss, you've made our jobs fun, like we're really contributing for a change," said Bill.

"I enjoy getting up and coming to work every day now, boss," said Judy.

"I enjoy the new challenges," said Stan. "It has really helped me get my master black belt certification much earlier than I thought I could," he added.

"Master black belt?" Joe exclaimed. "When did you get your master black belt certification, Stan?" asked Joe in a surprised tone.

"Last week, boss. I guess I forgot to mention it."

"Well, congratulations, Stan, I'm proud of you," said Joe.

"Me too," said Judy, "We should have a party to celebrate."

"This is all good to hear, guys, because I, or should I say we, all acknowledge the job that each of you have done in the last several weeks," said Joe.

"We?" asked Judy.

"The entire leadership team, Sam, Greg, Paul, me, we all see the difference you guys are making," said Joe.

"Well thanks, boss, just finally being able to do our jobs," said Stan. "Is that all boss?" asked Stan, "I have a meeting in ten minutes with Fabrics."

"No, that's not all," said Joe as he handed them their own personalized raise memo. "Go ahead, open them," said Joe.

"W-wow," said Manuel.

"Holy shit," said Bill, "Sorry, boss, I'm just so surprised."

"Thank you so much boss, I'm just shocked, but so happy," said Judy.

"Boss, I can really put this to good use," said Stan. "It's by far and away the biggest raise I've ever gotten," he added. "Now can I leave?" asked Stan.

"Hold on, Stan, I need to tell you one more thing, and then you can go," said Joe. "As you know, I've been very busy here lately and haven't been able to spend time directing you guys. And to be honest, I don't see that pattern changing much, at least in the short term" he said. "I'm just going to get right to the point. I'd like to ask Stan to be our lead black belt and run the day-to-day operations of our group, And since Stan is now a master black belt, it makes even more sense," he added. "Does anyone have a problem with this idea?"

"Are you kidding, boss?" said Judy, "I think it's a fantastic idea."

"Manuel, you OK with this?" Joe asked.

"Y-y-yes s-s-sir," he said.

"Bill?" he asked.

"Not a problem at all—he already kind of leads us every day anyway," he said.

"Stan?" asked Joe.

"I'm fine with it, boss," said Stan.

"Done! Stan, go to your meeting," said Joe. "And thanks again for everything you guys have been doing," he added.

Joe felt very good about what he had just done for his troops, and he knew that they all deserved their increases in pay. After Stan, Bill and Manuel had left the office, Judy knocked on Joe's door. Joe motioned for her to come in and asked, "What's up Judy?"

"Boss, I wanted to tell you what a wonderful thing you just did," said Judy.

"Judy, I was quite serious, you guys all deserved your raises, and I think you know that," Joe replied.

"Well, I can tell you this—I saw Stan's face and I think you helped him make a decision," she said.

"And what decision was that Judy?" asked Joe.

"I think he's going to propose marriage to Sally," she said.

Stunned, Joe's face broke into an ear-to-ear smile. "Wow, that's a pretty quick courtship," he said.

"It was love at first sight, boss," Judy said. "I've known Stan for quite a while, and I knew the day after he met Sally that she was something special to him," she said. "Anyway, I just wanted to thank you again and let you know what I think is going to happen with Stan."

"Glad I could help, but again, you guys all deserved your raises," said Joe.

Just then the phone rang, and it was Jerry. "Joe, the team from Corporate is here, and they want to talk about the way we've reduced our inventory levels. Do you have time to come meet with them?" he asked.

"I sure do, Jerry. You want me to go grab Sam?" he asked.

"If you don't mind, Joe. I would appreciate it," Jerry replied.

Joe tried Sam's cell phone, but didn't get an answer, so he literally ran to Sam's office to find him. Joe knew how nervous Jerry was about meeting with this corporate group alone. "Sam?" yelled Joe from across the plant floor. Sam looked around for the source of the voice and spotted Joe waving to him and signaling for him to come quickly.

"What's up, Joe, why are you in such a hurry?" he asked.

"The Corporate Purchasing team is here, and Jerry is nervous about being alone with them," Joe replied.

"OK, let's go," said Sam.

Everyone was already seated when Joe and Sam arrived, so they excused themselves for being late and sat down.

"Good morning everyone, I'm Cynthia Hall, Master Black Belt from AII's Corporate Headquarters," she said. "I'm here to help you with your parts supply system," she said. "I know you're like many of our portfolio companies that have parts outages on a regular basis, and I'm here to show you that there is a better way," she continued. "For example, on your J40, J50 and J60 product lines, I've reviewed your stock-out history and it's pretty dreadful," she said.

Sam started to put up his hand, but Joe stopped him and whispered, "Let her go, she obviously hasn't looked at the last six weeks worth of data."

"It's very clear to me that your minimum stock levels are much too low and need to be raised to avoid stock-outs," she continued. "I know that you must be thinking that you can't afford to raise them any higher because of cost, but I would tell you that you are wrong," she said. "You see, I'm a master black belt and I've been trained to analyze problems," she said rather pompously. "I'm here to fix your problems and I expect you to fully cooperate with my team while we're here. The system you should be using is called a MIN/MAX system, and if we implement the system correctly, you should see stock-outs decrease to no more than 5 percent of the time," said Cynthia."Who is your continuous improvement manager here at Barton?" she asked.

"That would be me, Joe Pecci," said Joe.

"And how large is your staff, Joe?" Cynthia asked.

"I have a master black belt and two black belts on my staff," Joe replied.

"Three people?" she said. "That's clearly not a large enough staff, Joe. I'll speak to your HR Manager about recruiting at least five more black belts," she said.

"With all due respect, Cynthia, I really don't need five more black belts," said Joe.

"What do you mean you don't need them? Of course you do," she snapped.

"I beg to differ, Cynthia, and I'm not going to hire even one more," he said.

"Excuse me, what did you say?" she replied angrily.

"I said, I'm not hiring a single additional black belt," Joe repeated. "We have all of the help we need."

"We'll see about that," she snapped back.

"I have a question for you, Cynthia," said Sam.

"And who might you be?" she asked.

"I'm Sam Henderson, Barton's Vice President of Operations," he replied.

"What is your question?" she snapped, obviously still upset with Joe's comments to her.

"Have you really looked at our data on stock-outs closely?" asked Sam.

"I just told you, I looked at your historical data and it looks awful," she said. "In fact I think your stock-out rate was on the order of 10 percent," she barked.

"And just how old is the data you used Cynthia?" asked Sam.

"Let's see," and she brought up her Excel file. "It is the past three years worth of data," she said.

"And what about the past two months, is that included?" asked Sam.

She reviewed her data and said, "No, it includes everything except the past three months."

"I thought so," said Sam.

"And just what did you mean by that comment, sir?" she asked with great irritation.

"I was thinking that since you are such a well trained master black belt, you would have known to use current data before making your assertions about Barton's stock-out situation," said Sam sarcastically. "If you had, you would have seen that for the last six weeks, we have had zero stock-outs at Barton," said Sam.

"What do you mean, zero stock-outs—no system will give you zero stock-outs. There must be something wrong with the data," she said sarcastically.

"No Cynthia, there's nothing wrong at all with the data, just the analysis," said Sam.

"How dare you speak to me in that manner," said Cynthia.

"Sam, she's really not interested in what we've done here. It's all about advancing her own cause," said Joe.

As everyone else in the room sat bewildered, Joe said, "Cynthia, if you care to listen, Jerry, Sam and I would be happy to explain how it is possible to have a system that will virtually achieve a zero stock-out condition and achieve it with much less inventory than you are proposing."

"Less inventory? Have you people lost your senses?" she shrieked.

"No, we've just found a different way than you're familiar with, that's all," said Joe.

"OK," said Cynthia, "let's hear about this amazing new method that I'm convinced will never work. No system will guarantee zero stock-outs," she repeated.

"First of all," said Joe, "we've implemented a new scheduling system here at Barton referred to as Drum-Buffer-Rope. Have you ever heard of DBR?" he asked.

"I have heard of it, but never seen it used," said Cynthia.

"One of the most important elements of DBR is that you must have the needed parts available 100 percent of the time," said Joe. "Most supply systems operate under the MIN/MAX system you have described. There are three basic rules to be applied under the, MIN/MAX system," Joe said. "Rule 1 is that you must determine the minimum and maximum stock levels. Rule 2 says that you must never exceed the maximum stock level." He continued, "And Rule 3 instructs you to reorder only when you go below the minimum stock level. Am I correct Cynthia?" asked Joe.

"Yes, you are so far," she said in a much calmer voice.

"The basic driving force behind these rules is that you must reduce the money spent on parts," said Joe. "So in order to save money, you must never buy more than the maximum and only order parts when you reach the minimum stock levels."He continued, "The problem that we have observed here at Barton, using this system with these three rules, is that it did not prevent stock-outs. Stock-outs occur for one primary reason, and that is that the lead time to replenish parts exceeds the minimum stock available," said Joe.

Cynthia snapped, "That's because you didn't set your minimums high enough or because you didn't calculate your lead times properly!"

"You're partially right, Cynthia, but that's not the total reason," said Joe. "There is this little thing called variability that enters into the equation as well." He continued, "So you're constantly seeing this cycle of high inventory when you receive parts, and it eventually dwindles down until you reach the reorder point, and then stock-outs frequently occur," he said.

"One of the other things that the MIN/MAX system instructs you to do is to hold the inventory at the lowest distribution point, just like we used to do," Joe explained. "We agree that some inventory should be held at the point of use, but it shouldn't be based on the MIN/MAX amounts. What we are using at Barton now is something called the TOC Distribution and Replenishment Model, which says that most of the inventory should be held at a higher level of the chain."

"What the hell is that?" asked Cynthia.

"It's a Theory of Constraint-based system that says, in a nutshell, that the point-of-use inventory should be replenished frequently based upon actual usage, rather than some minimum stock level," Joe explained. "We keep the majority of our stock in our warehouse and limit the amount in our point-of-use bins," he said. "The net result of using this TOC-based system is that because we're replenishing based upon what we're using, we have inventory levels that have been cut approximately in half, and we have zero stock-outs," Joe said.

"I don't believe you can use this kind of system and cut your inventory in half," said Cynthia.

"I think that the best thing we could do, Cynthia, is go to the shop floor and show you how our system works," said Joe. "And while we're there, you should talk to our operators about stock-out rates now versus the rates before we implemented this new system," he said. "Shall we go?" asked Joe.

They all left the conference room and headed to the shop floor to see, firsthand, how Barton's system actually worked. Sam walked with Cynthia, and along the way she asked Sam how much Barton had actually reduced its inventory since going to this new system.

"About 40 percent so far," said Sam.

"And you've had no stock-outs at all?" she asked in a much calmer voice.

"None at all," said Sam. "But please do as Joe suggested—talk to my operators."

Cynthia and her team spent at least two hours on the shop floor before signaling to go back to the conference room. Once there, Cynthia addressed the group.

"First of all, I want to say if I hadn't seen it, I wouldn't have believed it, but I did and I do," she said. "I must be honest, I had never heard of this TOC-based model before today, but I can assure you that I am impressed with it and it's certainly worth looking into much more," she said. "The fact that Barton has had nearly a 40 percent reduction in the amount of money tied up in inventory could translate into millions of dollars across our company," she said.

I also want to apologize to everyone for my arrogance early on, and I want you to know that I am humbled," she said. "And Joe, I do want to understand how you are able to get by with so few improvement people, so if you could make some time for me today or tomorrow, I would really appreciate it," she said.

"I have an idea, Cynthia," said Sam. "Since you're staying overnight, why don't we get together for a drink after work?"

"Great idea, Sam," said Joe, "and Cynthia, we could talk about how I am surviving with such a skimpy crew of people."

"Sounds great to me, guys. Where are we going?" asked Cynthia.

"I know this little, out-of-the-way bar that I think you would enjoy," said Joe.

"How do I get there, and what time?" she asked.

"I'll pick you up at your hotel around 5:30, if that's OK," Joe said.

"OK, see you then, and thanks Joe," she said.

"You're welcome, Cynthia," Joe replied.

While Cynthia and her crew met with Jerry to learn a bit more about the TOC replenishment model, Joe and Sam went outside for a cigarette.

"Sam, have you heard from Becky yet today?" asked Joe.

"No, as a matter of fact, I haven't," Sam replied.

"I think I'll call her and invite her to join us at Jonah's," said Joe. He called her, but got no answer and left a voice mail instead. "I wonder if she went back to Corporate, Sam?" said Joe.

"She didn't say anything to me about it," said Sam.

"So that was some meeting with Cynthia wasn't it?" asked Joe .

"Yes, it was," said Sam.

"She was really arrogant at the beginning, wasn't she?" said Joe.

"She was an outright bitch if you ask me!" joked Sam.

"You really challenged her, Sam, but she needed to hear what you had to say," said Joe.

"Well, I just hate it when people think they know everything when they really don't," Sam replied. "She came around though, and Joe, you explained our system really well, in very simple terms she could easily understand," said Sam.

At 5:30, Joe pulled into the parking lot of the hotel, and Cynthia was outside waiting for him. She opened the door, and Joe said, "You look really nice this evening, Cynthia, Ready to go?"

"Thanks for the compliment, Joe," she replied. "A woman always appreciates it when a man notices how she looks."

"By the way, I forgot to give you this today," said Joe as he handed her a copy of *The Goal.*

"What is it, Joe?" she asked.

"Cynthia, it's one of the best books ever written by a man named Dr. Eliyahu Goldratt, the inventor of the Theory of Constraints," said Joe. "This book changed my entire approach to manufacturing, and I think it will for you too."

"Well thanks Joe, that was awfully sweet of you," she said. "I hope we can find time to talk about how you manage to operate with so few improvement people," she said.

"We'll make time, Cynthia," said Joe.

As they pulled into Jonah's, Joe noticed Becky's car right away. "There she is," he said to himself.

"This, Cynthia, is the bar I was telling you about," said Joe. "By the way, where is the rest of your troop?" he asked.

"They decided to go out for dinner as a group," she replied.

As they walked in the door Becky saw Joe, and whatever she and Connor were looking at got put away rather quickly. Then she signaled for Joe and Cynthia to join them.

"Hi Joe," said Becky.

"Hi guys," said Joe. " I want you both to meet Cynthia Hall, she's a master black belt from American Industries."

Becky and Connor both stood to shake hands with Cynthia and introduce themselves. "Nice to meet you Cynthia," said Connor.

"Connor owns this bar," said Joe.

"Interesting décor Connor," said Cynthia.

"If I only had a dollar for every time I've heard that," laughed Connor. "The décor is just an extension of who I am," he added.

"I take it you used to be in manufacturing?" Cynthia asked.

"I guess you could say that," Connor replied.

"Cynthia, Connor used to work for Goldratt's consulting company," said Joe.

"Oh, then I'm honored to meet you," Cynthia said. "Joe just took me to school on the TOC replenishment model, so I'm anxious to hear more about it all."

"Joe, the usual?" asked Connor.

"Of course," said Joe.

"And you, Cynthia, what would you like to drink?" asked Connor.

"How about a nice glass of red wine?" said Cynthia.

"How about a glass of Chianti?" said Connor.

"Is that what you all are drinking?" she asked.

"It's all we ever drink Cynthia, at least since we all met Joe," said Becky.

"Well, when in Rome . . . " she replied.

Connor went and got her a glass and filled it.

Cynthia took a sip and said, "This is actually quite good," as she turned the bottle around to see the label. "Chianti Classico, I'll have to write that down."

"Guys, Cynthia and I have to discuss something, so if you'll excuse us, we're going to move to a different table," said Joe. "But we'll be back to join you in a bit."

"Cynthia, I need to give you a bit of background first, if that's OK with you?" said Joe.

"Of course it is," said Cynthia.

Joe used a napkin and drew his now famous piping diagram to explain the basics of the Theory of Constraints. He then drew his equally famous four-step process and asked her to tell him which step controlled the throughput of the process. She answered correctly. Joe then asked her why anyone would focus on the nonconstraints when the constraint controls the throughput, and she agreed it made no sense. They discussed Goldratt's Five Focusing Steps and the differences between a constraint and a nonconstraint, plus related issues like efficiencies not being a good metric except at the constraint. Cynthia understood everything, so Joe moved on.

"So Cynthia," Joe said, "I want to tell you about a different accounting method that we are using called Throughput Accounting." Joe wrote down the formulas for Net Profit, Return on Investment, and so on, and she grasped these equally well.

"So the method we use is Theory of Constraints integrated with Lean and Six Sigma," he explained. "We use TOC to identify the constraint and then focus all of our Lean and Six Sigma efforts only on the constraint. For us, it's all about focus and leverage—focusing on the constraint and then leveraging it," he explained.

"This clearly explains to me why you only need two black belts and one master black belt," she said.

"Yes Cynthia, while most places try and fix everything, we only focus on and fix what's really important, the constraint," said Joe. "Does it make sense to you, Cynthia?"

"Yes, it really does," she replied, "and if I understand you correctly, it goes like this—Identify the constraint, then exploit it, then subordinate everything else to the constraint. Right, Joe?

"Cynthia, it will all make much more sense to you when you read the book I gave you," said Joe. "You ready to join Becky and Connor?" he asked.

"Yes, I need some more Chianti too," Cynthia said with a smile. "And thank you, Joe for taking the time to explain all of this to me . . . I do have one question for you, Joe," she said.

"What's that, Cynthia?" ask Joe.

"If I could arrange it, would you be willing to come to New York and make a presentation to my group?" asked Cynthia. "They really need to hear this from the expert and not me."

"I'd be honored to Cynthia. Just let me know when and I'll be there," said Joe.

Sam had called to say he was running late, but eventually he showed up. As Sam was sitting down, Cynthia turned to him and said, "Sam, it's all about focus and leverage!" and everyone laughed.

"Sam, I need a cigarette, want to join me?" asked Joe.

"Sure Joe," said Sam and they walked outside.

"Sam, remember I couldn't get Becky to answer when I called her?" said Joe.

"Yeah, what about it?" said Sam.

"Well, it might not mean anything, but when I walked in, Becky was here with Connor. And when she saw me coming towards her and Connor, I don't know, she kind of acted reticent," said Joe.

"You think maybe she and Connor have something going on that they don't want us to know about, Joe?" asked Sam.

I don't know, but it seemed awfully strange to me," Joe replied.

"Let's just go back in and pretend you didn't see anything," said Sam.

The five of them sat and talked for hours about a variety of subjects, only interrupted when Connor received a phone call from Ron Parsons.

"Oh hi, Ron, how's the golf game?" said Connor.

Ron asked Connor when he was coming to Phoenix to help them with CCPM.

"I'm not sure when I can come, Ron," said Connor. "I know I told you next week, but some other things have come up that need my attention, so I'll have to get back to you."

Ron pressed the issue and wanted a more definitive answer from Connor.

"Just a minute, Ron, let me check on something here," said Connor. "Here, Joe, talk to Ron until I come back," Connor said as he motioned for Becky to go outside with him.

"Hi, Ron, what's up with you?" asked Joe.

Ron informed Joe that he was trying to get Connor to commit to a date to come to Phoenix.

"You mean to help you with CCPM? Wait Ron, here he comes now," said Joe.

"OK, Ron, I can come out for three days next week," said Connor. "I'll fly in Sunday night, but I have to fly back out Wednesday night," he said.

Ron asked Connor if three days would be enough time.

"Should be enough time, Ron," said Connor. "OK, Ron, I'll see you Monday , and if things change, I'll call you and let you know," he said.

The gathering was winding down now, and people began saying their goodnights.

"Cynthia, it was very nice to meet you," said Becky, "and I hope to see you again some time." She added, "I'm going back to the hotel now."

"I think I'd like to go too, said Cynthia. "Joe, would you mind running me back?"

"I can take you, Cynthia," said Becky.

"You don't mind?" Cynthia asked.

"Not at all," said Becky. "Connor, thanks for everything today, and I'll see you tomorrow," Becky said.

"I think I'm going to leave as well," said Joe.

"Me too," said Sam. "Connor, thanks for the company tonight, and we'll see you soon."

"Have fun in Phoenix," said Joe.

On the way out to their cars, Joe said, "Something's up with those two."

"I think you're right," said Sam. "I'll see you in the morning, Joe."

"Good night, Sam."

CHAPTER 20
Connor Goes to Simco

Monday morning was always a drag for Joe, but this Monday was a bit different. After the events at Jonah's on Thursday night, he was confused. One thing he was certain of—something different was going on between Connor and Becky, and he'd really like to know what it was. They had been acting so mysteriously lately and it was really bothering Joe. What could it be?

Connor arrived in Phoenix as scheduled Sunday afternoon, and Ron met him at the airport. "Hi Connor, thanks so much for coming out here to help us with CCPM," said Ron.

"My pleasure, Ron. I just wish I could give you more time, but some things have come up for me personally, and it's all the time I have right now," said Connor.

"Anything I can help you with, Connor?" asked Ron.

"No, it's something I have to take care of myself," Connor replied.

"Do you want to go check in before we hit the golf course?" asked Ron.

"I'm going to have to pass on the golf, Ron." Connor said. "I'm pretty tired and I just need to go to my hotel."

"But I thought you said this was one of the conditions for coming out here," said Ron. "I've got Simco's CEO and VP of Operations meeting us," he said.

"OK, then let's go ahead and play, I don't want to disappoint them," said Connor.

"Great, I'll give them a call," said Ron.

On their way to the golf course Ron asked, "So what's your plan for this week, Connor? And what do I need to set up, since your time is limited?"

"The first thing we need to do is meet with your leadership team,

Ron," said Connor. "I have to be able to read their pulse to make sure they're firmly behind this initiative."

"I thought maybe it might be a good idea for you to share a cart with our CEO today while we play golf," said Ron.

"That's probably a good idea, Ron," said Connor. "What's his name?"

"His name is Larry Levinson," said Ron.

"And the VP's name?" asked Connor.

"Steve Stevens," Ron said. "What else do I need to get ready for the week?" asked Ron.

"We need to establish a core team," said Connor. "I've put one together on paper," said Ron.

"Tell me about the team make-up, Ron," said Connor.

"I've got seven engineers all lined up, Connor, but we can add more if you think we need to," said Ron.

"So your engineers assemble the helicopters?" asked Connor.

"Well no, but they have the most technical know-how about helicopters."

"I haven't met any of them, but I can tell you that they're not your experts," said Connor.

"Sure they are Connor, what makes you think that they aren't?" asked Ron.

"Ron, the people that assemble the helicopters, the people in the trenches are your true experts, not your engineers," said Connor.

"But these guys have degrees in mechanical and electrical engineering, Connor," said Ron, "and a ton of experience. They know these helicopters inside and out."

"Look Ron, if you truly want CCPM to work, you need to select a team that is mostly made up of the people assembling them," said Connor. "I've been doing this for a long time, and if the solution—or in your case the project plan—isn't developed by the people doing the work, it simply won't work," he added.

Ron and Connor pulled into the country club, unpacked their clubs, and headed inside to check in. Ron saw Larry and Steve hitting balls on the driving range and pointed them out to Connor. Connor watched the two of them hit balls while Ron signed himself and Connor. It appeared a as though the Simco execs had spent a lot of time on a golf course.

"Would you like to hit a bucket of balls to warm up, Connor?" asked Ron.

"No, I think I'm ready. Let's go meet Larry and Steve," he said.

Ron and Connor walked outside. "Larry, Steve, I'd like you to meet Connor Jackson," said Ron.

"Hi Connor," said Larry as he shook Connor's hand.

"Nice to meet you," said Steve.

"We're really excited about you coming out to help us," said Larry. "Ron has told us so much about you, Connor," he added.

"I'm very happy to meet both of you," said Connor.

"You guys ready to play?" asked Ron. "I thought that Larry and Connor could ride together on the front nine, and then Steve and Connor could ride together on the back nine," he said. "It will give everyone a chance to talk about what's expected this week."

"Sounds like a great idea to me, Ron," said Larry.

"So, how about we play for a little money," said Larry.

"Sounds good to me," said Ron.

"Do you want to play teams or individuals?" asked Steve.

"How about you, Connor?" asked Ron.

"Either way is fun for me," he answered.

"Connor, what's your handicap?" asked Larry.

"I don't have one," he replied.

"You mean you haven't calculated one, or you're a scratch golfer?" asked Steve.

"That would be giving up an advantage if I told you," said Connor in a joking way.

"OK, so let's play as individuals with no handicaps," suggested Larry. "How about everyone throws in twenty-five bucks, and the winner takes all?" he said. Everyone agreed and they walked to the first tee.

Larry teed off first and hit a beautiful drive down the center of the fairway, much to his liking.

"Nice drive, Larry," said Connor.

Next up was Ron who promptly pushed his drive into the rough down the right-hand side of the fairway.

Steve pulled his drive left, and appeared to be stymied by a tree. He was not happy.

After much deliberation, Connor hit a 3-wood that started right, and then tailed down the center about ten yards past Larry.

"Great drive, Connor," said Larry. "Was that a 3-wood you hit that drive with?"

"Uh-huh," said Connor as Larry shook his head in disbelief.

As the cart moved to their drives, Larry started a conversation about what to expect this week. "Connor, I want to personally thank you for coming out to Phoenix to help us improve our operations," he said. "Realistically, how much of an improvement do you think we can achieve?" Larry asked.

"Good question, Larry," said Connor. "What is it that you want to improve?" he asked.

"Well," Larry began, "I know Ron has described what's going on here at Simco . . . ."

"To some degree," said Connor. "But I think I can describe what your operational performance looks like without having seen it," he asserted.

"Do tell," said Larry.

"First of all, in general your projects, or should I say, your assemblies are always late," said Connor. "It's not unusual for you to ask your customer for concessions on your delivery dates," he continued. "When you have project reviews, the reasons for delays are always outside the control of your project managers," said Connor.

"So far, you're right on the money," said Larry.

Larry and Connor finally arrived at Larry's ball, and after studying the scorecard to estimate the distance to the green, Larry hit it twenty feet from the pin.

"Not bad," said Connor.

They pulled up to Connor's ball, and without hesitation Connor selected a pitching wedge and with no practice swings, he hit a gorgeous shot inside ten feet of the pin.

"I think we're in trouble," said Larry. "Great shot Connor," he added.

They jumped into the cart, and Connor continued his description of Simco's operation. "I would also say that your assemblers typically bypass the project management plan that your engineers have created, and for good reason."

"Why do you say that?" asked Larry.

"Because they know that the assembly plan that they've been given is not the best ways to assemble helicopters," said Connor.

"I'm confused, Connor," said Larry. "Our engineers are experts in building helicopters, so why wouldn't they have developed the best plan?"

"Let me ask you a question, Larry," said Connor. "Exactly how many helicopters have your engineers actually assembled?"

"Well . . . none," Larry replied, and then quickly added, "Their job is to design the helicopters and develop assembly plans."

Both carts arrived at the green, and all four golfers lined up their next shots. Ron was about a foot off the green. He elected to chip it to the hole and left it about four feet short. Steve had about a thirty-footer, and he putted it to within three feet of the hole.

Larry lined up his twenty foot putt, looking at it from above and below the hole, just like you would see a pro doing on television. Connor thought to himself, "Larry is really competitive." He finally hit his putt and as it gets to the hole, it moved right on him by six inches for a tap-in par.

Connor looked at his putt and promptly knocked it square in the hole for a birdie. One hole complete, and Connor is one up on Larry and two up on Steve and Ron, as they both missed their short, par-saving putts.

"So Connor, you were talking about how our assemblers are not following the assembly plan that the engineers have given them," said Larry.

"Larry, a good plan or schedule, must have three critical components if it's going to work," said Connor. "First and foremost, it has to be believable to the people using it," he said. "Secondly," he continued, "it must be 'owned' by the people using it. And last, but not least," Connor concluded, "it has to be used. Your plans are not believable, not owned and not used," he explained.

"How do you know this, Connor?" asked Larry.

"Very simple, Larry," said Connor. "Because you didn't involve the people doing the work in developing the plan, it's not credible to them. And because you didn't include them, they don't 'own' it," he continued. "Because they don't own it, they don't use it," said Connor. "Instead, they do what are called "work-arounds."

"Larry," Connor said, "I challenge you to go to the shop floor with a copy of the engineering plan and watch an assembly. Make notes on the plan, and see if the assemblers are following the recommended sequence," he continued. "I promise you they won't be following the plan," Connor said.

The second hole was a par three, and because Connor had a birdie on the first hole, he hit first. He selected a pitching wedge and hit a gorgeous shot about eight feet to the left of the hole. Larry followed and hit his shot just inside Connor's about six feet to the right of the hole. Ron and Steve missed the green to the right and landed in a sand trap.

"Connor, are you telling me that the assemblers should have developed the assembly plan?" asked Larry.

"What I'm saying is that the development of the plan should have included them," said Connor. "You have to understand, Larry, the people doing the work are the true subject-matter experts," Connor explained. "You definitely need the engineers' input, but your assemblers know the best way," he said. "Think about it, Larry, if you want them to own the plan, let it be theirs."

"Makes perfect sense to me, Connor," said Larry. "I wish we would have known this a long time ago," he said. "Connor, you didn't answer my original question," said Larry. "How much of an improvement do you believe we can get?"

"I believe conservatively that you should see a 40 percent reduction in assembly time." Connor replied.

"Are you kidding me?" Larry exclaimed.

"It could be more, but I think you should reasonably expect that much," said Connor.

The round continued with the lead changing hands between Larry and Connor all day. The discussions about Simco's new direction also continued. Connor took the time to talk about common behaviors that exist in project-oriented organizations because of things like Parkinson's Law, the Student Syndrome and multitasking. Connor also explained the clear differences between a critical path and a critical chain, and why the concept of a chain is superior. Larry was like a sponge, soaking up everything Connor had to say, even making notes on his yardage book.

"So Connor, we're on the last hole and we're tied," said Larry. "How about a side bet?"

"What did you have in mind?" asked Connor.

"Dinner," said Larry.

"You mean, loser buys dinner for the winner?" asked Connor.

"Yep, that's exactly what I had in mind," said Larry.

"You're on, Larry," said Connor.

Both Larry and Connor had bogied number seventeen, so Ron and Steve hit their drives, both landing in the fairway. Larry hit next and shaped a beautiful right-to- left shot around the dogleg directly in the center of the fairway. "Beautiful shot, Larry, you must be hungry," Connor joked.

Connor pulled out his driver and elected to cut the corner of the dogleg on the left. He teed the ball high to get loft and hit a great left-to-right shot over the trees, ending up in the center of the fairway about thirty yards ahead of Larry's ball.

"What an incredible shot," said Steve.

"Wow," said Ron.

It seemed as though Connor saved his best for last.

Steve and Ron hit their second shots near the green, but both were short. Larry studied his shot and crafted a gorgeous shot to within six feet of the hole. Connor hit, and they watched his ball hit the green, bounce once and hit the flag stick, ending up about eighteen inches from the cup.

"Shit!" said Larry, "I hate buying dinner!"

Ron and Steve elected to finish the hole so they could watch the action.

Connor walked up to his putt and asked, "Is this a gimmee?"

"Hell, no," said Larry. "Not when dinner is on the line."

Larry took his time studying his putt from every possible direction and angle. As he was about ready to putt, Connor said, "Do you always pull your putts, Larry?"

Larry smiled and said, "Damn it, Connor, be quiet." He hit the putt and pushed it right, obviously over-compensating in response to Connor's comment.

Connor stood over his putt, waiting for Larry to make a similar comment, but when he didn't, Connor putt and left it short. It was clear to everyone that Connor had missed his putt intentionally.

"Oh well, better luck next time," he said with a smile.

"I'm buying dinner!" said Larry as he shook Connor's hand.

Dinner was good, and there were more in-depth discussions about what to expect during the three days Connor would be there. Larry gave Connor some facts and figures about the state of the business and—according to Larry's information—Simco had even deeper problems than Ron had described. Simco's on-time completion rate was hovering around 30 percent, and their customer retention rate was dropping at an alarming pace.

Connor saw this as a good thing from the "burning platform" perspective. Simco clearly had a reason for changing the way they approached their business, so leadership support shouldn't be a problem at all. Connor reiterated the key ingredients for a good schedule, which included being believable and realistic, owned by the people doing the work and one that will clearly be used. He took the time to explain some of the benefits that a good schedule would deliver, which included aligning the needed focus, reduction in multitasking, synchronization and meeting customer due dates. By the end of dinner, Larry was excited and enthusiastic to get started. Connor reminded Larry of the challenge he had issued him to go to the shop floor to see if the engineered project plan was being followed or not. Ron drove Connor to his hotel, and they made plans for Ron to pick him up at 6:00 a.m.

Ron and Connor arrived at Simco around 6:30 to find Larry out on the shop floor comparing the assembly plan with what the operators were actually doing .

"Good morning Larry, how's your comparison going?" asked Connor.

"Good morning Connor, it's exactly as you said it would be," Larry replied. "I've looked at three lines at different stages of assembly, and the assemblers are clearly not following the plan." He adds, "It's clear that there is no ownership of the plan we've given them."

As they walked the assembly process, Connor stopped to talk to the operators and supervisors to get their pulse of the plan. Their comments sowed that they simply thought the assembly plan was meaningless.

Connor suggested that he and Larry go to Larry's office to lay out the plan for the week. Larry suggested that they move to the conference room so that they could lay it all out on a flip chart.

"So Connor, it's obvious that nobody is following the assembly plan that our engineers created. Can we talk about what a good plan might look like?" asked Larry. "Not the actual assembly plan, but maybe the process for developing one," he added.

"Sure thing, Larry," said Connor. "Well, first of all, we've already talked about who should be building the project plan, but let's start referring to this as a schedule instead of a project. It really is a schedule, Larry," he added. "What I'd like to do is lay out, in a broad sense, the steps we need to take to create our schedule," said Connor as he moved to the flip chart.

"Remember, I explained the difference between the critical path and the critical chain, Larry?" Connor asked

"Yes, I remember, and as I recall, the biggest difference is that the critical chain includes resource dependencies, correct?" Larry replied.

"So the first step in our schedule development process needs to be something I'll call establishing a dependency network," said Connor. "This means that we have to identify all of the tasks required to assemble a helicopter, their correct sequence and the required resources," Connor added. "The people doing the work can tell you what the tasks are and the order in which to do them," said Connor. "Engineers should be used to making sure the schedule stays within all of the technical requirements," He said.

"Can you give me an example of that?" asked Larry.

"Sure," said Connor. "I know that you use bonding adhesives that have specific cure times, so the assemblers have to respect these times."

"OK, got it," said Larry.

"The tasks in your schedule can't be written in terms that are too general—they must be described in specific actions," said Connor. "And the task-to-task connections and required resources must be really well defined," he added. "In short, task dependencies and resource contentions must be linked. On a side note, we talked about the behaviors that we want exhibited on the shop floor and the ones we don't. Our schedule must not permit the multitasking we see with individual task-duration estimates," said Connor. "Likewise, we can't consent to the procrastination associated with the Student Syndrome and Parkinson's Law. These things need to be addressed head-on as we develop our schedule," he said.

"I understand all of these things Connor, but how do we avoid them?" asked Larry.

"We'll get to that, but not right now," said Connor.

"The next step in developing a coherent and believable schedule is that, up front, we must resolve any resource contention for tasks," said Connor. "If we don't resolve contention for resources, the schedule's credibility will suffer and it will be of no use," he added. "Like I said before, one of the problems with CPM is that its critical path doesn't satisfactorily consider resource contentions, so you're doomed before you even start," said Connor.

"I'm certain that is one of the primary reasons why we're always late completing our assemblies," said Larry.

"The next step is, in my opinion, the most important step of all—identifying the critical chain of the project," said Connor. "The critical chain is the constraint of the project and should always be the focal point," he said. "Here's one thing to remember, if the critical chain is late, the project is late." "Probably equally important as the critical chain is the development of the project buffer," said Connor. "The project buffer protects the project from uncertainty."

"How do you know how large to make the project buffer, Connor?" asked Larry.

"We'll get into that later too, Larry," said Connor. "What we have to do pretty soon is put together a core team made up of at least 70 percent assembly people and then give them some CCPM training," said Connor.

"Let me get with my guys and do that," said Larry. "Any particular qualifications we should focus on, Connor?"

"Only one—they need to be your best and most experienced people," Connor replied without hesitation. "One other thing," said Connor. "Let them volunteer, don't force anyone to be on the team."

Larry and his managers huddled together and developed a list of Simco's best and most experienced people. The list included three assemblers, two inspectors and seven engineers. But when they showed it to Connor, he asked, "Why so many engineers?"

"Because they know the aircraft—they designed it," said Larry.

"If you want this new schedule or plan to work, you've got to get outside your existing paradigm, Larry," said Connor. "No offense to the engineers, but they gave you the plan you have now, and I think you'll agree that it doesn't work," he said. "My recommendation is that you have six hourly assemblers from different stages in the assembly process, at least one hourly inspector and no more than two engineers," Connor said.

"One other point to consider when selecting team members," said Connor. "Try to pick a couple of informal leaders, people that others respect and admire. If you can get the leaders to positively participate on the team, then others will fall in line behind them," said Connor. "This transition to a new way of running your business will be met with resistance and skepticism simply because you've never given the workers an opportunity to design their future before," said Connor. "There are years of mistrust out there on the shop floor, so be ready for some pushback."

"But Connor, we've always involved our people," said Larry.

"Larry, this kind of involvement is totally different than someone being a token member of a team," replied Connor. "If this is to work, you must give them total responsibility with corresponding authority, and for some of your managers, that will be a difficult thing to embrace," he added.

"I know you're all worried about getting buy-in throughout the organization, but especially from your hourly workforce," said Connor. "TOC recognizes that the strongest force for change is, in fact, the initial resistance to it," he continued. "Once you have convinced the workforce that they can improve the current reality, the resistance to change will be broken," said Connor. "Although most TOC practitioners will tell you that there are six layers of resistance, I believe there are seven that must be addressed in a very distinct order," he said. Connor went to the flip chart and recorded all seven layers.

Seven Layers of Resistance

1. **Agreeing that there is a problem.**
2. **Agreeing on the problem.**
3. **Agreeing on the direction of the solution.**
4. **Agreeing that the solution will solve the problem.**
5. **Agreeing that the solution will not lead to significant negative side effects.**
6. **Agreeing on the way to overcome any obstacles that may appear when implementing the solution.**
7. **Agreeing to implement the solution.**

"The first step is that everyone must agree that there is a problem," said Connor.

"We certainly all know that we have a problem," said Larry.

"Don't be so sure, Larry," said Connor. "I've seen too many instances where companies took for granted that everyone knew there was a problem, when, in fact, the masses did not," he added. "Once everyone agrees that there is a problem, everyone must also agree on what the problem is."

"We all know what the problem is," said Larry.

"And what would the problem be, Larry?" asked Connor.

"We're not completing our assemblies fast enough," said Larry.

"Larry, if you asked people on the floor, I'm willing to bet that you'd get a completely different answer to that question," said Connor. "In fact, I'll bet the answer would be somewhere along the lines of, 'Management never listens to us,' " said Connor. "If you don't believe me, go ask some of your people."

"OK, I will right now," said Larry. Larry was gone for ten minutes, and when he came back, he confirmed what Connor had said about everyone having a different idea of what Simco's problems were.

Connor continued on with his explanation of layers of resistance. "Once everyone agrees that there is a problem and what the problem is, the next step is to get everyone to agree on a general direction that should be taken to develop a solution," Connor explained.

"This step will involve helping the team understand the problems associated with the way we currently schedule and manage projects," said Connor. "What I generally do is provide a half day of training on CPM versus CCPM, and the team realizes quickly that there are stark differences between the two methods," said Connor. "In that same training, we look for any possible negative side effects associated with developing a CCPM solution. We then spend the rest of the day discussing and agreeing on ways to overcome any obstacles that might block implementation of CCPM," Connor continued, "Finally, we agree to at least try to implement whatever the core team's solution might be."

"It is at this point that you, Larry, reinforce to the core team that their solution will be implemented. Will they make mistakes?" asked Connor rhetorically. "Yes, of course they will, but you'll work through them and let the core team create a different solution," Connor said. "If you want ownership of the solution, let the core team create it."

"One last point," said Connor. "During this discovery process, you, the management team, are going to hear some things that you don't want to hear, but you must listen and acknowledge what you've heard as being real," said Connor. "Avoid arguing about anything negative that comes up."

With the new criteria for team selection and a general direction to follow, Larry and the rest of his team painstakingly developed a list of potential candidates for the core team. When the list was complete, they discussed how best to address the group and recruit volunteers. They even laid out a presentation entitled, "Design a New Future." They met for the remainder of the day and scheduled a meeting with their potential team members for 8:00 a.m. on Tuesday. Everyone was excited about what they had accomplished, and they decide to call Connor in to let him see and hear it. Connor listened to what they'd put together and was generally quite happy with their approach and the upcoming presentation to the core team.

Then Connor asked Ron to drive him back to his hotel so that he could participate on a conference call in thirty minutes. On the way back to Connor's hotel, Ron and Connor discuss what had happened on this day.

"So Connor, based on your experience, how would you say we did today?" asked Ron.

"I'd say you did very well, but the proof will be how well everything is received by the potential core team members," Connor said. "You must follow the seven layers of resistance as I laid them out in order to have a successful kickoff meeting. How did you think it went Ron?" asked Connor.

"I think in general it went well, but I think it's going to be difficult for some members of our management team to let go of their command and control mentality," said Ron.

As they pulled into the parking lot, Ron recognized a familiar face, Becky Chen. "What's Becky doing here?" asked Ron.

"Err, uh she had some business in Phoenix and decided to stay overnight," said Connor, hurrying to get out of the car. "See you in the morning," Connor yelled back over his shoulder.

On his way back to Simco, Ron's phone rang and since he was driving, he put it on speaker. "Hello, this is Ron, how can I help you?" he said.

"Hi Ron, it's Sam. Just wondering how things went today?"

"It went great," said Ron. "I just dropped Connor off and I saw Becky at his hotel," he adds.

"Becky Chen?" asked Sam.

"Yeah, apparently she had some business in Phoenix and decided to meet Connor for dinner or something," Ron said.

"I wondered where Becky was today," said Sam.

"Connor did tell me he had a conference call in about fifteen minutes," said Ron.

"Did he say who the conference was with, Ron?" asked Sam.

"Nope, he just had to get here by 5:00 p.m. is all I know," said Ron.

"Let me know how everything is going, Ron, and thanks again for the new orders,"

"OK, talk to you soon, Sam," said Ron.

"What could Connor and Becky be up to?" Ron wondered.

Chapter 21
The Finale

On Tuesday morning Ron pulled into Connor's hotel, and Connor was nowhere in sight. After fifteen minutes of waiting, Ron decided to call him, thinking he might have overslept. The phone rang and an obvious sleepy voice answered, "Hello . . . this is Connor."

"Good morning, Connor . . . oversleep?" said Ron.

"Oh my gosh, what time is it?" asked Connor.

"It's about 6:20," Ron replied.

"Go ahead, Ron. I'll have Becky drop me off," said Connor. "Er, uhh, assuming she's still here," he said. "If she isn't, I'll get a cab . . . Go ahead Ron, I'll be there in forty-five minutes," said Connor.

"Sure you don't want me to wait for you?" asked Ron.

"No, I'll catch up to you," said Connor.

Ron drove away thinking that he knew why Connor overslept, and her name was Becky.

When Connor arrived, the conference room was full of unfamiliar faces, and he apologized for being late. He told everyone that he had a late night conference call that ran way over the allotted time. Ron thought he knew otherwise, but said nothing.

Larry was the first to speak. He welcomed everyone. He flashed his first slide on the screen, which read, Design a New Future. Larry laid out the state of the business to everyone, and for the first time ever at Simco, he actually shared factual financial results with the hourly workers in attendance. This, in itself, was a clear change from the norm, and it was rather effective. Larry went on to say that the project schedules the hourly workers had been forced to use were clearly a problem, and that continuing to use them would guarantee that Simco's orders would continue to be late. Larry was very persuasive and convincing, and Connor noticed that many employee heads were bobbing in agreement. Larry finished the first part of his presentation by apologizing for not recognizing the true subject-matter experts within Simco, the people doing the assembly work.

Larry introduced Connor to the group and asked him to say a few words. Connor moved to the front of the room and said, "I want to thank everyone for coming here this morning, and I hope to spend a lot of time working with all of you." He continued, "I think this is a major new step that Simco is taking, and the leadership clearly realizes that they need your help to be successful. One thing I want to say up front is that we don't want to force anyone to be on this core team, so anybody who wants to opt out, you're free to do so right now," he said. Nobody left which prompted Connor to ask the group," What did you think about what you heard from Larry this morning?"

One of the men at the table said, "So far, I like what I'm hearing."

"What is it that you liked hearing? asked Connor.

"The part about us being the subject-matter experts, because we are," said the man.

"Nothing against our engineers, but we know how to assemble these aircraft and it's not the way we've been told to do it," he said.

"We all believe that you all are exactly that," said Connor. "And because of that, we'd like some, or all of you, to be on what we call a core team, to tell us the best way to assemble helicopters. If you're interested in doing that, raise your hands," said Connor.

Everyone's hands rose in the air except one woman. "I have a question, if you don't mind," she said.

"Yes?" said Larry.

"Are you telling us that you are actually going to take our recommendations on how to assemble helicopters?" she asked.

Larry answered immediately, "That's not what I said."

"I thought so," said the woman.

Larry responded, "What I said was that we want you to tell us the best way, not just recommend how. There's a big difference between asking you for recommendations and you telling us the best way, don't you think?" he added.

Connor thought to himself, "What a great response from Larry," but said nothing.

"The bottom line is, we need your help desperately if we're going to turn this company into more than it is,", continued Larry. "I do hope you'll join us," he said.

"I will," said a man at the end of the table.

"I will too, as long as you're serious about us creating the right assembly process," said another man.

It was like a chain reaction with everyone except the two engineers saying yes.

Larry asked, "May I ask why you two haven't volunteered?"

"Well," said one of the engineers, "I wasn't sure if you really needed us or not."

Before Larry could answer, one of the hourly workers spoke up, "Of course we need you—someone has to keep us straight," and everyone laughed. "We know how to put these things together, but we need your technical knowledge to make sure we don't do something wrong," he added.

And with that, both of the engineers said they wanted to be a part of this effort. "If you're all ready, let's begin," said Connor.

"Larry, these guys won't really be needing your help or your staff's help right now, so we'll see you later," said Connor.

Larry smiled and says, "If you do need anything, just call me. Come on guys," he said, "Let's get out of this team's hair so they can show us the new way."

When everyone except the team had left the room, Connor explained how it was all going to work. "First, I'm going to give you some basic training on something called the Theory of Constraints, and then we're going to begin building your new production schedule," he said. For the next two hours Connor presented the basics of TOC and critical chain project management.

When the TOC training was complete, Connor gave them all their first assignment. "What I want you guys to do first is make a list of what are called major milestones," he said. "Major milestones are big things like installing the transmission or maybe the rotary blades. Once you've listed these milestones, I want you to list all of the individual tasks required to complete each milestone," he said. "For example, one of the milestones will be 'install transmission,' and there are many tasks that must be completed before you can claim that the milestone has been done, so list all of them directly underneath it, understand?" asked Connor. "Once you have all of the milestones and the specific tasks listed, I want you to put them in the order they must be done," said Connor. "Does everyone understand what I'm asking you to do?" asked Connor.

"I have a question for you," said one of the women.

"Yes?" said Connor.

"What if we don't agree on the order of the milestones or the tasks?" she asked.

"To be honest, I don't think you will, but remember, this isn't a one-day thing," he replied. "Keep in mind that there is only one 'best way' to assemble these helicopters, and your job is to define that way. You may even have to test some of the options before you arrive at your final list," said Connor. "If you need me, here is my cell phone number," he said as he wrote in on the flip chart.

"Where are you going, Mr. Jackson?" said one of the hourly team members. "What if we have a question about the assembly process?"

"I assure you, I don't know anything about how to assemble a helicopter," Connor replied. "Remember, you guys are the experts here, so you've got to find a way to work it out between yourselves. He adds, "As a last resort, you can call Larry or meet with a couple of the engineers. I'll be back again tomorrow morning to review your work," he added. "But conservatively, I would say this exercise will take at least four or five days to complete," he concluded.

The team did exactly as Connor had instructed, and they were very complete with their milestones and task listings, but when it came to agreeing on the order that things should happen, they discovered that it wasn't so easy. There were lots of discussions that might even be classified as arguments, but the team managed to trudge on. By late Tuesday afternoon, they couldn't agree on the final assembly order, so they paged Larry.

When Larry arrived, one of the team members asked, "Mr. Levinson, would it be possible for us to have a helicopter to test out some of our ideas?"

"First, please call me Larry, and second, like I told you, whatever you need, I will make it happen," he said. "I'll take care of that today so that you'll have it first thing in the morning, if that's soon enough?" Larry said.

"Yeah, that's great," the team member replied.

"By the way, where is Connor?" Larry asked.

"He left with some gorgeous Asian chick about three hours ago," said one of the team members. "He did say he'd be back in the morning though."

Around seven o'clock that evening, Ron was clearing off his desk getting ready to go home when he received a text message on his BlackBerry that read, "Something urgent has come up and I have to leave. The team has enough to keep themselves busy until I get back. Sorry for the short notice, but it can't be avoided, Connor."

"There must be a problem back at Barton," Ron thought. Before he left for the day, he decided to call Sam or Joe to see if there was a problem. He put his phone on speaker and called Sam.

"Sam Henderson here. How can I help you?"

"Hi Sam, it's Ron. Is everything OK back at Barton?"

"Everything's fine, Ron. Did we miss a shipment?" Sam asked with concern.

"No, no, nothing like that . . . it's just that I received a text from Connor a few minutes ago, and he said something urgent came up and he had to leave," said Ron. "I'm pretty sure Becky picked him up today," he added.

"I'm not sure what's going on with Connor," said Sam. "But if I see him, I'll ask him to call you."

"Thanks Sam, sorry to bother you so late," said Ron.

"Not a problem," said Sam.

The next morning Ron received a call from Sam asking him if he'd heard from Connor. "I'm a bit concerned, Ron because there's a sign on Jonah's that says "Closed Until Further Notice," said Sam. "There's no sign of Becky either, which has me equally concerned," he added.

"I can't imagine Connor closing Jonah's . . . could it be a health problems?" said Ron.

"I don't think so, but I'll check with Joe and see if he's heard anything," said Sam.

"Let me know Sam. Now I'm worried," said Ron.

Sam hung up and called Joe to see if he knew anything about Connor and Becky, but he didn't.

Later on in the day, Sam, Joe, Paul and Greg all received an urgent email telling them to come to American Industries headquarters for a meeting. The email said nothing about the subject of the meeting, but it did say, "No Preparation Necessary" in bold letters. The message also said that flight arrangements would be handled by American Industries.

Just then Sam's phone rang and it was Joe. "Sam, did you see the email from Cecil about going to New York tomorrow?" he asked.

"Yes, I just opened it, Joe," he replied.

"What could this meeting possibly be about Sam?" asked Joe.

"I have no idea," said Sam. "Could it be about the offer from the foreign investors?"

"I guess it could be, but surely they would have said something about it in the email," said Joe.

Later in the afternoon, Sam received a call from Larry Levinson, the CEO of Simco. "Hi Sam, this is Larry Levinson from Simco. I was wondering if you had any idea what this meeting was about at American Industries tomorrow?"

"You've been invited too?" Sam asked.

"Yes, and so has Ron," said Larry. "This is highly unusual, don't you think?" said Larry.

"Yes, it is," replied Sam. "I'll try my best to find out and call you back," said Sam.

"Thanks, Sam. Well, at least it will give me an opportunity to meet you guys. Ron has been raving about what you guys have done at Barton," said Larry.

"I look forward to meeting you too, Larry," said Sam.

"OK, call me if you find out anything," said Larry.

The phone rang again, and it was Sid Sanchez, the General Manager of Fabrics-R-Us. "Sam, this is Sid and I—"

Sam interrupted him. "Let me guess, you're calling to find out what the meeting in New York City tomorrow is all about?"

"Well, yes, how did you know that, Sam?" asked Sid.

"Just a sixth sense, Sid," said Sam jokingly. Sam explained about all of the calls he'd received about the same subject and told him he had no idea what it was about. Sid told him that Sally was invited too, which he thought was strange.

By the end of the afternoon, Sam had received no less than fifteen phone calls all relating to the meeting at American Industries headquarters. It was clear that the meeting in New York was secretive and with this list of attendees, it had to be something big. Later in the afternoon everyone on the attendee list received another email from the AII travel department telling them to meet at the airport around 7:00 a.m. and that they should check in through the flight information desk to confirm their travel arrangements.

The next morning everyone met, as instructed, at the airport. Apparently American Industries had chartered a large jet to transport everyone to New York City. Joe and all of his CI people were there, as were Paul, Jerry, Greg, Sam, and Benji, plus Sid Sanchez and Sally Bergland from Fabrics. Only Connor and Becky were missing, but maybe their absence meant something. Everyone checked in through security before boarding the plane. As they boarded, there were others already on the plane that Joe and Sam recognized—most notably Simco executives Larry Levinson and Steve Stevens and Ron Parsons, Simco's Sales Rep for Barton,. So apparently the flight had originated in Phoenix.

During the flight there were frequent, speculative conversations about the nature of the meeting in New York, until Sam finally whispered to Larry, "Larry, I think I know what's going on, why we're going to New York City today."

"What is it Sam, I'm really interested in hearing about this,: said Larry.

"Well," said Sam, "I'm pretty certain that we're going to be told that Barton has been purchased by a group of foreign investors."

"Really? Why do you think that, Sam?" asked Larry.

"Joe Pecci and I made a trip to American Industries recently and the board chairman of Barton told us that AII had received a purchase inquiry," he explained. "But we were told that it was confidential and not to say anything."

"Do you have any idea who intends to acquire Barton?" asked Larry.

"I don't have a clue, Larry," said Sam. "All we were told was that the initial inquiry was by a group of foreign investors."

"Well that concerns me," said Larry. "I certainly hope whoever buys it will keep the positive things you guys have done in place. Simco is a much better company now because of Barton, and I want to keep it that way," he added.

The conversations continued during the flight, but they were all based on speculation, just basically people guessing. The plane finally arrived at JFK, the landing was perfect and the plane pulled into the private arrival terminal gate. As the passengers exited the plane, they were met by three drivers, each with a separate sign with people's names emblazoned on them. One by one, they followed their designated drivers to three black stretch limos waiting to take them to AII. The trip to American Industries' headquarters took about forty-five minutes. They ascended in the elevator to the penthouse office suite. When the elevator door opened, they were welcomed by Cecil Graham, Barton's Board Chairman who led them to AII's executive conference room. They were offered numerous exotic pastries and other snacks plus a variety of drinks. Cecil told them to make themselves comfortable and said that the proceedings would start shortly.

"Much, much nicer than our executive conference room at Simco," said Larry as he looked around at the ornate décor of the room. It was almost like a shrine honoring past CEOs, board chairmen and other corporate dignitaries. Unlike the atmosphere during the flight to New York City, there was now a feeling of stillness as everyone awaited the arrival of American Industries' CEO, Thomas Ramsey. Ten minutes later the board room door opens and he entered. All eyes were on him as he stepped to the front of the room and welcomed everyone. What would he tell them? What announcement would he make? Finally, Thomas addressed the group.

"As you may or may not know, American Industries is a very successful private equity firm with a proud heritage. Like other private equity firms, our business model involves buying distressed or underperforming companies, fixing them and then selling them for a handsome profit," Thomas explained.

"Five years ago, American Industries purchased Barton Enterprises, which at the time was struggling to make a meager profit," he said. "For the first four and a half years, we thought maybe we might have made a mistake with this acquisition, but we now know it was the right decision," said Thomas. "Thanks primarily to Sam Henderson and Joe Pecci, Barton is now a viable business entity, making a very handsome profit.

"About six weeks ago, American Industries was approached by a group of investors inquiring about the possible purchase of Barton Enterprises," he explained. "When they approached us, our last reported margins were hovering around 5 percent, and quite frankly we were surprised by the inquiry," said Thomas. "But of course we listened," he added. "We continued talking with these investors, and over the course of our negotiations, Barton's profits began to move northward at an accelerated rate," he explained. "In fact, our last profit margin is now at almost 16 percent, and with the additional influx in orders from Simco, we expect the margins to be over 20 twenty percent in the next few months. This is obviously an important factor in the final selling price for any company," he said. "Yes, past history is equally important, but what's happening right now is also very important.

"Everyone in this room today has played some kind of role in turning Barton into a money-making machine," said Thomas, "and I want to personally thank everyone here for your efforts . . . so it is with great pleasure that I am announcing the sale of Barton Enterprises for a very handsome profit effective next Monday," said Thomas. "I personally had mixed emotions about selling Barton, but at the end of the day, it is simply a business deal where emotions don't count," he said. "In just a few minutes you'll get to meet the new owners, and I want to dispel any concerns that you might have about this group coming in and making wholesale changes to Barton's business model. These investors are fully aware of how tanks are built, and they have assured us that their satisfaction level is quite high." Thomas continued, "So if you'll follow me to our other conference room, I'll introduce you to the new and proud owners of Barton Enterprises."

The throng of interested employees, suppliers and customers followed Thomas to AII's other conference room, and when they reached the door, Thomas said, "Let me go in and check to see if the new owners are ready to meet you."

The level of anxiety increased with this new delay, but quickly subsided when the door opened. Everyone filed into the conference room and sat down, eagerly awaiting the arrival of the new owners. "Ladies and gentlemen, it is with great pleasure that I introduce Barton's new owners, Mr. and Mrs. Connor Jackson," said Thomas with a smile.

Once the absolute shock of this announcement settled in, the conference room erupted in applause and shouts of delight and contentment as euphoria replaced anxiety. Connor and Becky had clearly fooled the masses, and Sam and Joe both flashed back to that auspicious evening at Jonah's—the night Becky had a bit too much Chianti and casually mentioned that she, herself, might be interested in buying Barton.

Once the excitement of the announcement subsided, Becky and Connor addressed the group. "First of all, we both want to thank everyone for their outstanding contributions to Barton's success," said Becky. "You are the people who made this business venture possible, and Connor and I will be forever grateful to all of you. Your success is our success, and our rewards will be your rewards," she added.

Larry raised his hand and asked a question. "Connor, knowing that you are now a part owner in Barton, can I assume that you will no longer be helping us with CCPM?"

"Not a good assumption, Larry," said Connor. "On the contrary, I want Simco to grow and flourish because your success is directly linked to our success as a company," he explained. "Plus, Becky is the brains in this deal, so she'll be running the business side of the business, and I'll be continuing to be Connor," he said.

"That's a huge relief for Simco, Connor," said Larry.

"In fact Larry, we'll be adding some other people to the mix at Simco, others that are even better at CCPM than I am, so no need to worry at all," Connor added.

Stan raised his hand and asked if he could say something. "Since all of the people we love are here in this room, Sally and I would like to officially announce our engagement," he said. Once again there was spontaneous applause and excitement at this new announcement.

"Anyone else have any other shocking news to share with the group?" asked Connor.

Joe raised his hand.

"Yes Joe?" said Becky.

"I just received a call from my wife, Jennifer, right before this meeting," he said. "It seems as though Jennifer and I are going to be parents once again," he announced. "This one wasn't at all planned, but we're both very excited and happy," he added. Again the room was filled with applause and the spirit of surprise filled the air.

"Any other questions or announcements from the floor?" asked Becky.

Paul raised his hand and asked, "Do you plan on making any personnel changes at Barton?"

"Absolutely not!" said Becky. "We have the best team ever assembled at any company, and we have no plans to break up this winning combination. But having said this, Connor and I do plan on making other acquisitions, so don't be surprised if we call on some of you to help us with our due diligence and turnaround efforts," she added.

From across the room, Larry shouted a question, "Where are you going on your honeymoon?"

Becky and Connor looked at each other, smiled and said together, "We're going to Phoenix."

"Connor has a problem leaving jobs undone, and besides, I'd like to learn something from him," said Becky.

"Are you serious, Connor?"asked Larry. "Are you really coming back to Phoenix for your honeymoon?"

"We'll be there at 7:00 tomorrow morning, Larry," Connor replied.

The rest of the day was filled with laughter, dancing and, of course, the customary Chianti. The celebration lasted most of the afternoon and into the early evening when Joe thought to ask, "What time is our plane leaving?"

Connor spoke up and said, "Didn't we tell you, you're staying here in New York tonight."

"I need to call my wife," said Joe.

"Why in the world would you need to do that, Joe?" said Connor. He addressed the crowd, "Joe and everyone else, your spouse and/or your significant other will be here shortly to join in this joyous day with us. Actually, they should all be here any minute now," said Connor. "They would have been here earlier had it not been for a storm that grounded their plane and delayed their flight," he added.

Joe and Sam hadn't had a chance to talk about what had happened today, so they decided to go out on the balcony and grab a quick smoke before their wives arrived.

"So Joe, were you as shocked as I was today?" asked Sam.

"You mean about the purchase of Barton or Becky and Connor getting married?" asked Joe. "I don't know which one I was more surprised about, Sam," he added.

"To me, both were really exciting, and I think Barton will never be the same," said Sam. "What my one fear is—will Jonah's still be open?" said Sam, and they both laughed out loud.

Suddenly they heard someone yell—"They're here!" Just as Connor had promised, Joe's wife Jennifer and Sam's wife Peggy both walked into the conference room, and then came everyone else. The celebration was on, and of course the beverage of choice was Chianti for almost everyone. Somewhere around 8:00 p.m. Connor and Becky announced that they were leaving for their Phoenix-based honeymoon and that the celebration should not stop. Connor had arranged for an all-expenses paid private room and lavish party at their hotel and everyone took advantage of it, staying up until almost 1:00 p.m.

As he said he would, the next morning Connor arrived in Phoenix with his new wife Becky at his side, ready to meet with Simco's core team. Becky and Connor arrived at Simco, and Connor reviewed the core team's work. Connor introduced Becky to the group and let them know that they had done an excellent job laying out the new process in exact detail. Connor reviewed the basics of CCPM with the team, and they begin the process of developing an assembly schedule that actually reduced the time required to assemble the helicopters by about 40 percent. The team reached deep to remove as much waste as possible, and they removed the individual tasks durations from the project schedule and developed what they believed was an acceptable project buffer as well as feeding buffers for the noncritical chain tasks. The team then met with their IT Group to load the CCPM software and the individual tasks and milestones into the automated system.

Even though Becky was unfamiliar with the helicopter assembly process, she continued to amaze Connor with her pertinent questions when the team seemed to be stuck for answers to conflicts. She always seemed to know how to unlock the log jams when they occurred. Connor realized more and more what a great team he and Becky were and how successful their new business alliance would be.

The next morning the core team finally arrived at the first draft of their schedule and decided to ask Larry if they could try it out on their next production order. Larry and called his team in to hear a presentation by the core team. The core team confidently presented the new project plan, and it looked remarkably different than the one they had been using for the past three years. When the team finished their presentation, it was clear that there were two camps in the room. One camp was enthusiastic about trying the new assembly process, and one was very cautious and uncertain as to whether it would work. Larry made it clear to everyone that this new process was to be supported by everyone and that the core team was to be congratulated for their dedicated work. What Connor knew for certain was that because the core team had developed the new process, they would not let it fail, because they "owned" it.

One of the keys to this new process was that no helicopter would be started until it was full-kitted, meaning that all of the necessary parts, tools, documents, equipment and personnel were available. Gone were the days of starting a helicopter assembly only to run into things like parts shortages, missing or broken tools or human resources not being available when needed, all of which caused unnecessary delays. The core team had developed a very workable assembly schedule, and they felt very good about their work. Their major concern was whether leadership would allow them to execute it as is or not. They would soon find out, as Larry gave them the green light with his full backing.

The team believed that before they could implement a successful CCPM-based schedule, they needed to train their coworkers on the basics of CCPM and how to follow priorities. When Connor asked them who should provide the training, the core team felt that they would be more credible delivering it themselves. Connor agreed and helped them develop some basic training modules. The core team delivered the necessary training and set a target of the following Monday to implement what they had worked so hard to develop. The team had even developed poster-sized fever charts for the assemblers to post results on in order to make their progress visible. Monday morning came and they began using their new methodology. There were some minor glitches coming out of the gate, but the team was there to resolve them right away. The team kept tweaking their original plan, incorporating new ideas where they made sense—and where they didn't, they gave great feedback to the originator as to why. Suffice it to say that their plan was appropriately dynamic.

The team's assembly plan had called for a complete helicopter assembly to take no more than twenty-eight work days with fourteen days of project buffer for a total of forty-two days—which was down from sixty-eight days using their old method. After the first week the team had completed about 32 percent of the critical chain and had used only 16 percent of the project buffer, which clearly meant that they were ahead of schedule. And when the assembly moved into the red zone on the fever chart, the team took immediate actions to reduce the rate of buffer consumption, just as they had been trained. The team worked hard to make their plan work, and by the time they had finished the first helicopter, they had done so in thirty-two days instead of the forty-two days that their plan had estimated. Imagine that—what had normally taken sixty-eight days now took less than half that time. Larry and his leadership team were ecstatic.

The second and third helicopters took forty and thirty-five days to assemble, so based upon the first three aircraft, it was apparent that CCPM was firmly entrenched within Simco. The core team continued to meet on a regular basis and implemented new ideas on how to reduce the time to assemble even more. In fact, their first ten helicopters using this new schedule averaged only thirty-three days of assembly time. Simco's throughput and revenue stream jettisoned upward with matching profit gains, and it did not go unnoticed by Becky and Connor's new private equity firm, BecCon International.

In the coming year, BecCon International added both Simco and Fabrics-R-Us to their growing list of portfolio companies, with Becky seeming to always be able to select companies that turned out to be winners. She was a very talented woman, and their business model was simple, direct and repeatable, and very profitable. Becky and Connor typically used Sam, Joe and Paul to perform their due diligence, and if they purchased a company, they would send Sam and Joe in to fix it with a little help from Connor when they needed it. It was a winning strategy every time. And as for Jonah's? It was still there with the same old bartender serving Chianti and giving out free advice to anyone who wanted it. After all, isn't that what all bartenders do?

APPENDIXES

Appendix 1:	Theory of Constraints (TOC), Lean and Six Sigma (TLS)
Appendix 2:	Performance Metrics Using Cost Accounting (CA) and Throughput Accounting (TA)
Appendix 3:	Theory of Constraints (TOC) Thinking Process Tools
Appendix 4:	Interference Diagram (ID), Intermediate Objectives (IO) Map and ID/IO Simplified Strategy
Appendix 5:	Theory of Constraints Replenishment Model and Supply Chain
Appendix 6:	Drum-Buffer-Rope (DBR)
Appendix 7:	Critical Path Management (CPM) Versus Critical Chain Project Management (CCPM)
Appendix 8:	Supplemental System Tools—Plant Types, Control Point Theory and Volts Concepts

Appendix 1
Theory of Constraints (TOC), Lean and Six Sigma (TLS)

Over the past century there have been abundant attempts to improve the quality of both products and services throughout the world, and many different people have contributed to this improvement movement and the body of knowledge associated with it. If you take a moment and look back through the years, the list of improvement ideas and acronyms would fill several pages. If it is true that the past helps predict the future, then there will be many more new ideas come into existence.

Currently, three principal improvement methodologies—the Theory of Constraints (TOC), Lean, and Six Sigma—appear to dominate the subject matter of the improvement world, and each brings its own unique perspective to the improvement playing field. Each also has its own following of zealots and believers. And each proclaims that their single method is the way forward, providing the light and the truth, so to speak. It's almost as if each methodology is a religious experience of sorts. But does it really have to be this way? Is there a benefit in keeping these methods separate and apart from each other? Does each methodology have to exist in isolation from the others? Let's look at each methodology in a bit more detail to see if we can answer this question.

Theory of Constraints (TOC)

In the early 1980's Dr. Eliyahu Goldratt introduced the world to a new way of looking at profitability through his now famous Theory of Constraints (TOC), which was presented in his book *The Goal*. In principle, Goldratt's argued that instead of trying to *save money* through cost reductions, companies would be much more profitable if they focused instead on *making money*. But aren't the two ideas synonymous? The answer is—absolutely not! These two ideas represent very different and divergent approaches. Saving money is not the same as making money. And the management strategy you choose to employ to make money is very different than the one you employ to save money.

Goldratt's emphasis is that the goal of for-profit companies is to *make money now and in the future*. Goldratt analogized this concept using a chain. He stated that the weakest link in a chain controls the overall strength of the chain, and that any attempt to strengthen any link other than the weakest one will do nothing to improve the total strength of the chain. Organizationally this means that every action or decision taken by the organization must be judged by its impact on the organization's overall goal of making money. If the decision does not get you closer to that goal, then the decision is probably ineffective.

Goldratt defined a *system constraint* as anything that limits the system from achieving higher performance relative to its goal. So if the goal of the organization is to make money, then the systems constraint must be identified first. Goldratt explained that in order to determine whether an organization is moving toward its goal and not away from it, three simple questions must be asked and answered.

1. How much money does your organization generate?
2. How much money does your organization invest?
3. How much money does your organization spend to make it operate?

From his research Goldratt developed his own simplified system of accounting that he referred to as Throughput Accounting (TA). The basis for Goldratt's accounting system were three financially based, performance metrics:

Throughput (T): This is the rate that the organization generates "new" money primarily through sales. Goldratt further defined T as the money collected through the sale of a unit of product minus what it pays to its suppliers and others—or Totally Variable Costs (TVC). Therefore, T = Selling price minus Totally

Variable Costs, or T = SP – TVC. The bulk of the TVC would be raw materials, but could include any sales commissions and shipping costs associated with products.

Investment (I): The money an organization invests in items that it intends to sell. This category would include inventory, both raw materials and finished goods.

Operating Expense (OE): All the money an organization spends to operate, including labor costs, office supplies, employee benefits, phone bill, and electric bill and so on. All the money spent to support the organization.

What distinguishes Goldratt's definition of throughput from traditional definition is that throughput is not considered to be valuable until money exchanges hands between the organization and its customers. At any point in time before the sale the product is still considered Inventory, even in a finished goods status. Basically, any product that is produced and not sold to a customer is simply termed Inventory or Investment and it has a cost associated with it. This is a major departure from the traditional definition of throughput, and its overall implications are far reaching.
Goldratt expanded his TA definitions still further by defining net profit and return on investment as follows:

- *Net Profit* (NP) = Throughput minus Operating Expense or NP = T – OE

- *Return on Investment* (ROI) = (Throughput minus Operating Expense divided by Investment or ROI = (T – OE)/I

With these three simple measurements (T, I and OE), organizations are able to determine the immediate impact of their actions and decisions on the financial performance of their organization. Does it make sense that the superlative actions upon the system are those that increase T, while simultaneously reducing I and OE? You might wonder why a discussion of TOC started first with a financial definition. The relevance should become obvious shortly.

The Theory of Constraints operates under what Goldratt refers to as his Five Focusing Steps:

Step 1: Identify the system constraint. The constraint is commonly considered anything within a system that limits the system from achieving higher performance relative to its goal.

Step 2: Decide how to exploit the System Constraint. Exploitation implies getting more from what you already have. It requires that you understand why you are currently getting what you are getting, and what steps are necessary to maximize the throughput of the constraint. How do you get more from this constraining operation?

Step 3: Subordinate everything else to the System Constraint. The subordination implies that all other nonconstraint processes activate to the same level as the constraint. It seems contrary to popular belief, but sometimes in order to go faster, you have to go slower.

Step 4: If necessary, elevate the system constraint. Elevation implies more constraint capacity or resources, if the market demand on the system still exceeds current capacity. At this point, it may be required to spend some money to increase throughput—but only during Step 4 and not during Step 2.

Step 5: Return to step 1. When the constraint has rolled (moved) to a new location in the system, then go back to Step 1 and follow the sequence again.

So, you may be wondering why these Five Focusing Steps are important to someone who uses Lean, Six Sigma or the hybrid, Lean-Sigma. The facts are simple— without the understanding of the global system focus provided by TOC, many of the Lean and Six Sigma initiatives will fail to deliver significant bottom line improvement. The fundamental key to impacting the bottom line is directly proportional to the company's ability to drive throughput to higher levels while at the same time reducing Inventory and Operating Expense. The concept here is driving the system to make money, rather than saving money. Think about it, if your financial model is based upon how much cost you can remove from a process (reducing OE) then, your ROI has a mathematical limit. Likewise, if your focus is only on reducing Inventory, it too has a functional and mathematical lower limit. Throughput, on the other hand, is devoid of a theoretical upper limit. Ponder, just for a moment, the overall impact of simultaneously increasing T while reducing OE and I. The crucial focus of increasing T is what drives NP and ROI!

Lean

Much has been written about Lean over the past several years, but its basic philosophy is centered on a whole-systems approach that focuses on the existence and removal of non-value-added (NVA) activities within a process or system. These NVA activities are characterized as *waste* in the Lean vernacular. As an improvement initiative, Lean teaches you to recognize that waste is present within every process and that we should take extreme actions to either eliminate it or significantly reduce it. The entire premise for doing this action is to facilitate a flow of value through the entire process. If this is true, then it begs the question—What is value? There have been many attempts to define value, but the best definition is based on the *customer value* and not the producer value. In its simplest terms, value, is whatever the customer feels good about paying for. Customers know what they want, when they want it and how much it is reasonable to pay for it—so in the long run, value clarifies itself. Lean has become recognized as one of the most effective business improvement strategies used in the world today, but if this is so, then why are so many Lean implementations failing at such an alarming rate? In this case, failure implies the inability to not only achieve, but also sustain, the needed effort.

Six Sigma

Like Lean, much has been written about Six-Sigma methods and the now infamous acronym DMAIC. Whereas Lean is attempting to remove non-value-added and wasteful activities, Six Sigma is attempting to remove unnecessary and unwanted variation. Six Sigma uses the road map *Define, Measure, Analyze, Improve and Control* (DMAIC) to seek out sources of variation, and through various statistically based tools and techniques, attempts to limit (control) variation to the lowest possible level. The professed power of Six Sigma lies in the disciplined structure and use of the tools and techniques.

However, this supposed power sometimes ends up being a detriment to some companies because in many instances they will experience enormous information overload, coupled with a failure to launch the information into viable solutions. In essence, these companies are suffering from analysis paralysis. Like Lean, many Six Sigma initiatives have failed to deliver true quantifiable bottom line improvements and, therefore, have been abandoned. Six Sigma can be difficult to employ. It is heavily dependent on mathematics (statistics) and formula derivatives that quite frankly most people do not enjoy or involve themselves with. At times is seems as if you need to call Merlin the magician just to get started.

There is also popular hybrid of Lean and Six Sigma known as Lean-Sigma which, as the name suggests, is a merger of the two initiatives. The primary assumption of Lean-Sigma is that eliminating or reducing waste and variation in the system will lead to major cost reductions. It seems to make perfect sense that if each initiative delivers its own separate improvement, then combining output from both of them should optimize the process and result in a double-dip reduction in cost. However, in the final analysis, the primary functions of Lean and Six Sigma are aimed at cost savings. Saving money is indeed a strategy, but it's just not an effective strategy for making money. The overall issue is not with either one of these methodologies, but rather the belief that the way to increase profitability is through cost reduction. Cost reductions have implied mathematical limits, and once those limits are encountered, the improvement effort stops or slows down significantly. Consider this—have you ever heard of a company that has actually saved themselves into prosperity? If cost reduction is not the answer, then what is the best route to profitability?

Focus and Leverage

From what has been stated so far, you might think we have a negative view of Lean and Six Sigma, but such is not the case. In fact, TOC by itself cannot deliver sustainable bottom-line improvement. But it does provide the needed global system focus, and that focus is paramount to facilitating organizational growth. In fact, the primary reason why Lean and Six Sigma have failed to deliver acceptable ROI is they try to improve everything all at once, rather than focusing on the most important leverage points. They promote improvement because they can, and not because they must. It's like trying to solve world hunger—it's a tough job when you try to do it all at once. So let us discuss leverage points and what they mean.

Leverage

The foundational concepts of TOC can be presented in a simple, but understandable way as a reference environment. If you understand the reference, you understand the concept. If we use a diagram showing a simple piping system with the primary goal of delivering water, then the reference is defined. By presenting the concept in this format, the basic principles will be much easier to comprehend for people who have not yet had any experience with the Theory of Constraints.

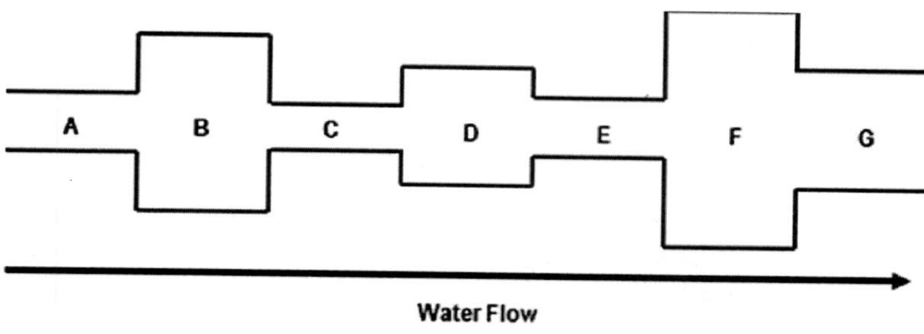

Figure 1: The Piping System

Figure 1 describes the piping system with different diameter pipes connected together supporting the water flowing through this system. The water flows from left to right from Section A through the entire length of the system until it exits at Section G. If you were given this water system and asked what you would do to increase the flow of water, or the throughput of water, through this system—how would you answer the question? For most responders, the answer would be to increase the pipe diameter of Section C since it is the choke point, or bottleneck, or constraint of this system. If you increased the diameter of any other pipe section, it would have absolutely no effect on the throughput of water through this system.

If you were asked how much you would increase the diameter of Section C—how would you answer that question? Most responders would answer by saying that the increased diameter of the Section C pipe would be determined by how much more water the system needed to deliver (loads on the system). So in order to satisfy the need (demand) for more water, you must have some type of metric for how much more water is needed (increased loads on the system). Let's say that you increased the diameter of the pipe in Section C to the same diameter as the pipe in Section D. What if the measured throughput of water out of Section G was still not enough to satisfy the new demand—what then? The new focus for system improvement would shift to the new constraints (the constraints have moved) which are now both Sections A and E. These two sections become interactive with each other. The diameter of these two pipes now becomes the new system constraint, and they need to be improved to meet the increased demand. So how does all of this apply to the real world?

Focus

The basic principles of understanding constraints are all around us. For example, instead of using the piping system to demonstrate the constraint, we could have substituted an electric circuit with different sized resistors and measured the flow of electricity through the circuit. The resistor location with the highest resistance to electrical flow would be the equivalent of Section C in the piping diagram. You could easily demonstrate that the flow of electricity through that system is completely dependent upon how much more electrical current was needed to satisfy the demand. And in order to increase the electrical output, you need to reduce the resistance of the resistor that was limiting the electrical flow.

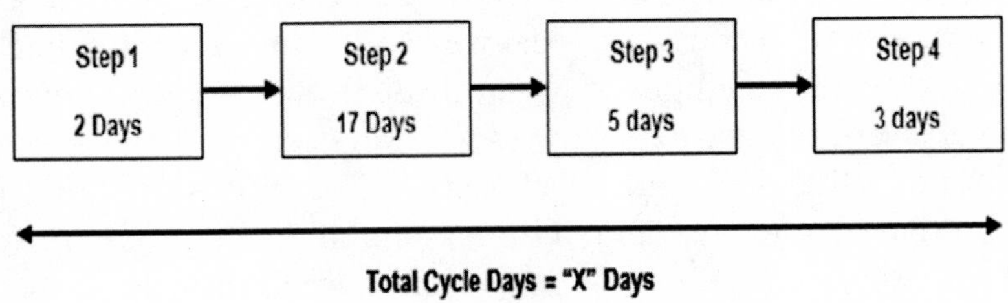

Figure 2: The Process

Figure 2 is another simple visual example of the same concept. Here we have a four-step process used to produce some kind of product or service. If we apply the same *systems thinking* and ask the same series of questions about this system, then we can effectively conclude that Step 2, at 17 days, is the process that is limiting the output from this system. By understanding this concept you now know where to *focus* your improvement efforts. Improving any other process in this system, except for Step 2, yields no system improvements *at all*. Globally, the system will improve only when Step 2 requires less time.

Rolling it ALL Up

With the foundational concepts of the three improvement initiatives laid out and defined, where does this take us? If you apply the methods of TOC first, and use TOC to analyze the system, and spend the necessary time to do it correctly, then you can employ the other methods of Lean and Six Sigma to help exploit the constraints. If the constraint quickly moves to a new location, then go back to Step 1 and start over. It is possible that the "fix and move" cycle can repeat several times before the system is stabilized and requires the implementation of Step 3—subordination.

If your current Lean or Six Sigma initiatives are suffering from a lack of real bottom-line improvement, then what is being presented here should be of interest to you. Why? Because the biggest reason many Lean and Six Sigma improvement initiatives fail to deliver sustainable bottom line improvement is that they are primarily focused on the *wrong* improvement point. The mistaken assumption is— if you improve everything, then hopefully you will achieve the benefit of something. This notion of improving something in hopes of saving a few dollars should be abandoned as wasteful. There is a better way. The necessary condition is that you take the time to understand what the problem really is. If you don't understand and *focus* on the real problem, it will be impossible to come up with the correct *leverage* to implement a solid solution. Take the time to slow down your thinking and understand precisely where to focus your improvements. If you think in terms of TLS (that is, the combination of TOC, Lean and Six Sigma), your results will be much more gratifying.

Just for a moment, imagine what would happen using the focusing power of the Theory of Constraints coupled with the improvement potential of both Lean and Six Sigma. The crucial component to real bottom-line improvement is to increase throughput through the system. Remember, throughput is not the same as output. Throughput only materializes when the sale occurs and fresh money is received from the customer and put back into your system. So by identifying and focusing the full improvement potential of Theory of Constraints, Lean and Six Sigma on the global system, it is possible to increase the throughput— perhaps exponentially.

The Importance of Three

TLS effectively combines all three methodologies into a single improvement consortium, and it allows you to use the best practices of each to solve most of the problems involved with implementing improvements.

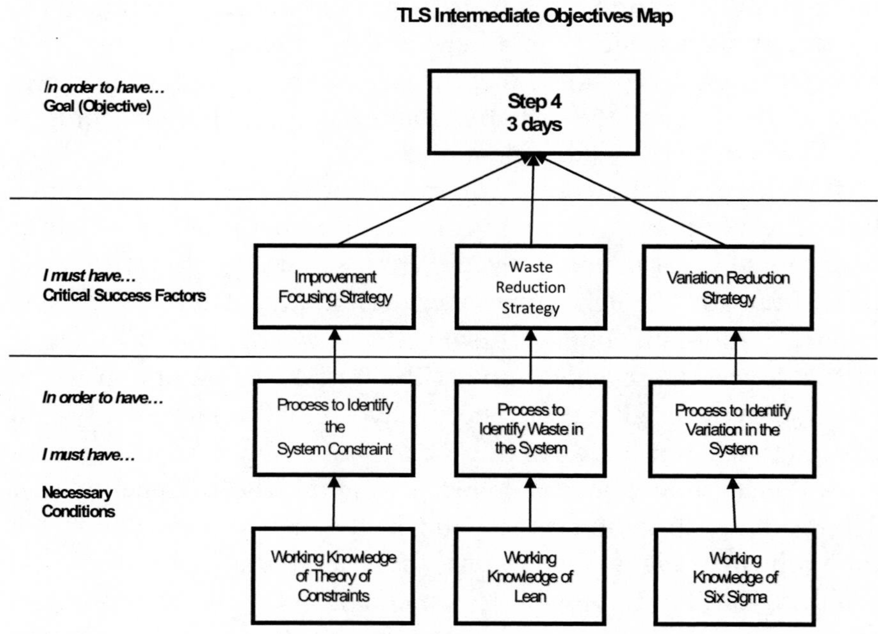

Figure 3. The Combined TLS Approach

But exactly how does this integration of methodologies work? Figure 3 provides the comprehensive answer. Using the IO Map you can define each of these methods as being a critical success factor to achieving your goal. Each supports the other in being able to move to the next level, which is the creation of the Optimum Process Improvement Methodology (OPIM). Each method, if used only in isolation, will fall short of the optimum method. But when these methods are combined, the optimum method can be realized. Having just one method or even two methods is not sufficient to complete the journey to the Optimum Process Improvement Method. All three working in tandem provide the optimum approach.

The IO Map succinctly defines the Critical Success Factors (CSFs) that must be in place to achieve Optimum Process Improvement Methodology. The CSFs are supported by the necessary conditions of the need for an improvement-focusing strategy, a waste-reduction strategy and a variation-reduction strategy. The first layer of necessary conditions translates into the need to have a working knowledge of the Theory of Constraints, Lean and Six Sigma. TOC provides the methods used to focus your improvement efforts (the constraint) while Lean and Six Sigma, with their many tools and techniques, can be used to reduce the waste and variation at the constraint and eventually in the system, as the constraint rolls from one location to another.

Russ Pirasteh and Bob Fox have published a wonderful new book on the integration of TOC, Lean and Six Sigma entitled *Profitability with No Boundaries.*[1] Pirasteh and Fox outline the results of a significant study (the first of its kind) aimed at providing a head-to-head comparison of Lean, Six Sigma and an integrated TOC-Lean-Six Sigma (iTLS) methodology. The response variable for the individual studies conducted during this project was the measurement of the financial benefits gained. It is the only documented study that demonstrates the potential power of this TLS integration. This two-and-a-half- study was performed at the facilities of a global electronics manufacturer with twenty-one different plants participating. In order to negate potential cultural effects, all twenty-one facilities were located within the U.S. It was a double-blind study with none of the team leaders knowing they were participants.

The authors used a variety of statistical tools to analyze the data, with the primary response variable being a coded, cost-accounting-

1 Pirasteh, Reza (Russ) M., Fox, Robert E., *Profitability with No Boudaries*, ASQ Quality Press. (2010)

based metric tied directly to cost savings. Their null hypothesis was a straightforward comparison of means whereby $\mu1 = \mu2 = \mu3$ corresponding to the average savings for Lean equal to the average savings for Six Sigma equal to the average savings for an integrated TOC, Lean and Six Sigma (iTLS). Their alternative hypothesis was that the three averages were not equal ($\mu1 \neq \mu2 \neq \mu3$). The authors first used One-Way ANOVA to demonstrate that there was no statistical difference between Lean and Six Sigma ($\mu1 \neq \mu2$) results. Since statistically, the Lean and Six Sigma results appeared to come from the same population, they combined both sets of results and compared the combined results to the iTLS results. The results of this comparison clearly indicated that there was a statistically significant difference between Lean, Six Sigma and iTLS. In fact, the savings contribution from iTLS accounted for 89 percent of the total savings. The inescapable conclusion from this study was that the interactive effects of iTLS were superior to the individual results obtained from using either Lean or Six Sigma.

For the last decade we have been using a comparable improvement methodology—first reported in the book, *The Ultimate Improvement Cycle*[2]—and we have achieved analogous results. Although our step-by-step method, or pathway, is somewhat different than the Pirasteh and Fox method, the basic beliefs are exactly the same. Significant bottom-line improvement can be achieved when using an integrated approach of TOC, Lean and Six Sigma, as compared to using individual TOC, Lean, Six Sigma or Lean-Six Sigma methodologies.

If you are truly interested in improving what your company does and how they do it, then arming yourself with the concepts of the TLS methodology should certainly point you in the right direction. The TLS approach is most likely not the end point in this game, but rather just a step to achieve the next level of understanding. There will be more and possibly even better methods proposed for future use. But as it stands today, understanding and implementing TLS carries the potential to lift your organization to heights not even dreamed of a few years ago. Good luck on your adventure.

---

2 Sproull, Robert A. *The Ultimate Improvement Cycle,* CRC Press. (2009)

Appendix 2: Performance Metrics Using Cost Accounting (CA) and Throughput Accounting (TA)

The Sock Maker

In the early 1900s Cost Accounting (CA) was in its early stages and beginning to be widely accepted and used. For a business owner there were many things to consider in the day-to-day operation of the business. One of the most important functions of the business owner was tending to the daily needs of the business financial situation. Keeping the books, calculating cost for raw materials, calculating labor cost and making sales were all important issues to be dealt with on a daily basis.

It was understood by business owners that in order to stay in business and make money the cost they paid for the products or service rendered had to be less than the selling price of their products or services. If it wasn't, then they would quickly go out of business. Then and now, the needs of business haven't changed much, but others things have changed.

The ideas and concepts about what was important to measure and how to measure it were starting to form and were being passed from one generation to the next. This was considered important information that you needed to know in order to be successful. Without this understanding, it was assumed that you would fail. Back then, the business structure and methods were different than they are today. The labor force was not nearly as reliable, and most workers did not work 40 hours a week. When they did work, they were not paid an hourly wage, but instead were paid using the piece-rate pay system. As an example, suppose you owned a knitting business, and the product you made and sold was socks. The employees in your business would knit socks as their job. With the piece-rate pay system, you paid the employees based on the number of socks they knitted in a day, or a week, or whatever unit of measure you used. If an employee knitted ten pairs of sock in a day, and you paid a piece rate of $1.00 for each pair knitted, then you owed that employee $10.00. However, if the employee didn't show up for work and did not knit any socks, then you owed nothing. In this type of work environment, labor was truly a variable cost and deserved to be allocated as a cost to the product. It just made sense in a piece-rate pay system. The more socks the employees knitted, the more money they could make. Also, as the business owner your labor costs were very precisely controlled. If employees didn't make any socks, then you didn't have to pay.

In time, metrics for calculating labor costs changed and the labor rates changed as well. Many employees were now paid a daily rate instead of a piece rate. Labor costs had now shifted from a truly variable cost per unit to a fixed cost per day. In other words, the employees got that same amount of money per day no matter how many pairs of socks they knitted or didn't knit. As time went by, the employee labor rates shifted again. This time labor rates shifted from a daily rate to an hourly rate. With the new hourly rate came the more standardized work week of forty hours, or eight hours a day, five days a week. With the hourly rate the labor costs now become fixed.

With these changes, it became apparent to the sock-knitting business owner that in order to get the biggest bang for the labor buck, the owner needed to produce as many pairs of socks as he could in a day in order to offset the rising labor costs. The most obvious way to do that was to keep all of your sock knitters busy all of the time making socks. In other words, efficiency was a key ingredient and needed to be increased. If the owner could make more pairs of socks in the same amount of time, then his labor cost per pair of socks would go down. This was the solution the business owner was looking for—reducing his costs. If everyone was busy making more and more socks, and they could make a lot of socks in a day, then his new labor cost per pair of socks could be reduced! This had to be the answer— look how cheap he could make socks now! Or so he thought.

With these new found levels of high efficiency came another problem. The owner quickly noticed that he had to buy more and more raw materials just to keep his employees working at such high efficiency levels. The raw materials were expensive, but he had to have them. The owner knew that his past success was directly linked to his ability to maintain such high efficiency and keep his cost low. More and more raw materials were brought in. More and more socks were made. The socks were now being made much faster than he could sell them. What he needed now was more warehouse space to store all of those wonderfully cheap socks! So at great expense, the owner built another warehouse to store more and more cheap socks. The owner had lots and lots of inventory of very cheap socks. According to his numbers the socks now were costing next to nothing to make. He was saving lots of money! Wasn't he?

Soon the creditors started to show up and want their money. The owner was getting behind on his bills to his raw material suppliers. He had warehouses full of very cheap socks, but he wasn't selling his socks at the same rate he was making them. He was just making more socks. He rationalized that he had to keep the costs down, and in order to do that he had to have the efficiency numbers high. The business owner soon realized that he had to save even more money. He had to cut his costs even more, so he had to lay people off and reduce his workforce to save even more money. How did he ever get into a situation like this? His business was highly efficient. His cost per pair of socks was very low. He saved the maximum amount of money he could, and yet he was going out of business—How come?

Reality had changed and labor costing had changed (labor shifted from a variable cost to a fixed cost), but the cost accounting rules did not change. The owner was still trying to treat his labor cost as a variable cost. Even today many businesses still try to treat their labor cost as a variable cost and allocate the labor cost to individual products. When the labor costs are allocated to a product, then companies try and take the next step—they work hard to improve efficiency and drive down the labor costs per part, or unit. This erroneous thought process is ingrained in their mind, and they believe that this action will somehow reduce labor costs. And if you can reduce labor costs, they think, then you are making more profit. But take just a moment and reflect back on the consequences of the sock maker's experience with cost savings and the high efficiency model. Are these end results anywhere close to what the business owner really wanted to have happen? Was this the real outcome business owners really wanted from high efficiency?

The Efficiency Model

The efficiency model, when measured and implemented at the wrong system location will have devastating effects on your perceived results. The end results will actually be the opposite of what you expected to happen. I wonder why with all of the technology improvements accomplished through the years, why it is still acceptable to use cost accounting rules from the early 1900s?

Cost Accounting

The primary focus of Cost Accounting is per part or per unit cost reductions. Because perceived cost reductions are viewed so favorably, is it any wonder why there is so much emphasis on efficiency? And yet cost reductions don't seem to be the answer. There have been many highly efficient companies that have come close to going out of busines or have gone out of business. Have you ever heard of a company that has saved themselves into prosperity? Think about it, any perceived savings that the sock maker thought he was getting were quickly eroded by buying more raw materials. In fact, it ended up costing the sock maker much more money than he realized and not saving him anything! He was doing all of the recommended practices and yet he was failing—How come?

Many companies will emphatically state that the primary *goal* of their company is to *make money*, and yet they spend the largest portion of their time trying to *save money.* It would appear they've forgotten what their goal really is. The strategy you employ to make money is vastly different than the strategy you would employ to save money. For most companies, the assumption is that saving money is equal to making money—that is, if you somehow save some money it's the same as making money. This is simply not true. These two concepts are divergent in their thinking—each takes you in a different direction with different results. If the real *goal* of your company is to save money, then the very best way to accomplish your goal is to *go out of business*. This action will save you the maximum amount of money—goal accomplished! However, if the goal of your company is to make money, then a different strategy must be employed—maximizing throughput through the system.

Throughput Accounting

Suppose we consider again the same example using the sock maker. Suppose the sock maker wants to make three times as many socks as he is making now. What does he have to do? Using the piece-rate pay system he would have to hire three times as many employees to be sock makers and pay them a piece rate of $1.00 per pair. So in order to make three times as many pairs of socks, the labor rate must go up—he has to hire three times as many people. In the piece-rate world getting three times as much through the system will cost him three times as much in labor. But let us suppose our sock maker is paying an hourly wage rather than a piece rate, and he figures out a way to make three more pairs of socks, per worker, per day. By being able to make three times as much, how much do his labor costs go up? They *do not* go up at all! His labor rate stays exactly the same. He still pays the workers an hourly rate whether they make one pair of socks or ten pairs of socks. He only has to pay the employees one, not a rate based on the number of socks made. His only increase in cost comes from buying more raw materials to make the socks. So why does modern day cost accounting still try to allocate a labor cost per unit of work and then claim that increased efficiency drives down the cost per part? It does no such thing! In today's reality, labor costs are fixed not variable!

Perhaps it is possible that some of these cost accounting rules and methods might be wrong and mislead the user into thinking some results are better than they really are. Is it possible that there might be another way to look logically at the practice of accounting that will truly get us closer to the goal? What if there was another way? A way that provides an alternative accounting method that allows us to remove, or abandon or ignore the CA rules that are causing so much trouble? Let's have a look at Throughput Accounting.

Throughput Accounting is not necessarily a frontal attack on Cost Accounting. However, it is a different way to view the accounting measures, solve issues and manage the company at a much higher success and profitability level—an update of the *accounting rules*, if you will, that is much more in line with current business reality.

Throughput Accounting uses primarily three performance metrics—Throughput (T), Investment (I) and Operating Expense (OE). These metrics are a simplified methodology that removes all of the mystery of accounting and rolls it into three simple measures.

1. *Throughput* is the rate at which inventory is converted into sales. If you make lots of products and put them in a warehouse, that is not throughput—*it's inventory*. The products or services only count as throughput if they are sold to the customer and fresh money comes back into the business system.

2. *Investment/Inventory* is the money an organization invests in items that it intends to sell. This category would include inventory, both raw materials and finished goods. This includes buildings, machines and other equipment used to make products for sale, knowing that any or all of these investments could at some point in time, be sold for cash.

3. *Operating Expens*e is all of the money spent generating the Throughput. This includes, rent, electrical, phone, benefits and wages. It is any money spent that does not fit within one of the first two TA categories.

When you read and understand these definitions it seems likely that all the money within your company can be categorized to fit within one of these three measures.

In thinking about TA it is important to consider the following thoughts: TA is neither costing nor Cost Accounting. Instead, TA is focused on cash without the need for allocation to a specific product. This concept includes the variable and fixed expenses for a product. The only slight variation would be the calculation for Total Variable Cost (TVC). In this case the TVC is a cost that is truly variable to a product or service, such as raw materials, paying a sales commission or shipping charges. The sum total of these costs becomes the product TVC. TVC is *only the cost* associated with each product. Some would argue that labor should also be added as a variable cost per product. Not true! Labor is no longer a variable cost, it's a fixed cost. With the hourly labor measures, you pay employees for vacation, holidays and sick leave. You pay them while they are making nothing! The employees cost you exactly the same amount of money whether they are at work or not. Using this example, labor is an operating expense and not a variable cost associated with products.

The following definitions apply to TA:

1. Throughput (T) = Product Selling Price (SP) – the Total Variable Cost (TVC). Or T = SP – TVC.
2. Net Profit (NP) = Throughput (T) minus Operational Ex pense (OE). Or NP = T – OE
3. Return on Investment (ROI) = Net Profit (NP) divided by Inventory (I). Or ROI = NP/I
4. Productivity (P) = Throughput (T) divided by Operating Expense (OE). Or P = T/OE
5. Inventory Turns (IT) = Throughput (T) divided by Inven tory Value (IV). Or IT = T/I

Some would argue that TA falls short because it is not able to pigeon hole all of the categories of CA into TA categories. Things like interest payments on loans, or payment of stock holder dividends or depreciation of machines or facilities. However, this argument appears to be invalid. Which one of those specific categories can't be placed into one of the TA categories? The baseline TA concept is really very simple. It you have to write a check to somebody else, it's either an Investment (I) or an Operating Expense (OE). It's an investment if it is something you can sell for money at some point in time. It's an operating expense if you can't. Put this debt in the category that makes the most sense. On the other hand, if somebody is writing a check to you, and you get to make a deposit, then it's probably Throughput (T). Cost accounting rules have made it much more complicated and difficult than it needs to be. When you make it that complex and difficult and intently argue about the semantics, the stranglehold that CA has on your thinking becomes even more obvious.

TA is really focused on providing the necessary information that allows decision makers to make better decisions. If the goal of the company is truly to make money, then any decisions being considered should get the company closer to the goal and not further away. Effective decision-making is well suited to an effective T, I & OE analysis.

This analysis can show the impact of any local decisions on the bottom line of the company. Ideally good business decisions will cause:

1. Throughput (T) to increase.
2. Investment/Inventory to decrease or stay the same. It is also possible that investment can go up as long as the effect on T is exponential. In others words, sometime a very well placed investment can cause the T to skyrocket.
3. Operating expenses decrease or stay the same. It is not always necessary to decrease OE to have a dramatic effect. Consider the situation where the T actually doubles and you didn't have to hire anyone new to do it, nor did you have to lay anyone off.

The decision-making process becomes much easier when these factors are considered. The movement either up or down, of these three measures should provide sufficient information for good strategy and good decisions. Any good decision should be based on global impacts to the company and not just a single unit or process in isolation. If your thinking is limited to the lowest level of the organization, and you are focused on the wrong area, then the positive impact will never be seen or felt by the entire organization.

Comparing Cost Accounting (CA) and Throughput Accounting (TA)

Priority	**Common Practice**	**Common Sense**
1.	**OE**	**T**
2.	**T**	**I**
3.	**I**	**OE**
	Cost World Thinking	**Throughput World Thinking**

Figure 1.Common Practive vs. Common Sense

If we compare these two concepts at the highest level, then CA is all about the actions you take to try and *save money*, and TA is about the action you take to *make money*. Once you've made the cost reductions and you still need more, what do you do next? Where else can you reduce costs? On the other hand, making money, at least in theory, is infinite. What is the limit on how much money your company can make now? Figure 1 compares the top level priorities of these two accounting approaches. With these differences in priorities it is easy to see why CA is focused on saving money, and TA is focused on making money. So consider the real goal of your company before you decide which path to take.

You can pick up the newspaper almost any day of the week and see the effects of these priorities. You can read about company XYZ that is going to lay off 500 employees in order to reduce costs and become more efficient and align themselves to be more vertical with the customer and . . . blah, blah, blah! What these companies are really saying is they have forgotten how to make money. They are so focused on saving money that they have forgotten what the real goal of the company is.

So, how did all of this come about? Why are things happening the way there are? If all of this CA and saving money is so good, then how come so many companies seem to be in trouble or worse yet—bankrupt! There are many reasons and some could be debated for weeks, if not months or years. But however many reasons there may be, all of them are not equal. Some reasons are bigger players than others, and as such have had a far greater impact. Let's look at the cost model associated with both the CA and TA concepts. It provides an interesting history about why things are the way they are. Figure 2 defines the cost model concept for both CA and TA.

The product depicted in Figure 2 is exactly the same for both models. It indicates the same selling price, same manufacturing process, same everything. In the CA model you notice the layers of allocated cost that are applied to each product as some percentage of the cost, or allocated rate. The sum total of all of these costs, whatever it may be, equal what CA considers to be the cost to manufacture. Let's look at each layer.

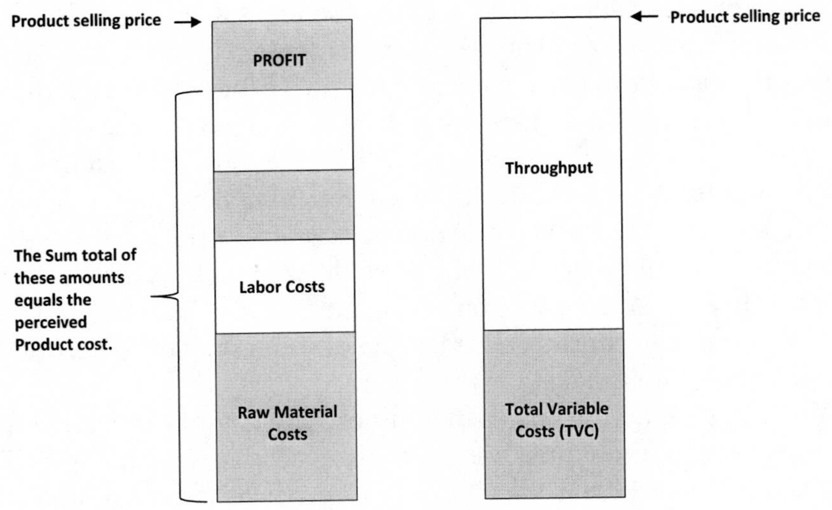

Figure 2: Cost Model Comparisons

Raw Materials—This is the total cost of all the raw materials used in the product you make. An average raw material cost for most companies might be around 40%, but some can, and do, go much higher.

Labor Costs—This is the allocated labor cost per parts. It is usually calculated based on some type of total parts per hour, or day, or production batch, or order, or some other value. Then the total labor cost is divided by the number of parts produced to arive at the percent of labor to be allocated to each part.

Overhead Costs—This is the allocated percentage per part to pay for all of the overhead costs. These are items like the management staff, administrative jobs, training and so on. Usually these types of overhead assignments cover many type of parts, but also no part in particular. Human Resources or even Finance are examples of organizations that fit in the overhead category. You need to have some place to charge and collect your overhead costs.

Corporate General and Administrative—This is the allocated cost that pays for all of the corporate staff and everything they provide.

Profit—This is the location where you add the percentage of profit you want to receive for your product.

Selling Price (SP)—This is the selling price for your product once you've gone through and added together all of the manufacturing cost categories and the percentage of profit.

There very well could be more layers in your company, but in the end the hope is that when you add up all of the costs and sell to the market, or consumer, or the next guy in the supply chain, your selling price is always greater than your manufacturing costs. If it is, then you have made a profit.

But in reality the selling price is not determined by the manufacturer, but rather by the consumer. If the price is too high they won't buy your product and will look elsewhere. So if that happens, what are your choices? Somehow you have to lower your cost and selling price in order to make your product more attractive to the consumer. So how do you do that? You could cut your profit margins, but most organizations do not like to do that. If you can't do that, then what else do you look for? How about overhead cost? You can slow down or stop doing some of the things associated with overhead, for example, training. You could cut your raw materials expense. Perhaps find a different a vendor, or maybe buy cheaper parts. If you do that, then what about the quality risk? How about cutting labor costs? If you could just get more efficient, then your labor costs would go down. If labor costs go down, then we can make more profit – correct? I think by now you understand the cycle of chaos that takes place when you focus on efficiency—disaster usually follows in short order. Such is life in the cost model cycle.

In your company if you *do not* pay your employees using the piece-rate pay system, then the assumption of using allocated labor costs, or any costs, is invalid! Why is the stigma of allocated costs so strong in CA? The assumption that higher efficiency reduces the cost per part is also invalid. In today's reality of the per hour rate the cost remains the same.

The TA cost model contains only Total Variable Cost (TVC) and Throughput (T). The calculation is simple: T = SP-TVC. Throughput, in essence, equals the dollars remaining from selling the product after you have subtracted the TVC cost. Nothing is allocated, nothing is assumed, it's just a simple cash calculation from the sale.

Appendix 3
Theory of Constraints (TOC) Thinking Process Tools

The Systems Thinking Tools

The Systems Thinking tools were developed and popularized by Dr. Eliyahu Goldratt. These tools are a series of thinking processes that can be used individually to solve problems, or they can be used in a defined sequence to conduct a full analysis. It is not the intention of this book that the reader will become proficient in using these tools; rather the intent is to make the reader aware that such tools do exist and to present a basic discussion about what these tools do and how they work.

Current Reality Tree (CRT)

The CRT is used to determine current reality at a single point in time. It's a snapshot, if you will, of a system in its current existence. It is an assemblage of entity statements linked together using *sufficiency* logic. Sufficiency is based on "if" and "then" statements. In other words, *If* (Entity "A") . . . *then* (Entity "B"). The CRT is the tool of choice for defining and logically connecting the current state of activities within a system.

The foundational structure of the CRT is comprised of entities commonly referred to as *Undesirable Effects* (UDEs). The UDE list is best populated by asking the question; "*In my current reality it bothers me that . . .* ?" Determine the best statement that answers the question. The UDEs become the collection of *all* the bad things (Undesirable Effects) that seem to be happening at the same time. Sometimes what appear to be many random negative events, all happening in isolation of each other, are actually events that can be linked together *using cause-effect-cause* relationships. These different, apparently random events that appear unrelated can be logically connected using a CRT. As it turns out, random events are not nearly as random as we think they are.

Using sufficiency logic to determine the cause-effect–cause relationships between events provides a detailed and clear understanding about why particular events seem to be happening over and over again. Figure 1 defines a basic structure for a CRT.

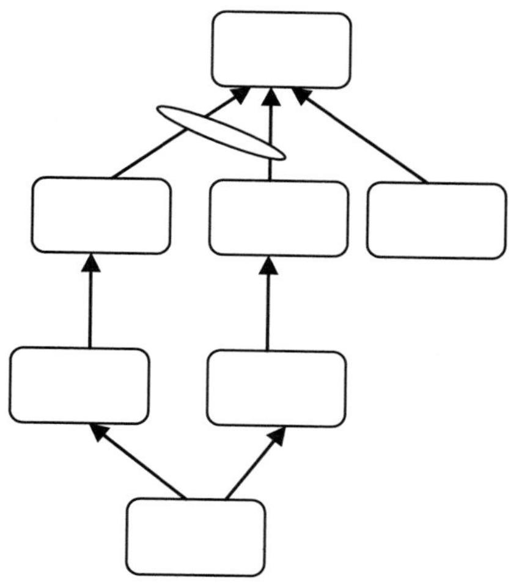

Figure 1: Basic Structure of a CRT

Once the CRT is completed, logically connected and verified, it is possible that a single UDE (the core problem) at the bottom or near the bottom of the tree is actually creating all of the other UDEs. With the core problem now identified it becomes clear where to focus the improvement effort. In the figure, the ellipse between two arrows is the logical "and" statement—meaning that both entities must exist to cause the stated effect.

Conflict Resolution Diagram (CRD)

The CRD, often referred to as the "Evaporating Cloud" as it was originally developed, is a powerful tool for resolving conflict. How many times have you been in a situation where on the one hand somebody wants something, while on the other hand you want something different? The thing they want is different than what you want. How can you possibly come to an agreement if you both want different things? For years people have used negotiation to resolve conflicts. The problem is in a negotiation both sides are required to give up something. You compromise and give up parts of what you want, and the other side give up parts of what they want. Therein lies the problem with a compromise – neither side really ends up getting what they really want. What if there was a way for you to have what you wanted and the other side to have what they wanted? Neither side would be required to compromise on their desired requirement. Would that be of interest you? Enter the CRD. This is by far the most effective tool available to clearly define a conflict and surface the assumptions that cause the conflict to continue to be a conflict. If both sides could get what they wanted, then a conflict would not exist.

The CRD uses necessity-based logic with the statement *In order to have . . . I must have . . .* And it is constructed from these three components:

- Objective
- Requirements
- Prerequisites

The objective becomes the common ground between both parties. It's the statement about what both parties really want. It should be stated succinctly and at a high enough level to meet the needs of the two parties.

The requirements are the necessary conditions that both must have to be able to meet the objective.

The prerequisite is an assumed necessary condition to be able to achieve the requirement. It is usually the two prerequisite entities that will be in conflict with each other. One entity may say, "do something," while the opposite entity may proclaim, "don't do it." One entity may say, "change" and the other entity says, "don't change." The battleground is now set—we've established the conflict. Figure 2 shows one way to configure the structure of CRD.

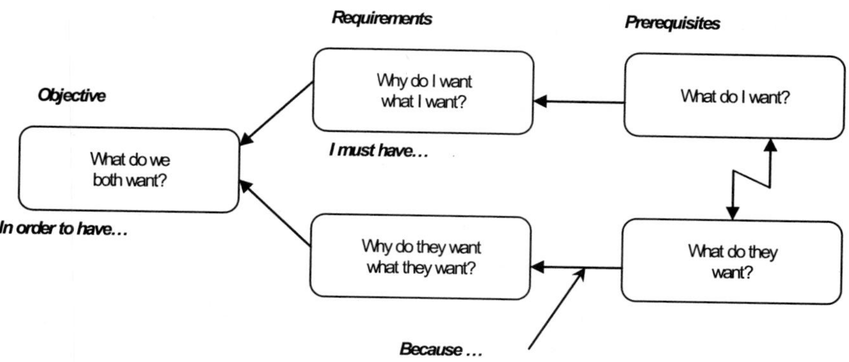

Figure 2: The CRD Structure

With the structure in place and the conflict precisely verbalized, you can surface the assumptions. The assumptions are located on the arrows between the entities. These lines are solid lines because there are assumptions that exist. You can surface the assumptions by stating, In order to have (Objective), I must have (Requirement) . . . because . . . assumption? Do this for each arrow and list the assumptions. If you can dissolve an assumption and make it go away, then the conflict can be resolved. The line is no longer solid—it doesn't exist. If you invalidate an assumption, the conflict no longer exists. If we replace the invalid assumption with a new idea, then we have an *Injection*.

Future Reality Tree (FRT)

How many times has it happened that we think we have a good idea only to find out that our idea wasn't so good? You usually find out when you implement your "good" idea, and then bad things start to happen. What if there was a way to test an idea before it was implemented to determine if the idea generates the results you want to have happen? A way, if you will, to run the movie in fast forward and see if we like the ending. Such a tool does exist and it's called the Future Reality Tree (FRT). With an FRT you can logically test the virtues of an idea before it is implemented and look for those unwanted, undesirable effects that might happen. If you can predict what might go wrong, and you have a way to overcome the negative effect, then the bad things shouldn't happen. Such is the function of an FRT. Figure 3 shows the FRT Structure.

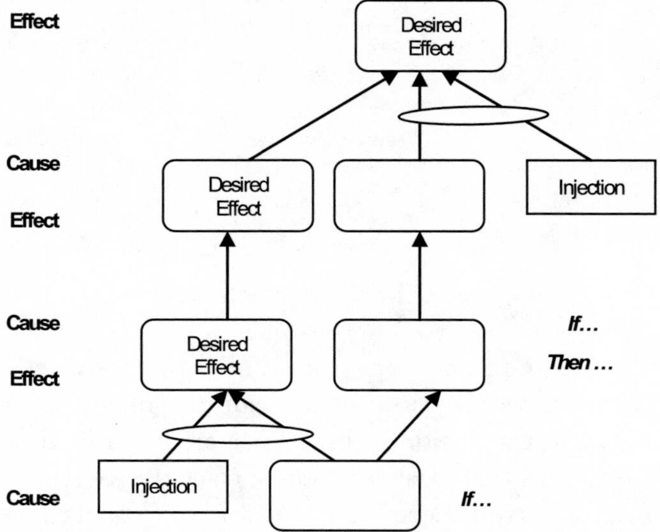

Figure 3: The FRT Structure

An FRT is constructed using sufficiency with the *If . . . Then . . .* statements. What you are looking for is the *Desired Effects*—the good things that happen from implementing your idea. The FRT can also provide advanced warning for the Negative Effects—the bad things that might happen. If you find negative effects (branches) coming from your idea then think of an *Injection*—an idea that overcomes the negative effect and makes it positive again. The more negative effects you can overcome, the more powerful your idea, and the greater the chance that the implementation becomes successful.

Prerequisite Tree (PRT)

Once you have tested your idea using the FRT, and you decide your idea is worth moving forward with, then the PRT becomes the tool to surface the obstacles to your idea. Ask yourself, "Why can't I do this right now?" What are the reasons or obstacles that stand between you and completing your idea? You might even try presenting your idea to someone else. They offer suggestions such as, "It's a great idea, but . . ." As soon as they say "but," they will offer their opinion as to why the idea won't work. This means they have surfaced an obstacle that you might have to overcome to make your idea real. The purpose behind a PRT is to surface and overcome as many obstacles as you can so your idea will be implemented as smoothly as it possibly can. Figure 4 shows the structure of a PRT.

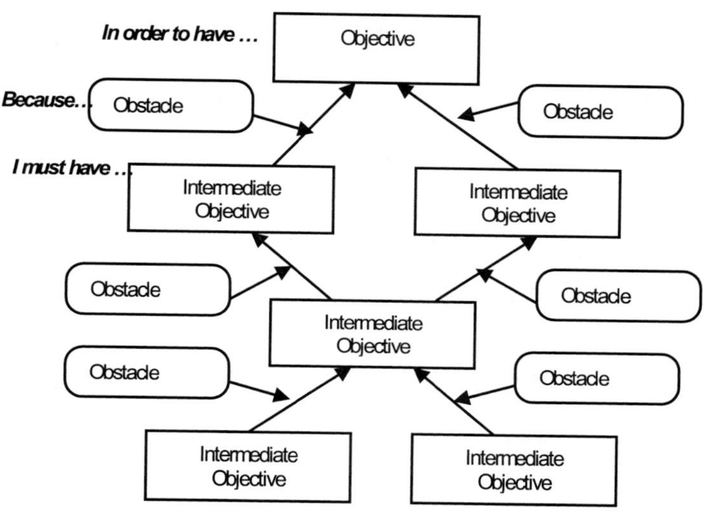

Figure 4: The Structure of a PRT

Think of as many reasons as you can "why" your idea won't work. What stops you right now from doing this? With each obstacles you surface, counter that thought with an *Intermediate Objective* that makes the obstacle no longer an obstacle. The PRT is read from the top down. You are looking for the logical connections between the Intermediate Objectives (IO) that makes the obstacle go away. If you achieve the defined IO, then the obstacle is removed and is no longer a problem. Once all of the IO's are completed the objective can be achieved.

Transition Trees (TT)

The final tool is the Transition Tree (TT). Based on popularity, it is not a tool that is often used. However, the TT can provide an excellent logical structure for going deeper and being more fractal in your thinking. It is designed at a level that requires the definition of *actions* to be taken, and needs to be filled.

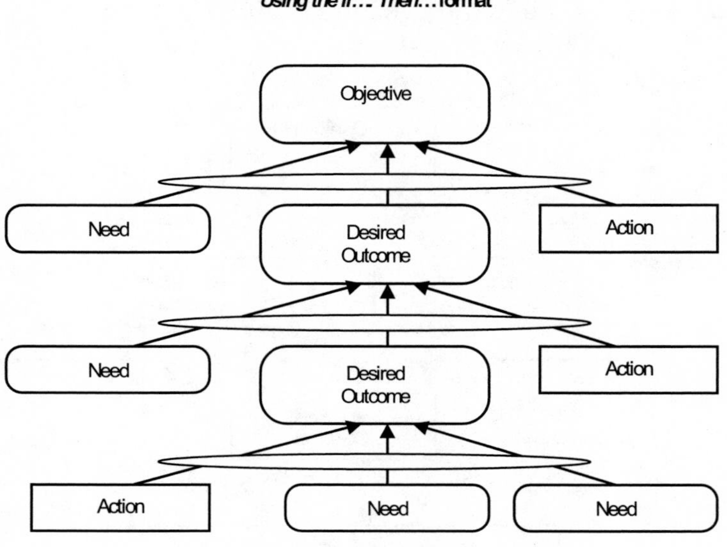

Figure 5: TT Structure and Format

The basis of the TT is sufficiency, and it is read with the *If . . . then . . .* statements. Figure 5 shows the structure of the TT.

If you encounter an Intermediate Objective (IO) in your PRT that may be particularly difficult to achieve, then the Transition Tree (TT) is an excellent tool to define the actions necessary to meet the needs to accomplish the IO.

The TT is comprised of an *Objective, Actions* and *Needs*. The Objective can be defined as the difficult IO from the PRT, or any other objective you might have that benefits from planning at a detailed level. With the objective in mind, consider what need you are trying to fill and what action you can take to immediately make it happen. When you read the TT from the bottom up, the intrinsic order of the actions, desired outcomes and need are clearly defined. Start at the bottom, complete that action, and achieve your desired effect, then take the next action, which fills a need and continue until the objective is accomplished. At this level of detail, actions could be equal to making phone calls, writing a paper, doing a presentation, whatever the action is that you can start today. The trick here is: *Take action.*

The Full Thinking Process (TP) Analysis

The TP tools can be used on a standalone basis and they can also be used in a specific sequence to drive a complete systems analysis. With the full level of analysis you are trying to answer three questions:

1. What Do I change? Identifying the core problem.
2. What do I change to? Determining the best solution to solve the problem.
3. How to cause the change to happen? The steps to implement your great idea.

Figure 6 display the sequence when conducting the full thinking analysis.

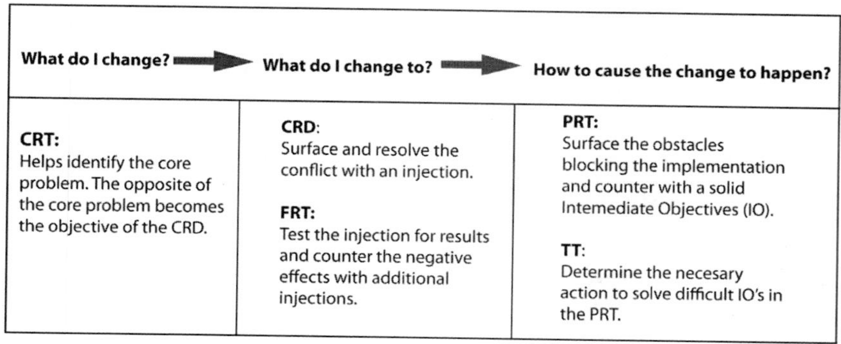

Figure 6: The Full Analysis Sequence

The full Thinking Processes analysis can be time consuming and possibly frustrating, but certainly worth the effort to find the core problem, provide the correct injection (idea) and determine the best way to implement the new idea.

Appendix 4
Interference Diagram (ID), Intermediate Objectives (IO) Map and ID/IO Simplifed Strategy

Introduction

When Eli Goldratt[3] first exposed the world to his then radical Systems Thinking Processes he presented them as the logical tools to express, and document, logical thinking in a very structured format. The improvement quest was centered on the ability to answer three questions:

1. What do I change? (What problem are you trying to solve?)
2. What do I change to? (What is the best solution to solve the problem?)
3. How do I cause the change to happen? (Implementing the solution into reality.)

Goldratt developed the five systems thinking tools to accomplish the necessary thinking tasks to succinctly solve a problem. Each of the five thinking tools aids the user with the ability to apply the tool as a singular component, or to use the tools in a sequential combination to strengthen the logical analysis even more. The five systems thinking tools are:

1. Current Reality Tree (CRT)
2. Evaporating Cloud (EC)
3. Future Reality Tree (FRT)
4. Perquisite Tree (PRT)
5. Transition Tree (TT)

---

3 Goldratt, Eliyahu, Cox, Jeff, *The Goal: A Process of Ongoing Improvement*, North River Press, Great Barrington, MA., (1992)

Today, these five tools still remain as the foundational cornerstone of the Thinking Processes for the Theory of Constraints (TOC). These thinking tools have, through time, proven their worth to better understand and analyze simple, as well as, complex problems. For any of you who have been through a Systems Thinking Processes course and learned how to use these tools properly and effectively, you understand the "how" and "why" a good analysis can command a rigorous and sometimes sustained effort to accomplish the task. In others words, developing a useful and solid analyses using the Thinking Process tools can take some considerable effort. In some respects the time commitment required to do a good systems analysis has been a downside to using the thinking tools and has, in turn, caused many people to ignore the tools and turn their heads to the real power and usefulness they can provide.

Over the years Global dynamics have evolved to a level of forcefulness that instant gratification is now considered the norm – put your nickel in and get something out NOW! The dynamics of this global phenomenon have pushed us all to chant the mantra of - "Better, Faster, and Cheaper!" Waiting any amount of time for something to happen no longer seems to be an acceptable option - it's the world we live in. There are situations and problems that are not accompanied by the luxury of the required time to figure them out. This requirement to be "Better, Faster and Cheaper" has not gone unnoticed in the network of the world's Systems Thinkers.

The Evolution of the Thinking Processes

If an idea is presented to the world, and it's a good idea, then somebody, somewhere, somehow will improve the idea and expand it to another level. The "improved" idea will overcome some of the prior inertia of the obstacles and issues that seemed to exist. If the idea is really good and accepted by many people, then the evolution of the idea continues. Each new level of improvement removes more of the obstacles from the previous level and each new level is presented as a form of unification of ideas from the previous level(s). This unification notion becomes the idea of doing more with less, or combining for better results. For instance, instead of doing three separate tasks, now you do one task and get better and faster results. In other words, through the steps of unification an idea can now become easier and more usable by more people. Such is the case for the TOC Systems Thinking Processes - a good idea that continues to evolve.

The Apparent Problem

As a person who has taught many Systems Thinking courses I've had the opportunity to present the Systems Thinking tools to a wide variety of people. The intellectual levels, the passion, and the job functions have been spread over a variety of individuals and industries. Teaching these courses has also delivered a wide range of results. In some classes there was 100% completion and in other classes results were dismal with a 75-80% failure rate. Failure rate in this case, is defined as those students who did not finish the course, which was usually related to the time commitment required.

In the early days of teaching this course the preferred approach was to provide a level playing field for all students and make it as linear as possible. The desire for doing this was to reduce as much variation as possible in the learning environment. However, even after creating the utopic venue, there were some surprises. In a typical class the students would be divided into teams so that each team had a minimum of two members and, in some cases three or more, if required. Each team was given a two page write-up (case study) about a fictitious company that was having problems. The assumed linear thinking was that everyone who read the paper would discover the same problems and ALL readers would eventually reach the same conclusions for the Undesirable Effects (UDE's). Such was not the case. In a class with ten (10) students and five (5) teams it was very predictable that these five teams would develop five different core problems when they constructed their Current Reality Tree (CRT). It is a ponderous thought to speculate how it was possible for five different teams; each analyzing the exact same problem, to come up with five different answers? It was also a surprise to discover, that in most cases, each of the five different answers could be plausible! There was also another observation – the confidence level of the students in thinking they had correctly discovered the core problem was absent. It seemed that the constant question from the group was, "Is this the right core problem?" Even when a core problem was stated (defined), the lingering question became. "Is this REALLY the core problem?"

When you apply a truly scientific method towards problem solving then, a potpourri of answers should not be possible – only one answer should be correct! And yet, at the same time, it appeared as if more than one answer could, in fact, be correct? Why? The answers provided by the students were not the same, and yet they all seemed to be related. It seemed that what was actually being exposed was a listing of the "obstacles" or "interferences" that stopped them from achieving what they wanted! All of the answers (the perceived core problems) presented were all plausible reasons (interferences) to better understand "why" what they wanted more of *could not* be achieved. This epiphany created a path back to a thinking tool that I had previously used– the Interference Diagram (ID).

The Interference Diagram (ID)

When the interference diagram was first being developed and drawn on whiteboards, it was done so, not with the intention of replacing or linking any of the current Systems Thinking Tools, but rather to fill the void of a necessity for completing the analysis in less time. The ID is a thoughtful mind mapping tool that can quickly point a team, or individual, in essentially the right direction to solve a problem and not be required construct a Current Reality Tree (CRT). In essence, the Interference Diagram (ID) was able to answer the question: "What to change." In this case, the "What to change" became a list of the many entities (Obstacles/Interferences) and not just a single entity (Core Problem).

The first uses of the ID came from Bob Fox at the TOC Center, New Haven, CT, circa 1995. Since then, the use and structure of the ID tool *has not* been well documented, published or transferred to the public at large, but rather used by a limited number of practitioners within the TOC network. The simplicity of the ID and the underlying robust concept to solve problems has been applauded by ID users. The global influence of the ID to solve problems is colossal. Unlike the other thinking tools the ID is not based on logic, but rather on intuition. The arrows in this diagram are just arrows without sufficiency or necessity. The applied thinking is not to develop or isolate a single answer, but rather to list the obstacles/interferences that block the achievement of the desired objective.

It has often been said that the biggest obstacle to solving a problem is to first be able to preciously define the problem. If you are not sure what problem you are trying to solve then, it is awfully difficult to determine the correct solution. In other words, if you don't know where you are going, then any path you decide to take is sufficient to get you there – you'll just never know when you get there. The ID structure and concepts are very simple and yet, very powerful in the results provided.

Interference Diagram (ID) Types

There are actually two different ways to apply an ID. The first application is using the ID as a thinking tool to exploit a known constraint. The second application involves using the ID in combination with the Intermediate Objectives (IO) map. The second application offers a fast and highly effective way to develop an overall strategy plan and implementation plan. We will discuss the second application later.

First, let's consider the exploitation of a constraint within a system. When the system's constraint is identified, then the exploitation question becomes—"How do I get more from the constraint?" What are the "interferences" that slow down or stop the constraint from doing more and or doing better? It is possible that there could be several interferences that block the enriched performance of the constraint. This list of "interferences" becomes the reasons "why" the constraint cannot do more. The interference list is best compiled from the resources that use the constraints. The constraint users can provide the subject matter expertise to define the interferences and are most familiar with the constraint and how it works, or doesn't work. When constraint users are asked the question: "What stops (interferes with) you getting more from this operation?"—chances are good that the user resources will be brutally honest with their answers. What becomes important at this stage of information gathering is to filter the "emotional" response from the "logical" responses. You'll need to determine is if the response is really a system problem, or strictly a personal annoyance or gripe. This analysis will provide better results if the emotional responses are removed up front before placing the statement on the interference list.

The entities on the list simply imply those "interferences" that stop the constraint from doing more - those interferences that "steal" time away from the constraint. In order to get more from the constraint, you must reduce the impact of the interferences, or remove them completely. Any interference that can be reduced or eliminated will free up additional time for the constraint to work more. As an example, let's go through the building steps to construct an ID that is used to exploit a constraint in a production system. In our example let say that we have identified one particular machine in a production line as the constraint. We will refer to it as "Machine XYZ." Let's define the steps to construct.

Step 1 – Define the Goal/Objective
The goal/objective should be something that you really want, but something that doesn't exist in your current reality. For our example, we will choose as the objective: "More parts from the XYZ machine." This can be written on a whiteboard or in the center of a piece of paper.

Step 2 – Define the interferences
Step 2 is best accomplished using observation of the system and interviews with the operators. When observing the constraint look for those things that slow down or stop the constraint from working. What are the interferences that take time away from achieving more of the objective? If the identified constraint is truly a system constraint, then keeping it busy all the time and getting more output will be paramount to successfully gaining more system throughput. A possible list of obstacles/interferences might include:

1. Parts not available to work.
2. Operator on break/lunch.
3. Operator has to find his own parts.
4. Operator is looking for the Supervisor.
5. Operator is attending training.
6. Machine is broken.

The list could be extensive and varied. What is most important is to identify are those things that stop the constraint from doing more. Observation of the constraint might reveal others things that impact time at the machine, such as, having to do setups for a different product. All of the observation and interview items combined equal the list of obstacles/interferences that hinder achieving the objective

"More parts from the XYZ machine." There is not a set limit to the number of interferences that need to be gathered. Rather, you should list as many as you think necessary to fully describe "why" the machine stops working.

Step 3 – Quantify the Time Component for ALL interferences
Quantifying the time component associated with the interferences, becomes important to fully understand and appreciate the impact of the interference on the available time. The time component will help filter the important few from the trivial many and help express those items with the greatest impact. Knowing the impact of the time component will also be useful in determining the priority ranking for which interferences to reduce, or eliminate, first. Some of the interferences will be more important than others – they are not all equal. When you accurately quantify the time component for the interference, it also allows for excellent Pareto analysis. Pareto analysis will align the interference, based on time distribution, and determine which interference is most impactful, and the intrinsic order of improvement. Pareto allows the *focus* necessary to gain the most *leverage* from the action implemented. However, it is also not realistic to assume that ALL interferences can be reduced and/or eliminated. There will be some interferences that do not offer themselves as candidates for elimination, but rather as entities that can benefit from a reduced time impact. In other words, if an entity with a time impact of 45 minutes can subsequently be reduced to 15 minutes, then the benefit gained for the system is 30 minutes more time for the constraint. In other cases, the interferences cannot be reduced or eliminated at all. In our example, the time for breaks and lunch cannot be removed. Employees are allowed lunch and break time. However, as an alternative you could gain some machine time by having an alternate person or crew to work the machine during lunch and breaks.

What you are really looking for in Step 3 is to quantify with time, those activities that are stealing time away from your constraint operation. If you can eliminate, reduce, or off-load some of these activities, then more time is available to get more parts through the constraint. If interferences are known, and corrected, then the end result should equate to more output from the machine and more throughput through the system.

Step 4 – Alternatives to the Interferences

The interference list defines all of the obstacles/interferences that stand in the way of having more of what you want. If these interferences/obstacles did not exist, then achieving the goal would be easier. With the interferences defined, you should be able to counter the seemingly negative effect of the obstacles/interferences with an Injection/Intermediate Objective (IO). This action can be accomplished by asking the question: "What must exist so that the interference no longer exists?" Whatever your answer might be is the Injection/ Intermediate Objective to overcome the negative impact of the interference. Continue working your way down the list and create an Injection/Intermediate Objective for each Inference/Obstacles listed. The items on Injection/Intermediate Objectives list are the things that must be accomplished to reduce, or eliminate the negative effects of the inferences. If not, then consider revising your Injection/ Intermediate Objective list until the answers are sufficient to remove the obstacles/interferences. With the addition of Injections/Intermediate Objectives the list should provide sufficient "ideas" to move you closer to the objective/goal you have established. With the list in place you have now preciously defined "What to change to."

Obstacles/Interferences	Intermediate Objective/Injections
1. Parts not available to work	1. Parts are kitted and ready for use.
2. Operator in on break/lunch.	2. Train an alternate crew or person.
3. Operator has to find his own parts.	3. Parts delivered to operator.
4. Operator is looking for the Supervisor.	4. Supervisor notification system.
5. Operator is looking for paper work.	5. Paperwork follows job in the system.
6. Machine is broken.	6. Preventive maintenance (priority #1).

Figure 1 presents an example of what a completed Interference Diagram might look like for our example. The circle contains the objective and each of the interferences is listed around a circle. The direction of the arrows makes no difference because these arrows are based on the ID user's intuition and not necessity or sufficiency logic.

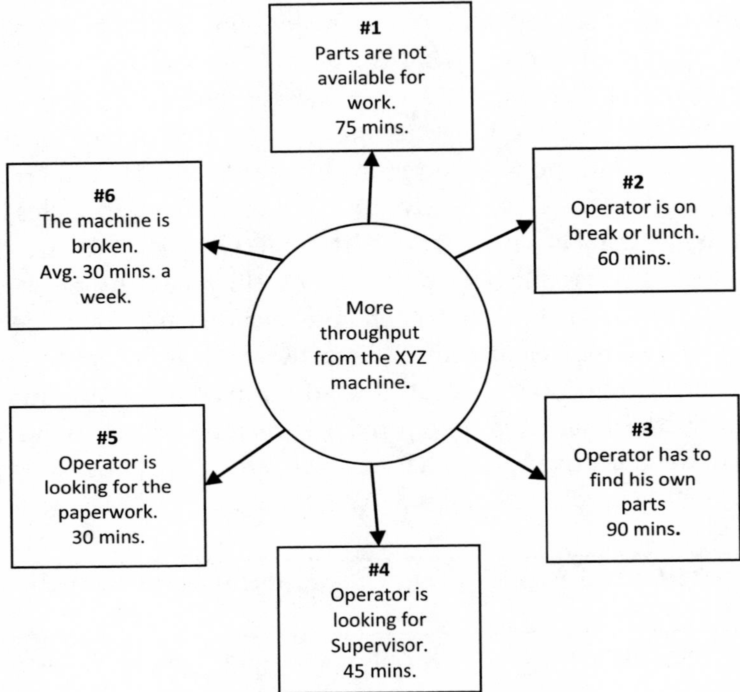

Figure 1: Completed Interference Diagram (ID)

Notice in the figure that the interference times have been added for every interference identified. This allows for a quick visual of the time impact.

When using the Pareto analysis you should base it on available machine time. This will succinctly show the impact of the interferences. If the available machine time for the XYZ machine is considered to be 8 hours, for one shift, then the available time is 480 minutes (60 min X 8 hours = 480 minutes) during an 8 hour period. When you use the 480 minutes as the baseline to measure the impact of the interferences, the results will show the conflict between the time available to work and the time the machine actually spends working. Figure 2 shows an example setup of the Excel input sheet to show the interference description, total minutes the interference consumes, and the percentage impact on the total minutes available. As you can see the leading time impact comes from not having parts available at the machine to work on. Fixing this interference alone could provide an additional 90 minutes of throughput time every day.

#	Description	Daily minutes	Percent Interference
1	Parts not available	75	16%
2	Breaks & Lunch	60	13%
3	Operator finding parts	90	19%
4	Looking for Supervisor	45	9%
5	Looking for paperwork	30	6%
6	Machine is broken[1]	6	1%

Total Interference minutes[2]	306	
Available work minutes[3]	174	
Total Available minutes	480	
Utilization Percentage		36%

[1]6 minutes is calculated from a weekly average of 30 mins (30 mins/ 5 days)
[2]Σ interference minutes
[3]Available mins - Interference mins.

Figure 2: The simple Excel setup

From this spreadsheet setup you can display two additional charts that help drive the point home for the impact of the interferences. With the interference percentage calculated you can create a pie-chart to visually display the breakout and "Interference Impact." Figure 3 displays the Interference Impact for our example.

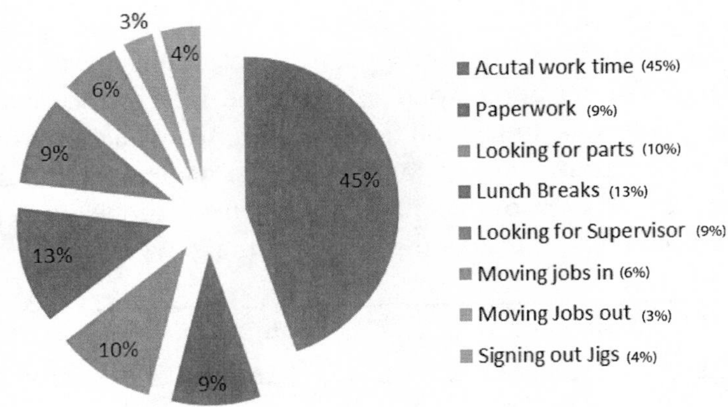

Figure 3: The "Interference Impact."

Figure 3 shows that only 36% of the total time available is actually used to make parts on this machine. The other 64% of the time is consumed by the interferences. Figure 4 displays the interferences in a Pareto analysis to show the intrinsic (descending) order of improvement. Those interferences listed highest on the list should be reduced or eliminated first, if possible, to gain the most benefit.

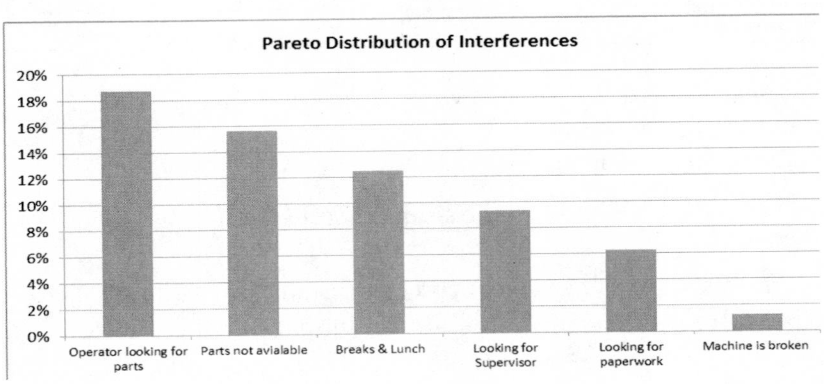

Figure 4. Pareto distribution of Inferences.

When the ID is used to analyze and exploit a constraint it can be a quick and effective tool to generate good ideas quickly. This method, when used in conjunction with Pareto analysis, can quickly provide the visual tool to determine the impactful interferences and provide the *focus* and *leverage* on those few important actions that will provide the highest levels of improvement.

Interference Diagram (ID) for Strategy

In the previous example we showed how to use the ID to exploit a constraint, now let's look at the second application—strategy development. When using the ID for strategy development you want to *focus* on a higher level (more global) objective/goal, especially if the input audience is cross-functional. The Objective/Goal has to be at a high enough level to satisfy all parties concerned. If you drive the Objective/Goal too low, some organizations will complain that it does not apply to them. When using the ID for the purpose of strategy development, it is best if used in tandem with the Intermediate Objectives (IO) map. The combined thinking power of the ID/IO map is referred to as Simplified Strategy and will enable an effective strategy, and detailed implementation plan, to be developed. In this case, the IO map provides the intrinsic order (sequence) of the tactical actions to accomplish the overall strategy.

When the ID is used in a strategy development scenario it is not a constraint you are looking for. Instead, what you want to define is the strategic Objective/Goal that you really want to achieve. When the objective/goal has been defined then, look next for the "interferences" that slow down or stop the progression towards the goal. Usually, there can be several interferences that block the path to success. If there is one thing people are really good at, it's their ability to express their vocal rational about "why" something won't work, or why you cannot have something you want. When you present your idea to someone else, or to a group, the common reaction is, "that's a great idea, but...." As soon as the person says "but" they will interject the reason "why" they think the idea won't work. "It's a great idea but, the boss will never approve it." Or, "That's a good idea but, it's not the way we do it here." Or maybe even, "It's a good idea but, it will be too expensive to do." What they are telling you is what they think the interferences/obstacles are that will hinder your ability to succeed. In order to get more of what you want, you must reduce the impact of the interferences/obstacles, or remove them completely. As an example, let's go through the steps to construct an ID that will be used for strategy development.

Step 1 – ID Strategy – Define the goal/objective
The objective/goal for the strategy application of the ID is focused on strategic direction rather than a constraint and generally answers the questions: "Where do we go from here?" The objective has to be at a level high enough to include the many. However, with that said, it is also important to understand that good strategy development can happen within a specific organization, such as Engineering, Procurement, or Manufacturing. Think in terms of a higher level objective/goal for this scenario when dealing with a single organization, or combining the objectives of many organizations into a single strategy at a higher level. The objective/goal that you pick might seem elusive, but it should also be necessary to get where you want to go. The focused end point of the journey.

The ID tool can work well in a group setting and allow the user to surface obstacles/interferences across many different organizations. Suppose for our example we defined the objective as "Increasing Revenue."

Step 2 – Define the Obstacles/Interferences
When a group consensus is realized, and the objective has been clearly defined, then you need to look for the obstacles/interferences to characterize "why" you can't have what you want. Again, when using the ID for strategy development the obstacles/interferences can, and most probably will, cross many organizational functions. There is no minimum or maximum number of obstacles/interferences required. Rather, you should be looking for a list of an interferences that is comprehensive enough to surface those entities that are really standing in the way of your success. Suppose, for this example, our cross functional team listed the following obstacles/interferences for achieving the objective/goal of "Increased Revenue." The obstacles/interference list might look something like this:

Obstacles/Interferences

1. Not enough sales
2. No markets to grow into
3. Customer has low perception of our product
4. Products are priced too high
5. Competitor has higher quality
6. Production takes too long

This list defines the obstacles/interferences that are perceived to currently exist and block successful achievement of the goal. These are the things that stand in the way of being able to achieve "Increased Revenue." This list can, and probably will, seem a bit overwhelming when you look at it, but don't lose faith just yet. Let's do the rest of the steps and see if we can tame the beast.

Step 3 – Define the Intermediate Objectives/Injections

As part of the ongoing group discussion, you'll want to define the Intermediate Objectives/Injections. In Step 3 what you want to surface are those intermediate objectives (IO) that must exist to make the obstacles/interference go away and not be a problem anymore. Ask the group this question; "What must exist in order for the obstacle/interference not to be a problem anymore?" When you think of the actions required for eliminating or reducing the obstacles/interferences—be BOLD. Describe what you think is really necessary to counter the problem(s) to accomplish the stated objective. Don't shy away from intermediate objectives/injections just because you think you cannot make them happen. If they are important for the overall objective, then write them down, no matter how far out there they might seem. Here are some possible intermediate objective examples for the obstacles on the list:

Obstacles/Interferences	Intermediate Objectives/ Injections
1. Not enough sales	1. Increased sales
2. No markets to grow into	2. Explore/find new markets

3. Customer has low perception of our product	3. Customers have high product perception
4. Products are priced too high	4. Products priced competitively
5. Competitor has higher quality	5. Quality higher than competitor's
6. Production takes too long	6. Lead-time reduced (Increase throughput)

With the intermediate objectives/injections defined you now have the list of the required actions to eliminate the obstacles/interferences and make them go away. It is a foreboding list and at first glance it's appears almost impossible to achieve any of these actions. Figure 5 provides an example of the basic structure and layout for using the ID for strategy development.

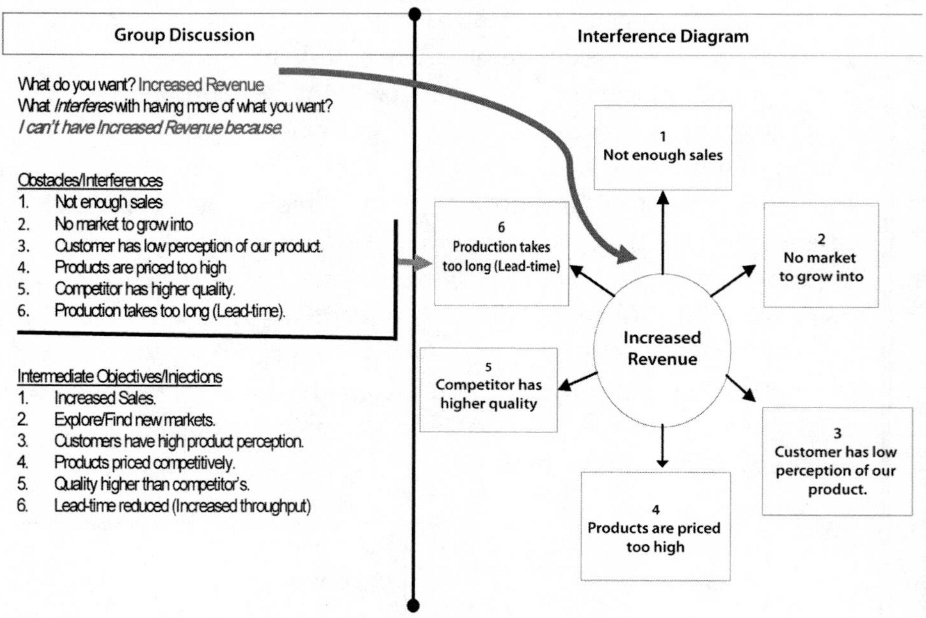

Figure 5: Converting from Discussion to an Interference Diagram (ID).

With this section complete the next step is to layout and constructs the Intermediate Objective (IO) map to govern the implementation plan and determine the tactical actions to accomplish the objective.

Intermediate Objectives (IO) Map

The Intermediate Objectives (IO) map was developed by H. William (Bill) Dettmer[4], and in the spirit of combining methods (Unification) within a methodology this tool fits the criteria. The IO map has been refined over the years to become a very practical and useful organizational and thinking tool. Instead of using the full spectrum of the Thinking Process tools to conduct an analysis, the IO map combines the Prerequisite Tree (PRT) and the Conflict Diagram (CD) into a single tool. In his paper about Intermediate Objective mapping, Dettmer defined the IO Map as a Prerequisite Tree (PRT) without any obstacles defined. Dettmer's primary intent for this tool was to simplify the construction and accuracy of the CRT—to focus the attention on a better defined objective, rather than a core problem. In this context the IO map can be used to surface the undesirable effects (UDE's). In most cases, the UDE's can be discovered by verbalizing the exact opposite of the desired intermediate objectives that are listed. These UDE's then become the building blocks for a Current Reality Tree (CRT). It makes sense that UDE's can come from the IO's. UDE's are what currently exist and the IO's are what you want to exist. In essence, the IO's are what "you want" and the opposite wording of the IO's would embrace the UDE list.

Dettmer also defines an expanded function for the IO map, indicating that it serves well the purpose of strategy development, and as such, it does provide a robust tool to do that. The IO map used a standalone technique can provide the necessary clarity and direction to accomplish a needed strategy.

The IO Map is a very concise organizational thinking tool based on necessity logic. The IO map allows the user to define the IO's and then the intrinsic order of the IO task completion by using necessity logic. In other words, it is read with necessity as the outcome. *In order to have... (Entity Statement at the tip of the arrow), I must have...*

4 Dettmer, H.W., *The Intermediate Objectives Map, http://goalsys.com/books/documents/IOMapPaper.pdf*, November, 2008.

(Entity Statement at the base of the arrow). Necessity logic states, in essence, that entity B must exist before you can have entity A. The entity cannot be there just sometimes, or most of the time, but, instead necessity states it MUST be there. The existence of entity B is not a causal existence. Necessity requires that the "B entity" exist before the "A entity" can be achieved.

The structure of the IO map is really very simple. There are three primary levels, or thinking levels required to construct the IO map. The first level is defining the GOAL. The second level identifies the *Critical Success Factors (CSF)* or, those intermediate objectives that must exist prior to achieving the Goal. The third level is populated with the remaining *necessary conditions* required to achieve the Critical Success Factors (CSF). Figure 6 provides an example of the basic structure of an IO map.

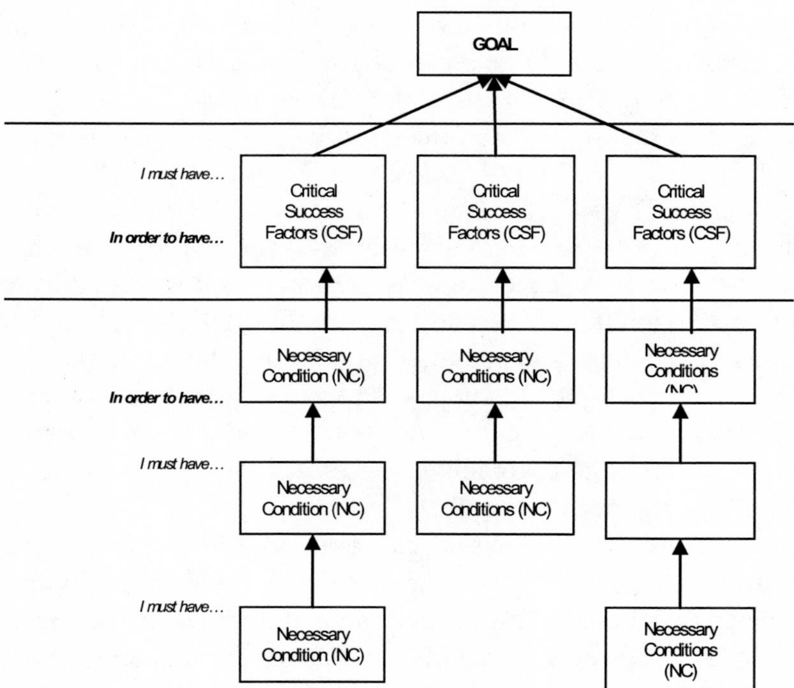

Figure 6. Example structure of the Intermediate Objective (IO) Map.

Figure 7 shows an example of the IO map that was created using our IO list example.

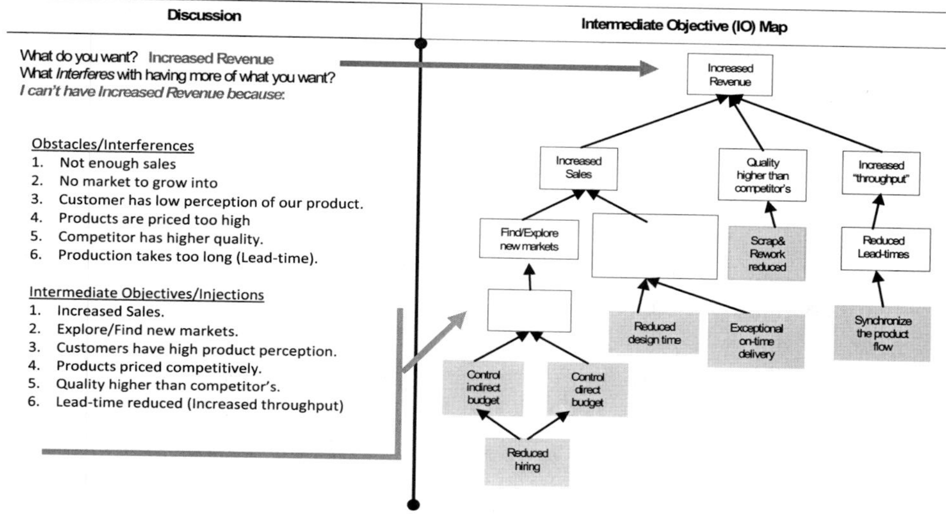

Figure 7: Converting from Objectives/Injections to the IO Map

You'll notice the shaded IO's in the diagram. These are the IO's that were surfaced when building the IO map. These IO's did not appear on the original IO list, but instead surfaced after construction began on the IO map.

The ID/IO Simplified Strategy

Now that you have an understanding of both the Interference Diagram (ID) and the Intermediate Objective (IO) map and how they can be used as standalone techniques to generate some impressive improvement results, let's talk about how they can be combined. The Simplified Strategy is a way to combine these two tools, depending on the situation being analyzed and the desired outcome required. It is possible that when using the ID to define the interferences, they are actually obstacles that are not necessarily time driven, but rather event driven. The ID allows you to define the obstacle/interference, if they are not already well know. Sometimes, the obstacles do not provide the means to implement a simple solution in isolation, but rather are collectively connected by necessity. In other words, when you develop the list of obstacles using the ID, the IO list becomes the verbalization opposite of the obstacle rather than just an injection. You are looking for the IO's that must exist in reality to make the obstacle/interference not a problem anymore. What happens next is the listing of IO's becomes just that—a list of IO's. Now, with the IO mapping tool you can establish the logical necessity between single IO events (entities) that requires another predecessor event (entity) before the event can happen. In other words, there is a logical dependency and intrinsic order in the sequence. Just randomly selecting and completing of IO's will not satisfactorily achieve the goal. When you analyze the IO list you realize that ALL of the IO's need to be completed, but which one do you start with first? When this is the case, the IO map can be used to determine the sequence and order of completion. From the IO list you can determine which events are Critical Success Factors (CSF's) and which ones are the Necessary Conditions (NC's.) By using the IO to map to determine the necessity between the events, it becomes exactly clear which IO you need to start with to implement your strategy. Each level of the IO becomes logically connected to formally outline the "strategy" and "tactics." In other words, the goal is the strategy and the Critical Success Factors are the tactics to accomplish the goal. At the next level the Critical Success Factors become the strategy and the Necessary Conditions become the tactics. The same thinking applies down through the next levels of Necessary Conditions. When you reach the bottom of an IO chain, then you know what action you need to take first to start the process moving up through the IO's. By using the IO map as a problem solving supplement to the ID it provides the needed organization to logically align the IO's. The ID map will provide the well-defined obstacles/interferences to better focus the creation of the correct IO's to negate the obstacles. Consider also, that sometimes it is very difficult to generate a good solution without first understanding what exactly the problem is.

Even though these tools can be used in combination it might not always be necessary to do so. In fact the power of these tools allows them to be used in reverse order if so desired. If you already understand what you need to do, then the IO map can be your beginning tool. If, however, you are not so sure why you cannot achieve a particular goal, then the ID helps identify the obstacles/ interferences. Even if you begin with the IO map and you discover a particular IO that is necessary, but you're just not sure how to make it happen, then you can use the ID as a subset of the IO map to discover the interferences for achieving that IO. If you remove the interferences for the IO, then you can achieve the IO. When you achieve that particular IO you can move on to the next one. If you already know how to accomplish that IO, then fine. If not, then use the ID again to surface the interferences. Figure 8 shows a possible template for the combined approach.

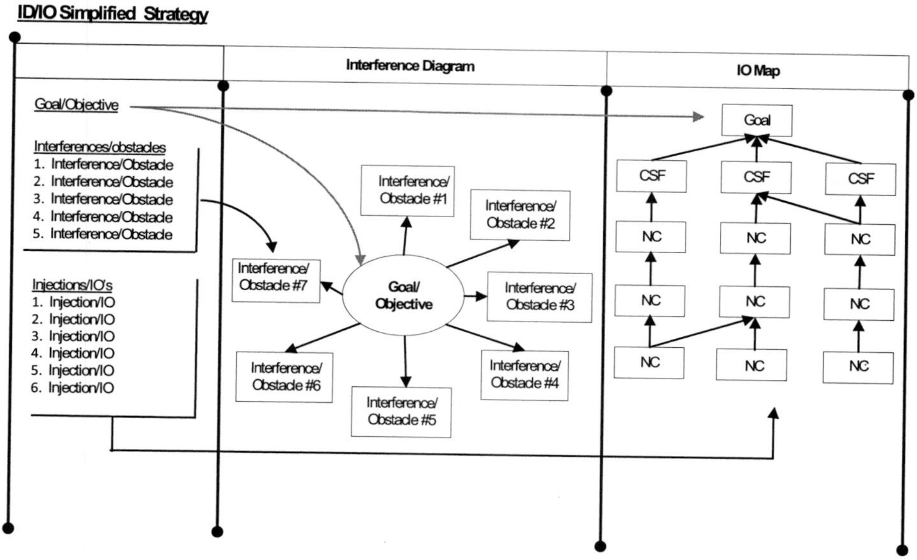

ID/IO Simplified Strategy

Interference Diagram
IO Map
Goal/Objective
Interferences/obstacles
1. Interference/Obstacle
2. Interference/Obstacle
3. Interference/Obstacle
4. Interference/Obstacle
5. Interference/Obstacle
Injections/IO's
1. Injection/IO
2. Injection/IO
3. Injection/IO
4. Injection/IO
5. Injection/IO
6. Injection/IO
Goal/ Objective
Interference/ Obstacle #1
Interference/ Obstacle #2
Interference/ Obstacle #3
Interference/ Obstacle #4
Interference/ Obstacle #5
Interference/ Obstacle #6
Interference/ Obstacle #7
Goal
CSF
CSF
CSF
NC
NC
NC
NC
NC
NC
NC
NC
NC

Figure 8: The combined ID/IO Simplified Strategy

With the ID/IO Simplified Strategy complete you now have the outline necessary to prepare an effective and accurate Implementation Plan. The intent of the IO map is not to provide implementation detail at a low level, but rather to provide milestones or markers to make sure you are walking the right path. For each IO listed you can provide the required detail about how it will be completed.

Conclusions

In a world that requires "Better, faster, cheaper", the Simplified Strategy approach of the Interference Diagram (ID) and Intermediate Objective (IO) Map (ID/IO) can provide exceptional results in a shorter period of time. By combining the power of these thinking tools into the ID/IO, the user will benefit from an effective and complete analysis that is completed in significantly reduced time. These tools, used in either a standalone environment or a combined approach, will provide the thinking necessary to develop good results. The speed with which these tools can be used is an enormous benefit over the original System Thinking tools to allow the ability to answer the three questions:

> What do I change?
> What do I change to?
> How do I cause the change to happen?

The structure and concept behind these tools makes them easily adaptable and well understood and accepted in a group situation to allow for faster collection of data and analysis of issues.

Appendix 5
Theory of Constraints Replenishment Model and Supply Chain

The Supply Chain

Most, if not all, businesses are linked one way or another to some kind of supply chain. They needs parts or raw materials from somebody else in order to do what they do and pass it on to the next system in line until it finally arrives at the end consumer. Depending on what you make and how fast you make it, the supply chain can be your best friend or worst enemy. If it works well, it's your best friend. If it doesn't work well, it's your worst enemy.

The fundamental problem with most supply-chain systems is that they have remained stagnant in their thinking through time, while business reality has flexed in a cycle of constant change—sometimes at an exponential rate. There are many new supply-chain software applications, each proposing that it will solve the problems associated with the supply chain. These new software applications have come about mostly because of advances in computer technology, but few have solved the real issues of the supply chain. It is true that these systems can provide an enormous amount of information very fast, but sometimes system speed is less important than having access to the correct information. What difference does it make how fast you get the information if it's the wrong information?

The new business reality has caused a need for change in supply-chain systems, but most systems have not changed. Businesses now are required to build products more cheaply, have higher quality and deliver those products faster. These are the new rules of competition. You either play by the rules or get out of the way. The rules in business have changed, and yet many businesses insist on doing business the same "old" way. How come? Usually, the most common answer given is—"Because that's the way we've always done it." The old system and the old rules may have worked for some period of time, but times are changing. If the supply- chain system has not changed to align with the new rules, then the gap between supply-chain output and system needs will grow even larger. If the supply-chain system is not changed to meet future needs, then there is very little hope of getting different results.

Many supply-chain systems were designed to solve a problem, and the problem they were trying to solve was the needed availability of parts, raw materials or inventory— the right part/material, in the right location, at the right time. These systems were designed to hold inventory in check—that is, don't buy too much, but also don't allow stock-out situations to occur. Then and now, managing the supply chain is a tough job. There are many variables that can require constant attention. You don't want to run out of parts, and yet, sometimes, you still run out of parts. You don't want excess inventory, and yet sometimes, you have too much inventory. This constant negative cycle of sometimes too much and sometimes too little has persisted through time. The supply problems encountered years ago are still the problems being encountered today.

The Minimum/Maximum Supply Chain

For many companies the supply chain/inventory system of choice is one often referred to as the minimum/maximum (MIN/MAX) system. Parts (or inventory) are evaluated based on need and usage, and some type of maximum and minimum levels are established for each item. The traditional rules and measures for these systems are usually quite simple:

- Rule 1: Determine the maximum and minimum levels for each item.
- Rule 2: Don't exceed the maximum level.
- Rule 3: Don't reorder until you go below the minimum level.

The foundational assumptions behind these rules and measures are primarily based in Cost Accounting (CA) and commonly referred to as cost-world thinking. In order to save money and minimize your expenditures for supply parts/inventory, you must reduce, or at least hold in check, the amount of money you spend for these items. In order to reduce the amount of money you spend on these items, you must *never* buy more than the maximum amount. Also, in order to reduce the money spent on these items, you must not spend money until absolutely necessary, and order parts only when they reach the minimum level.

These assumptions seem valid, and if implemented correctly and monitored should provide a supply system that controls dollars and maintains inventory within the minimum and maximum levels. However, most systems of this type, even in the perfect world, don't seem to generate the desired results that are required. For some reason, there always seem to be situations of excess inventory for some items and of stock-out situations for others. There always seem to be constant gyrations (variation) between too much inventory and too little inventory. The whole operational concept behind the minimum/maximum systems was supposed to prevent these kinds of occurrences from happening, and yet they still do. How come?

Consequences of Cost Accounting Metrics

Perhaps the best way to make this point is with a couple of examples. The first example deals with a company that measured and rewarded their procurement staff based on the amount of money they *saved* with procurement purchases. For the procurement staff their primary scheme to accomplish this objective was to buy in bulk. For the most part, this was usually quite easy to accomplish. Their suppliers preferred, and sometimes demanded, that their customers buy in bulk to receive the benefit of *quantity discounts*. The more you bought, the less it cost per unit. The assumption being that the purchase price per part (unit) could be driven to the lowest possible level by buying in bulk and the company would save the maximum amount of money on their purchase. It seemed like a great idea and certainly a way to meet the objective of *saving money*. Sometimes these supply items were procured in amounts well in excess of the maximum, but the company got them at a great price!

By employing this cost-saving strategy, the company had a warehouse full of low-cost inventory that had used a large portion of dollars. The problem was this—they didn't have the right mix of inventory to build even a single product. They had too many of some items, even though they were *all* purchased at the lowest price, and not enough of other items. The bigger problem was they ran out of money to purchase any more parts—especially the parts they desperately needed! Do you suppose they wished they had at least some of the money back so they could buy the right parts, in the right quantity, at the right time so they could produce products?

Another cost saving example is the tale of a company who was a contractor to the government. In their contract with the Government the Government had offered a very lucrative clause to save money. This company was given a budgeted amount to buy parts on a yearly basis. Based on this budgeted amount, the Government offered to split fifty-fifty any amount the company could underrun their parts budget. The company took the total budgeted dollars and divided it by twelve to establish the monthly parts budget. They also held back a percentage of the budgeted amount each month so they could claim cost savings and split the difference. Any parts purchase that would have exceeded the targeted monthly budget was postponed until the next month, even if it was urgently needed. The ability of this company to make money slowed dramatically. They were literally jumping over dollars to pick up pennies. There were many jobs waiting for parts that couldn't finish until they had the parts to finish, but they had to wait, sometimes for several days or weeks, to get the parts, because of the cost-saving mentality.

In both of these examples it's an issue of bad cost metrics driving the bad behavior. In both of these cases, cost savings were employed as the primary strategy. In the first example, the company ultimately went bankrupt and went out of business. They couldn't pay back the loans on the money they had borrowed to buy all of the low cost parts because they couldn't make any products. In the second example the company avoided bankruptcy because they provided a needed service for the Government; they were ultimately spared by seeing the error of their ways, and they decided to spend the budgeted dollars to buy the needed parts.

The System Analysis

If the system, as a whole, isn't producing the desired results, then what segment of the system needs to be changed to produce the desired results? Perhaps the minimum and maximum levels are the wrong rules to engage, and saving money is the wrong financial measure to consider. In order to solve today's problems we must think at an order of magnitude higher than we were thinking when we developed yesterday's solutions. In other words, yesterday's solutions are causing most of today's problems.

One of the most important aspects of any manufacturing, production or assembly operation system is to have and maintain the ability to supply raw materials or parts at a very predictable level. If the parts availability goes to zero, then production activities stop. The continual availability of parts, accurately monitored, implies a supply-chain system that contains all of the necessary and robust features to support the customer-demand requirements.

The Most Common Supply-chain system

The minimum/maximum supply-chain system was developed years ago, and at the time it brought forward some favorable improvements. Then and now, the functional theory behind the supply-chain minimum/maximum concept is that supplies and materials should be distributed and stored at the lowest possible level of the user chain. In essence this is a *push system*—one that pushes parts through the system to the lowest possible level. It seems to make some sense. Parts must be available at the lowest level in order to be used. In this type of system the parts are consumed until the minimum quantity is exceeded, and then an order is placed for more parts. The parts order goes up the chain from the point-of-use (POU) location back to some kind of central supply center, or orders are placed directly back to the vendor depending on the situation. When the orders are received at the central supply center, they are pushed back down the chain to the lowest POU locations. Figure 1 defines a simplified version of this parts-flow activity. This flow might not be applicable to all situations, but to most it will make sense. Some companies and smaller businesses will have fewer steps, in that they order directly from a vendor and receive parts back into their business without the need for large, more complex, distribution systems. However, the thinking behind the minimum/maximum system will still apply, even to those smaller businesses. Larger companies or those with numerous geographical locations will most likely have developed some type of a central supply and/or distribution locations that feed the next level of the supply distribution system. Regional warehouse versus local distribution points. The distribution points in turn feed the companies or business segments that use the raw material and parts at the final POU to build products. Some distribution systems may even be more complex than what is displayed here. But even with increased complexity, the results they are trying to achieve remain the same— get the parts to where they need to be when they need to be there.

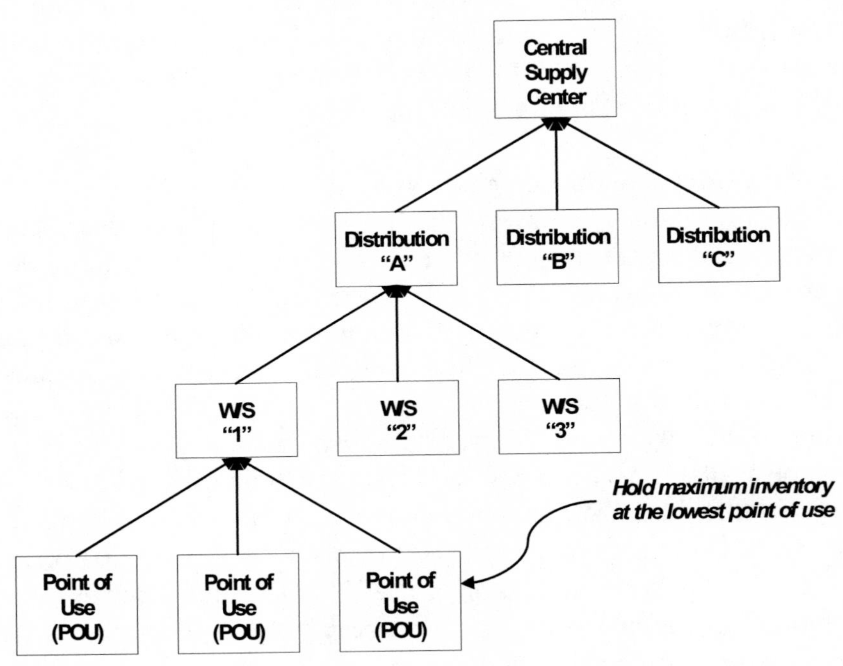

Figure 1. Parts and Inventory Flow from Central Distribution Location to POU Locations.

The model of a central supply system versus a decentralized system has volleyed back and forth for many years. Some say the supply system should be centralized at the user location to make supply activities easier and more responsive. Others argue that the supply activities should be decentralized to save money and reduce operating expense. Even with these continuing arguments, it seems that the current vogue is for the decentralized model of supply systems.

For all of its intent to save money and reduce operating expenses, the decentralized system can and does cause enormous hardships on the very systems it is designed to support. With all of the intended good this type of system is supposed to provide, there are some top-level rules that drive the system into chaos. Let's look at some of these rules and understand the negative aspects that derive from them. Table 1 provides a summary listing of the top-level rules for the maximum/minimum supply system.

Table 1

Top-level Rules for Minimum/Maximum Supply System
1. The system reorder amount is the maximum amount no matter how many parts are currently in the bin box.
2. Most supply systems only allow for one order at a time to be present.
3. Orders for parts are triggered only after the minimum amount has been exceeded.
4. Total part inventory is held at the lowest possible level of the distribution chain—the point-of-use (POU) location.
5. Parts are inventoried once or twice a month and orders placed, as required.

Even though the minimum/maximum system appears to control the supply needs and cover the inventory demands, there are some significant negatives effects caused by using this system.

First and foremost, there is the problem of being reactive to an inventory or parts situation, rather than proactive. When minimum stock levels are used as the trigger to reorder parts, some supply-chain systems—as they are currently organized and used—will have a difficult time keeping up with the demands being placed upon them. And there is an increased probability that stock-outs will occur, maybe for long periods of time.

Stock-outs occur most often when the lead time to replenish the part exceeds the minimum stock available. In others words, availability of the part between the minimum amount and zero is totally depleted before the part can be replenished from the vendor. Figure 3 displays a graphical representation of this stock-out effect. The curved line shows the item usage through time and the possibility of a stock-out situation.

Variation also exists with this scenario, and stock-outs can either happen in a shorter or longer time frame—depending on the actual part usage. These stock-out situations are a recurring problem in systems that use minimum stock levels as the trigger to reorder parts.

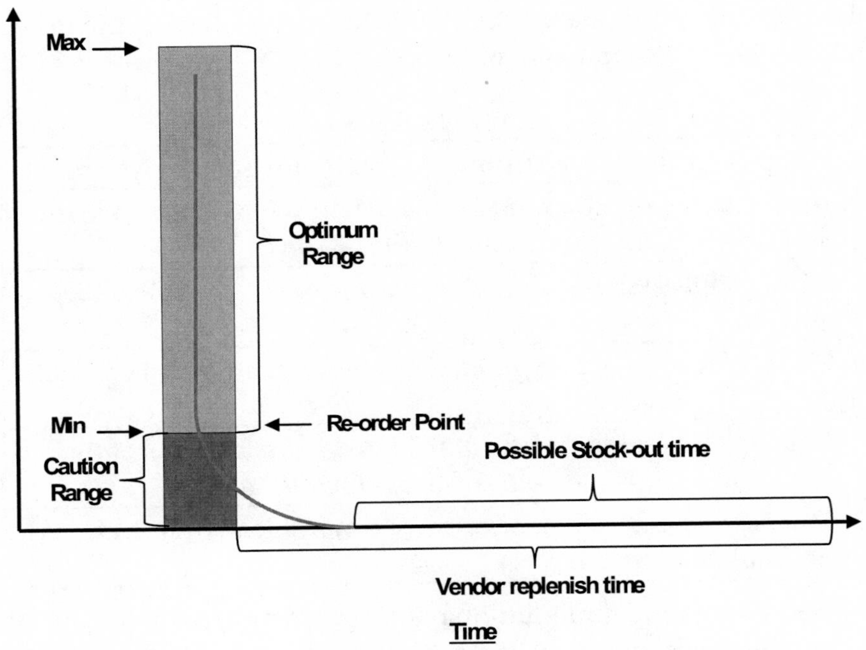

Figure 3: Minimum/Maximum Parts Model

Of course, when parts are reordered, they are ordered at a level equal to the maximum amount, and the problem appears to quickly correct itself. However, there can be a significantly large segment of time between stock-out and correction, and if the part is urgently needed, its nonavailability can cause havoc in the assembly sequence. Some might argue that the solution to the problem is to simply increase the minimum amount to trigger a reorder sooner in the process and avoid the stock-out situation. It is possible this solution could provide some short-term relief, but in the long run it causes inventory levels to go up and stay up. It is also possible that if you raise the minimum level, then the maximum level must be raised also. Many companies use a ratio variable to calculate the spread between mini-companies use a ratio variable to calculate the spread between minimum and maximum. If that's the case, then total inventory levels will go up, which costs more money to maintain. This is totally counter to the cost accounting rules.

The minimum/maximum supply chain is based totally on being in a reactive mode—waiting for the part to reach minimum stock level before a reorder request is activated. In many companies the most used parts are managed using the minimum/maximum concepts and can frequently be out of stock. This MIN/MAX supply system also creates the disadvantage of having maybe several thousand dollars or hundreds of thousands of dollars tied up in inventory that may or may not get used before it becomes obsolete, modified or dated because of expiration. If additional money is spent buying parts that might not be needed, at least in the quantity defined by the maximum limit, then you have effectively diverted money that could have been used to buy needed parts.

As an example for purposes of discussion, suppose we pick a random part with a minimum/maximum level already established, and we track this part for a twenty-six week period using the current system rules and follow the flow and cyclical events that take place. What happens at the end of the twenty-six weeks? For this example, we will assume the following:

- The maximum level is ninety items.
- The minimum reorder point is twenty items.
- The lead time to replenish this part from the vendor averages four weeks. The average is based on the fact that there are times when this part can deliver faster (three weeks) and other times it delivers slower (five weeks).
- Usage of these parts varies by week, but on average is equal to about ten items per week.

Table 2 shows the reorder trigger happening when current inventory drops below the minimum amount of twenty items. The first reorder would trigger between weeks six and seven, and again between weeks seventeen and eighteen, and again between weeks twenty-five and twenty-six. During this twenty-six week period there would be a total of about eight weeks of stock-out time. Remember: There is an average of four weeks of vendor lead time to replenish this part. This repeating cycle of maximum inventory and stock-outs becomes the norm, and the scenario is repeated time and time again.

Table 2. Simulated Data for Minimum/Maximum Supply System.

Week	Current Inventory	Actual Items Used	End of Week Inventory	Items Added (Replenish)
1	90	10	80	
2	80	15	65	
3	65	15	50	
4	50	15	35	
5	35	5	30	
6	30	15	15	
7	15	15	0	
8	0	0	0	
9	0	0	0	
10	0	0	0	90
11	90	15	75	
12	75	15	60	
13	60	8	52	
14	52	12	40	
15	40	10	30	
16	30	10	20	
17	20	15	5	
18	5	5	0	
19	0	0	0	
20	0	0	0	
21	90	15	75	90
22	75	18	57	
23	57	15	42	
24	42	12	30	
25	30	15	15	
26	15	15	0	

Figure 4 uses the data from Table 2 to graphically display the results of the minimum/maximum system, and it shows the negative consequences that can occur in this system. If the vendor lead time is not considered as an important reorder variable, then stock-outs will continue to occur. Stock-outs can become a very predictable negative effect in this system.

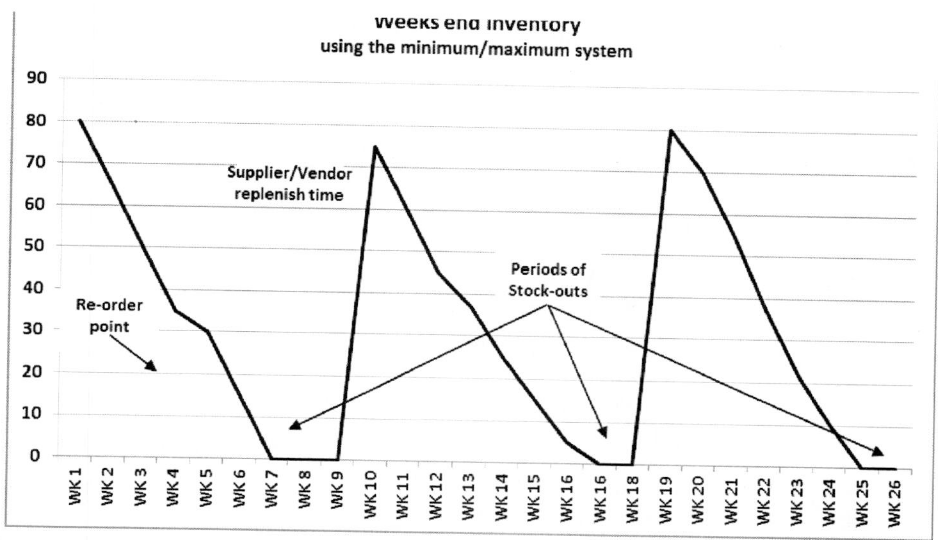

Figure 4: Consequences of Min/Max Supply System

The graph shows the negative consequences of the supply system and demonstrates why supply-chain systems using the maximum/minimum concepts will periodically create excessive inventory and stock-out situations. The primary reason this happens is because part lead times are not properly taken into account.

In most cases, the most prominent measures for the minimum/maximum systems are focused in cost world (dollars) thinking, rather than system needs. If the lead times from the vendors are not considered, then there remains a high probability that stock-outs will continue. The stock-out situation exacerbates itself even further when at the POU a user has experienced a stock-out situation in the past. In that situation the users will often try to protect themselves against stock-outs by taking more than is needed,.

It is also possible that some companies will preorder inventory based on some type of forecast for the coming year. This strategy exacerbates the problem even more. At best, it is extremely difficult to forecast what a consumer may or may not buy. This problem is encountered at the manufacturing level and the retail level. Manufacturers will produce excess finished good inventory that must be stored at a great cost or sold to retailers at a discounted price. Because of the flaws in their forecast methods, some stores are left with large amounts of inventory when new models or products are released. This becomes most visible when stores offer "year-end clearance sales" or "inventory liquidation" events. They guessed wrong with the forecast and have much more inventory than they can sell. In many cases because stores couldn't get enough of the hot-selling product, they missed out on sales. Now they must sell any remaining inventory, sometimes at bargain prices, to generate enough cash to go buy more inventories for the coming year. This cycle of too much and too little repeats itself year after year.

The Robust Supply System

One of the primary operating functions of the supply-chain system is to build and hold inventory at the lowest possible distribution level. This assumption is both correct and incorrect. The correct inventory should be held at the POU location, but not based on minimum/maximum amounts. Instead, the necessary inventory should be based on the vendor lead times to replenish and maintain sufficient inventory to buffer the variations that exist in lead time. The TOC Distribution and Replenishment Model is a robust parts replenishment system that allows the user to be proactive in managing the supply-chain system. It's also a system based on usage, either daily or weekly, but not the minimum amount. Some parts/inventory will require much more vigilance in day-to-day management.

Table 3 defines the suggested criteria required to implement a TOC Distribution and Replenishment Model in a supply-chain system.

Table 3: Criteria for the TOC Distribution and Replenishment Model

1. The system reorder amount needs to be based on daily or weekly usage and part lead time to replenish.

2. The system needs to allow for multiple replenish orders, if required.
3. Orders are triggered based on buffer requirements, with possible daily actions, as required.
4. All parts/inventory must be available when needed.
5. Parts inventory is held at a higher level, preferably at central supply locations or comes directly from the supplier /vendor.
6. Part buffer determined by usage rate and replenish supplier/ven dor lead time. Baseline buffer should be equal to 1.5. If lead-time is 1 week, buffer is set at 1.5 weeks. Adjust as required, based on historical data.

The TOC Distribution and Replenishment Model argues that the majority of the inventory should be held at a higher level in the distribution system (supply chain) and not at the lowest level. It is still important to keep what is needed at the lowest levels, but don't try to hold the total inventory at that location. The TOC model is based on the characteristics of a "V" plant distribution model. The "V" plant model assumes that distribution is fractal from a single location—in this case either a central supply location or a supplier/vendor location (the base of the "V")—and (see Figure 1) distribution is made to different locations (the arms of the "V"). The "V" plant concept is not unlike any supply-chain distribution methodology. However, using a "V" plant method has some negative consequences, especially when working under the minimum/maximum rules (as shown in Figure 2.) If one is not careful to understand these consequences, the system can suffer dramatically. One of the major negative consequences of "V" distribution is distributing items too early and sending them down the wrong path to the wrong location. In other words, inventory is released too early and possibly to the wrong destination. This is especially likely to when the same type of inventory or part is used in several locations.

Has it ever happened that at one location you have a stock-out situation, and one of the rapid response criteria for finding the part is to check another production line within a company or call back to the distribution center? If this is the case, then parts/inventory distribution has taken place too early in the system. Sometimes, it's not that the system does not have the right parts/inventory; it's just that they are in the wrong location. Distribution from a higher level in the chain has been completed too quickly.

The TOC Distribution and Replenishment Model also argues that the use of minimum/maximum amounts should be abolished. Instead the inventory should be monitored based on daily or weekly usage, with replenishment occurring at a minimum weekly and possibly daily for highly used items. The end result of these actions will be sufficient inventory in the right location at the right time—with zero or minimal stock-outs—to support production activity. Instead of using the minimum amount to trigger the reorder process, it should be triggered by daily usage and vendor lead time to replenish.

As an example, suppose we apply the TOC Distribution and Replenishment Model rules to exactly the same criteria discussed earlier. We will use the same part simulation, and the same period of time, with the same usage numbers. The difference will be in this simulation we will change the rules to fit the TOC Distribution and Replenishment Model—based on usage amount and vendor lead time rather than minimum and maximum amount.

Table 4
TOC Distribution and Replenishment Model

Current Inventory	Actual Items Used	Weeks end inventory	Items added (Replenish)	
WK 1	90	10	80	
WK 2	80	15	65	
WK 3	65	15	50	
WK 4	50	15	35	10
WK 5	45	5	40	15
WK 6	55	15	40	15

WK 7	55	15	40	15
WK 8	55	10	45	5
WK 9	50	10	40	15
WK 10	55	15	40	15
WK 11	55	15	40	10
WK 12	50	15	35	10
WK 13	45	8	37	15
WK 14	52	12	40	15
WK 15	55	10	45	15
WK 16	60	10	50	8
WK 16	58	5	53	12
WK 18	65	10	55	10
WK 19	65	10	55	10
WK 20	65	10	55	5
WK 21	60	15	45	10
WK 22	55	18	37	10
WK 23	47	15	32	10
WK 24	42	12	30	15
WK 25	45	10	35	18
WK 26	53	15	38	15

Table 4 presents the simulated data for a random reorder scenario using the TOC Distribution and Replenishment Model. In this example we will assume the following:

- Maximum level is ninety items. (This is the start point for the current inventory.)
- There is no minimum reorder point; instead reorder is based on usage and vendor lead time.
- Lead time to replenish is still four weeks.
- Average usage of the part is about ten per week.

The Table 4 data also assumes that no parts inventory is held at the next higher level and that the parts replenishment has to come from the vendor and consumes the allotted vendor lead time. However, if the parts/inventory were held at a higher level in the distribution chain (central supply or a distribution point), and replenish happened daily and/or weekly, then the total inventory required could go even lower than the data suggests. This could happen because distribution is completed weekly rather than waiting the full four weeks for delivery. The part usage rates are exactly the same as the previous run and the starting inventory is equal to ninety parts. This also assumes we have a weekly parts/inventory replenish after the initial four weeks of lead time has expired. In other words, every week we have delivered what was ordered four weeks ago. In the TOC scenario the reorder point is at the end of each week based on usage. The total number of parts used is the same number of parts that should be reordered.

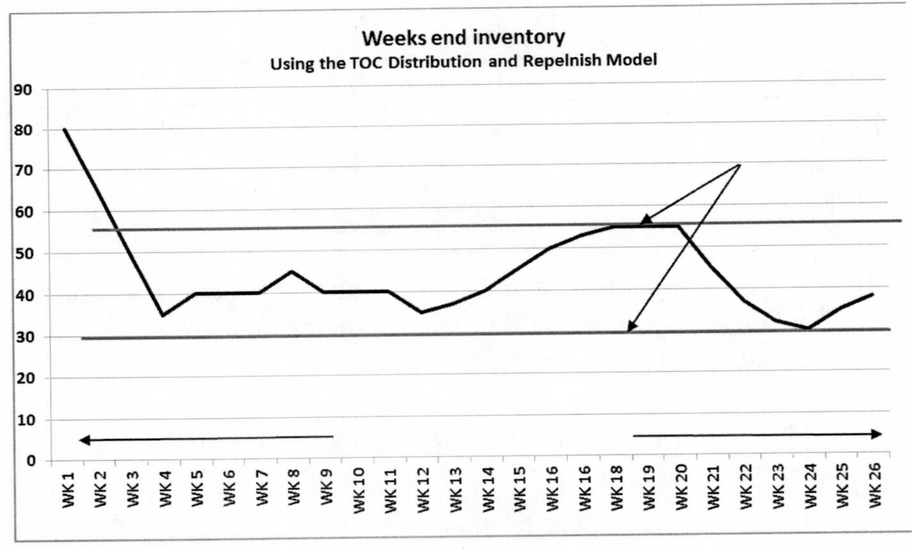

Figure 5: Overall Effect of TOC Method

Figure 5 shows the effects of using the TOC Distribution and Replenishment Model. What is most notable is that total inventory required through time has decreased from ninety items to approximately forty-two items. In essence, the required inventory has been cut in half. Also notable is the fact that there are no stock-out situations present.

When the TOC Distribution and Replenishment Model is used to manage the supply chain there is always sufficient parts inventory to continue production work. The total inventory is also much more stable, through time, without the large gaps and gyrations from zero inventories available to maximum inventory as noted on the first run (Figure 4) using the minimum/maximum system.

Perhaps the best way to explain the TOC Distribution and Replenishment Model is with an easy example. Consider a soda vending machine. When the supplier (the soda vendor) opens the door on a vending machine, it is very easy to calculate the distribution of products sold, or the point-of-use consumption. The soda person knows immediately which inventory has to be replaced and to what level to replace it. The soda person is holding the inventory at the next highest level, which in on the soda truck, so it's easy to make the required distribution when needed. He doesn't leave six cases of soda when only twenty cans are needed. If he were to do that, when he got to the next vending machine he might have run out of the necessary soda because he made distribution too early at the last stop. After completing the required daily distribution to the vending machines, the soda person returns to the warehouse or distribution point to replenish the supply on the soda truck and get ready for the next day's distribution. When the warehouse makes distribution to the soda truck, they move up one level in the chain and replenish from their supplier. This type of system does require discipline to gain the most benefits. It assumes that regular and needed checks are taking place at the inventory locations to determine the replenishment needs. If these points are not checked on a regular basis, it is possible for the system to experience stock-out situations.

Conclusions

The distinct contrast in results between simulated data runs using the minimum/maximum supply system and the TOC Distribution and Replenishment Model are undeniable. The true benefits of a TOC-based parts replenishment system are many, but the most significant impact is realized in these two areas.

The first benefit is the reduction of total inventory required to manage and maintain the total supply-chain system. This inventory reduction could lead to a significant dollar savings in total inventory required, perhaps thousands of dollars.

The second benefit is the elimination of stock-out situations. Without a doubt, not having parts available is an expensive situation because it slows throughput through the production system. Production lines sit idle, waiting for parts to become available. Or worse yet, they start making products that aren't needed only because parts are available, and everyone needs to be kept busy. Stock-out situations increase frustration, not only in not being able to complete the work, but also in the time spent waiting for parts to become available. When this happens, orders will be delivered late, and customers will be frustrated.

Looking for parts and experiencing part shortages are a continuing problem in most supply-chain systems. These problems are not caused by the production people, but by the negative effects of the supply-chain system and the way it is used. If the current supply system is maintained, then the output (results) from that system cannot be expected to change much, if at all. However, if new levels of output are required from the system now and in the future, then new thinking must be applied to solve the parts supply-system issues. The concepts and methodologies of the TOC Distribution and Replenishment Model can positively impact the ability to produce products on time and in the correct quantity.

Appendix 6
Drum-Buffer-Rope (DBR)

In his book *The Goal*, Eliyahu Goldratt effectively uses a story written in a novel format to walk the reader through the steps necessary to move a manufacturing organization from the traditional manufacturing concepts to a facility managed using the concepts of Drum-Buffer-Rope (DBR). This nontraditional approach through logical thinking is masterminded by a character named Jonah. Jonah is able to help Alex Rogo understand the invalid thinking and assumptions being used to manage his plant and the negative consequences associated with that type of thinking. By helping Alex focus his thinking on how the plant is being managed, Jonah helps Alex logically discover a new and better way. And Drum-Buffer-Rope (DBR) is the centerpiece of this process.

The thinking behind DBR is really quite simple, but mostly just logical. Thinking logically is nothing new, but it is not the way most people think. The fundamental view of DBR is to focus on the system as a whole rather than only a single segment of the system—at least until you have clearly identified the constraint. This idea of looking at the *global system* is a major shift in the way systems have previously been viewed and managed. Prior to global-systems thinking, the pervasive point of view was (and still is) that any systems improvement, at any location, would improve the overall system. The idea being that the sum total of several isolated improvements would somehow equal an improved to the overall system. But such is not the case. The effects of employing the "shotgun" approach to systems management can cause a series of devastating systemic effects.

A system can be defined as a sequence of steps or processes that are linked together to produce *something* as an end result. With that definition in mind, it's easy to understand how virtually everything can be linked to some kind of a system.

Engineering organizations have systems, banks have systems and grocery stores have systems. Almost anything you can think of is the product of a system. By design, a system can be as small and unique as two processes linked together, where the output of one process becomes the input for the next process. Or systems can be very complex, with many processes linked together, maybe even hundreds or more. Just because a system is complex does not mean it can't be improved—it just means it's complex, and that's OK. Even in a system as simple as two linked processes, one of those two processes will constrain the other. It's just the nature of how things work. If a systems constraint did not exist, then the system should, at least theoretically, be able to produce at infinite capacity. But infinite capacity is not a level that is ever achieved from a system. *All* systems are restricted, at some point in time, by some type of output limitation. This limitation is usually determined by the presence of some kind of system-capacity limit. No matter how good the system is, there is still only so much it can do. Sooner or later whatever kind of system is being analyzed, it is will reach its maximum system capacity and be unable to produce more. If higher system outputs are required beyond the current capacity, then the system must be changed.

Variation

For years, if not decades, people and organizations have dedicated considerable time and effort to remove variation from systems. The utopian goal is to remove as much variation as possible from the system. No matter how much planning is employed, no matter how much effort is extended, variation will still exist! If you were asked; how long it takes you to get to work every day, your response might be something like, "about thirty minutes." The instant you answer with the word *about*, you have introduced variation into the system. You know that historically speaking, some days you get to work in twenty-five minutes and yet others days it can take thirty-five or forty minutes. In your "get to work" system, things can happen that will either speed up the process or slow it down.

Variation exists in everything, especially within a system. You understand that some processes will produce at a faster or slower rate than others, and this is the premise behind variation. Because of variation, the output from a system will not be linear, but rather it will operate within a range that changes. This variable range is known as *statistical fluctuation*, and it exists in every system. It's important to understand that you cannot make variation go away. The theory and practice of Six Sigma has pioneered the race to variation reduction. But even with the most valiant efforts of time and money, not all variation can be removed. You can reduce the amount and severity of variation, but it will still exist. Once you understand that variation is a constant variable in any system, it's easier to understand that at some point you will reach the minimum variation that is controllable in the system, and any efforts to reduce variation beyond that point are fruitless. Perhaps, instead of spending so much time and effort on techniques to remove variation, the focus should really be on techniques to manage variation.

Managing Variation with DBR

When viewing a system through the eyes of DBR, it becomes quickly apparent that improving every step in the process is not required, nor will the sum total of all of those discrete system improvements equal an improved overall system. When conducting a full systems analysis, with the intent of implementing DBR, an important consideration to know and understand is the location of the *system constraint*, or slowest operation. In Goldratt's Five Focusing Steps, this is Step 1—Find the constraint. Once you know where the slowest operation resides, you now have the information necessary to know where to focus your attention within the system. Why is it important to understand where the slowest operation is? Because this is the location that controls and determines the output for your entire system. In essence, the entire system will produce no faster than the slowest operation can produce. (The system can produce less, but it won't produce more.)

With the constraining operation identified, you have collectively quarantined the "drum" beat for your system. Knowing the drumbeat is of strategic importance to implement and gain any system improvements. The drum provides you with the necessary information of knowing where to focus your improvement efforts. Historically, many organizations can and do conduct many improvement projects on a yearly basis. The mantra seems to be that every organization and every process should strive for improvement. The thought is that each organization is improving at some level of frequency to make the whole system better. However, the sum of many efforts does not always equal what is good for the whole. The problem with this type of thinking is it is a totally unfocused *shotgun* approach to solve the problem. In effect, it presents an improvement policy that states: if I select a wide enough range, then I should hit the target, or at least come close to the target. When you take the shotgun approach you might hit everything a little bit, but miss the full impact required to make real change and improvements. If your shotgun approach includes trying to improve nonconstraints, and most do, then the system as a whole gains nothing! The improvement of nonconstraints in isolation of the entire system, without a comprehensive analysis, is just a way of dealing with symptoms and not the real issue (constraint). Without the ability and the accurate information necessary to focus on the real issues, the disease goes merrily on. Improvement of nonconstraints is a noble gesture, but one that yields little, if any, real improvements. Every process within a system does not need to be improved at the same time! Some system processes are more important than others. Without knowing where your constraint resides, your efforts to improve will be unfocused and consequently worthless, serving only to consume large amounts of money, resources, and time.

Once the systems constraint is identified, it must be subjected to the red carpet treatment. Nothing in your system is more important than the constraint— nothing! Once you have this information, you must decide how to best manage the constraint. If the output from your entire system depends solely on the output of the constraint, then it certainly merits special considerations. One of those considerations is to *exploit* the constraint, which is Step 2 of the Five Focusing Steps. Exploitation means that you evaluate the process to get the most out the constraint activity.

Rarely is a constraint being utilized at, or near, the maximum that it can do. The exploitation effort means looking for things that the constraints can stop doing. This could be an excellent opportunity to employ the Interference Diagram (ID) to define the interferences that stop you from getting more from your constraint. You may want to implement Lean concepts to reduce waste or Six Sigma to better control variation and quality. It might also mean taking actions as simple as keeping the machine, or process, busy during break time and lunch time, or perhaps implementing a second shift or a third shift, or even off-loading work to nonconstrained processes or resources. Exploitation *does not* mean buying a new machine or adding more resources, at least not yet. It simply means finding ways to get more out of the current process than you are currently getting. There is a very high probability that during the exploitation exercise, the constraint capacity could be improved above and beyond the capacity of the next constraint in the system. If such is the case, then go back to Step 1 and redefine the constraint. In a normal improvement effort, this repeating cycle between Steps 1 and 2 might be completed many times before the system is stabilized. When the system becomes stable, then go to Step 3 in the Five Focusing Steps and ratify the subordination rule to synchronize the product flow. The end result is to stabilize and synchronize the system, and then focus on the constraint. Let the nonconstraints work as required to produce sufficient quantities to keep the constraint busy.

The second consideration is to make sure the constraints are busy all the time. Never let the constraint run out of work to do. If the constraint stops or slows down, then the entire system will stop or slow down. The best way to accomplish this objective is to make sure there is always work in the queue in front of the constraint. In other words, create a *buffer* of work in front of the constraint. The entire system output has total dependency on the constraint output, and constraint output is directly proportional to system output. Think in terms of the right amount of work, in the right location and at the right time. The system constraint not only determines the amount of throughput you can achieve, but it also determines the correct amount of work-in-process (WIP) inventory that should be maintained in the system. The correct inventory level will be reached almost by default when system subordination is actively pursued and implemented.

The *rope* is actually a mechanism that controls two different functions. First, it is the mechanism that determines how much and when to release inventory into the system. The most common practice is to tie an artificial "rope" from the constraint operation back to the front of the line. When the constraint produces and completes one unit of work and passes it to the next operation, then the rope is pulled to signal the front end of the line to release one more unit of work into the system. Rope signaling systems can vary. The rope signal is equal to the output of the constraint operation, no more and no less. This release mechanism, tied to the drumbeat of the constraint, will allow for a synchronized work flow and a smooth transition of work through the system.

The second function of the rope is to initiate and maintain subordination for all other processes in the line. By default, following the cadence of the rope release signal causes subordination to the remaining nonconstraint processes to be executed. The nonconstraints processes can only work on what has been released to work on. By releasing work only to the drumbeat, all other operations are held in check to the rule of subordination. Even if the nonconstraints can do more work, they are restricted by subordination and only allowed to work on parts or products required by the constraint.

The systems inventory not only includes the work located at the *buffer*, but also the cumulative total of inventory (work) at other process locations as well. It is possible, and recommended, that you establish an additional buffer at the shipping location. The shipping buffer can be used to help control any system variation that occurs after the constraint. Bad things can and do happen after processing at the constraint. The constraint buffer provides the necessary protection in front of the constraint, and the shipping buffer provides protection after the constraint. The shipping buffer is just a mechanism to absorb and manage the inevitable variation that will occur. Buffer sizing at these two locations is a variable, but you do need to start with something. Consider, as a starting point for the buffer at the drum (the constraint) location to be about one and a half for whatever units of time you are measuring. For example, if your constraints can produce ten units in one day, then the buffer should be set at fifteen units (or 10 x 1.5 = 15). You may decide in time that the buffer is too large or too small, so you can adjust it either up or down depending on the need. The shipping buffer could be three or four days or less depending on the speed of product through the ystem. It doesn't need to be necessarily large in quantity or long in time. It just needs to be sufficient to protect against variation after the constraint. It's also important to consider your shipping buffer time in your scheduling calculation to determine the correct release date into the system for on-time delivery. If you watch your buffer locations carefully, you can make good decisions to increase or decrease them based on some supportive historical data. If the buffer is constantly on the high end, then reduce it. If it is constantly on the low end, then increase it. Apply the rule of common sense to determine the correct buffer.

When you know and understand the constraint location, and you buffer the work activity, and you send the correct release signal to the front of the line to release more work, then you have in essence implemented a system of synchronized flow. Figure 1 defines the DBR steps and integration.

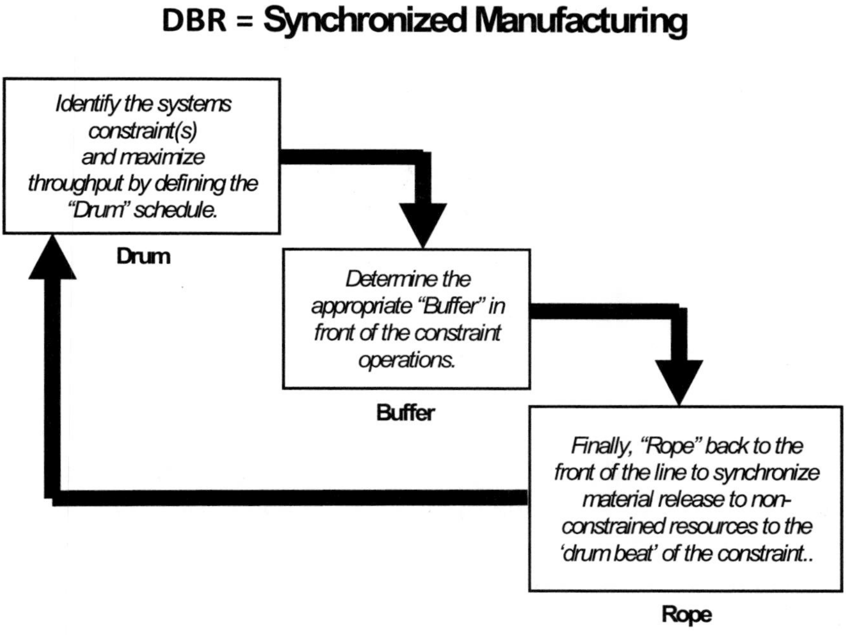

DBR = Synchronized Manufacturing

Identify the systems constraint(s) and maximize throughput by defining the "Drum" schedule.

Drum

Determine the appropriate "Buffer" in front of the constraint operations.

Buffer

Finally, "Rope" back to the front of the line to synchronize material release to non-constrained resources to the 'drum beat' of the constraint..

Rope

Figure 1. DBR Steps and Flow.

But wait! With a synchronized flow, and actively implementing system subordination, there is a very high probability that the performance metric of *efficiency* will deteriorate quickly, at least for some period of time. It will manifest an unacceptable efficiency performance metric that is considered undesirable by most companies. The new mantra will be to "stop the synchronization nonsense and improve the efficiency." Be careful what you consider to be nonsense. In this case, the real nonsense is the efficiency metric. When the synchronized flow is implemented, then excess capacity at non-constraints will be quickly exposed, at least for some period of time. Based on the efficiency metrics it will appear that everything is falling apart, and you are headed in the wrong direction. But through time, the new system reality and thinking will expose new evidence about what is actually happening in the system. The new reality is this:

- Throughput rates will increase.
- Lead times through the system will be reduced.
- Work-in-process inventory will go down.
- On-time delivery will improve.

If you consider these results to be nonsense, then think of the possible consequences if you return to the "high efficiency" metric:

- Throughput rates will decrease.
- Lead times through the system will become longer.
- Work-in process inventory will go up.
- On-time delivery will go down.

So think carefully when answering the question about which one of these methods is really the nonsensical approach.

Types of Constraints

Constraints can exist in one of two types. The first type is the *internal constraint*— which means that the market demand for your product is higher than the capacity of the system to produce it. Customers want much more of what you offer then what you can produce. It's a good situation to be in, but only up to a point. If you can't figure out a way to meet market demand, then your competitors will usually figure out a way to do it for you. This situation is ideal for implementing traditional DBR to meet the demand and capture more market.

The second type of constraint is an *external constraint*. In this case the market demand is less than your ability to produce. The market is buying less, in some case much less than you can produce. This is a less desirable situation, but one that nonetheless can exist. This situation usually means that there is not an internal constraint to contend with. If this is the case, then it is somewhat improbable that traditional DBR will provide an acceptable answer. Instead, in this situation, a modified or simplified form of DBR might be more practical. Consider S-DBR.

DBR Variants:

Simplified Drum-Buffer-Rope (S-DBR)

The concept of S-DBR was developed by H.W. Dettmer and E. Schragenheim is defined in their book *Manufactruing at Warp Speed.*[5] The S-DBR concept assumes that the constraint is external to the system and resides in the market segment. Customers aren't buying as much product as you can make, or there is significant variation in market demand, which can cause the constraint to float back and forth between internal to external locations. In this situation, the constraint becomes interactive by moving between the market constraint (external) and the production constraint (internal). This oscillating cycle between internal and external constraints can cause its own brand of chaos in deciding which market segments should be pursued and which ones might be better left alone. Either way it is a decision that must be dealt with.

In the scenario of an external constraint, the drum is determined and activated only when the system has firm orders in place. The rope is now determined by the orders that actually exist, which are released based on due dates. If the orders exceed the capacity of the system, then the constraint has become internal and different actions must be taken. This also assumes that the internal constraint will exist only for short periods of time and can be overcome by actions like implementing additional shifts or short-term overtime. Dettmer and Schagenheim have argued, quite successfully, that the market is the true constraint of any system. There is much more reading available about this concept at Dettmer's Goal Systems web site (http://www.goalsys.com).

Multiple Drum-Buffer-Rope (M-DBR)

There is another unique situation that can require the implementation of a third type of DBR, known as Multiple-Drum-Buffer-Rope (M-DBR). The situation for M-DBR is created when a single buffer location is required to supply products to more than one assembly

5 Dettmer, H.W., Schragenheim, E., *Manufacturing at Warp Speed: Optimizing Supply Chain Financial Performance*, CRC Press. (2000)

line, and each assembly has its own drum that is keeping pace at a different rhythm. Figure 2 shows an example of an M-DBR configuration.

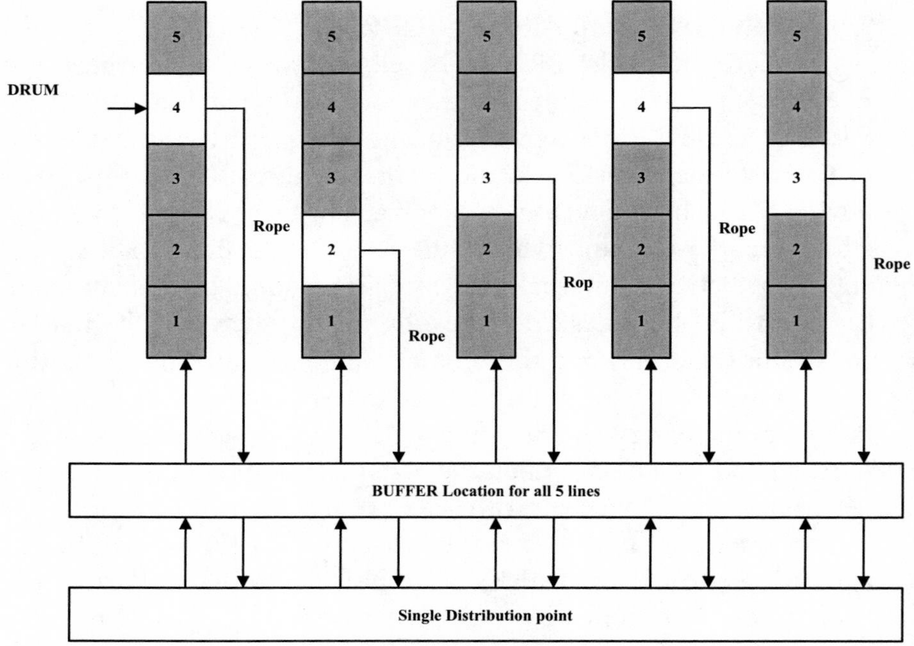

Figure 2. The M-DBR Model

An example might be a surface mount technology (SMT) machine that is required to make different types of circuit cards for different assemblies, and each circuit card assembly flows down different assembly lines. It's similar to moving from the apex of an "A" plant into the base of a "V" plant, with different parts now required for a number of different "I" lines (see Appendix 8 for discussion on plant types). The demand (drumbeat) for each "I" line will vary, but each line requires its input from a single SMT machine or a series of SMT machines.
In the configuration of multiple drums, there are also multiple ropes, and each has different requirements. There are two signal points for the rope. The first would be back to the buffer to release more work for that particular line. The second rope goes back to the SMT machine to support the needs of the buffer, which in turn releases work at the front of the SMT line.

The advantage of this concept is to reduce the tendency for economic batch size quantity at the SMT. Many organizations believe when they set up a machine to make parts, they should make as many parts as they can, especially if the machine is expensive, or the setup times seem especially long. The thought that this economic batch size quantity somehow saves money is, at best, absurd. The economic batch size only serves to slow down throughput in the system. No money has been saved at all! In fact, it will cost additional amounts of money because throughput will have been damaged (revenue lost) and the dollars will have been spent to buy those raw materials and parts that aren't needed yet. Instead, you should manage the constraint, conduct the setups in the sequence and frequency required from the drumbeat in the lines and solve the problem of shorter setup times as they occur using Single Minute Exchange of Dies (SMED) techniques. The action of the machine should be to support the buffer for the various "I" line drums, not maintain "high efficiency" at the expense of making money (remember the goal of a company?).

An additional variant of this same concept can also exist in a production/manufacturing situation where the buffer supports different lines, but the buffered product is the same for each "I" line. An example of this situation might be a maintenance and repair organization (MRO) for aircraft. The lines in this case would be equivalent to hangar space. The drum would be the length of time required to repair each aircraft, and the buffer is equal to the number of aircraft waiting to enter the repair system. Each hangar can and does repair the same type of aircraft. The difference becomes the duration of the repair cycle time. Some will be faster and some will be slower. It's the total repair time duration that determines the drumbeat in each "I" line. Aircraft waiting in the buffer would be required to have the repair problem isolated (to some reasonable level), and fully ready to enter with the necessary repair parts, the ability to move aircraft in and out of the hangar and a crew waiting and ready to perform the repair.

The Total View

Even with all the respectable improvements that can be achieved with a synchronized flow using traditional DBR, S-DBR or even M-DBR, there can also be some problems associated with achievement, especially with traditional DBR. It's not a bad problem, just one you need to be aware of. When you follow Goldratt's Five Focusing Steps, it is possible during Step 2 (the exploitation step) that a constraint can be improved to the point that it is no longer the constraint, and at times this can happen very quickly. When it does happen, you have effectively "rolled" the constraint to a new location, which means you only finished Step 2 before it is now time to go back to Step 1 again. The original system process that was considered to be the constraint today is no longer the constraint tomorrow. These types of rapid system improvements can obviously cause some problems. When a new constraint is identified in the system, then the system effectively has a new drumbeat. When that happens, you also have to move the buffer location to reside in front of the new constraint, and you have to move the rope signal from this new location back to the release point at the front of the line. In some systems it might be possible to roll the constraint several times to several different locations before an acceptable level of system stability is achieved. This fast action of fixing and rolling the constraint can and does cause a certain amount of chaos in a system. Workers will quickly become confused about "Who is the constraint today?" Improvements can happen so fast that the negative effects of change will outweigh the positive effects of improvement. This was a problem recognized early on by some implementers of TOC and DBR concepts, and there are some simple and robust solutions to overcome this phenomenon. (See Appendix 8, Supplemental System Tools—Plant Types, Control Point Theory and Volts Concepts.)

Appendix 7
Critical Path Management (CPM) Versus Critical Chain Project Management (CCPM)

If you have ever been involved in project management, then it is easy to understand the frustration associated with trying to manage projects that are over budget, have missed delivery due dates and on many occasions, have not achieved the required technical objectives. All of these issues seem to be commonplace in today's project management world— but why? When you look closely at your projects it appears that the same types of problems and issues seem to be happening over and over again. If the issues remain the same, and they become very predictable, then the problems might have a direct relationship to the project management tools and methods that we use. If we keep using the same tools and methods, then it is very predictable that we will keep getting the same results.

To better understand the tools and methods, let's look take a closer look at the Critical Path Method (CPM) and the Critical Chain Project Management (CCPM) methods. We will look at each one separately, discuss the basics and understand the differences.

Critical Path Method

The current potpourri of project management tools were developed in the early 1950s and, with the exception of newer PC tools and applications, the project management methodologies and concepts have stayed virtually unchanged throughout that time. The basic technology back then, and now, is a methodology known as "Critical Path Method," or CPM. At the fundamental concept level, CPM looks at all project tasks on the schedule and determines the longest sequence of tasks, based on successor and predecessor relationships, required to complete the project. Those linked tasks with the longest durations in time sequences are defined as the "Critical Path." If any task on the critical path starts late or finishes late, then it is highly probable the entire project will finish late. It seems to make sense with this linkage and sequencing that the most important tasks have been identified in the project. As such, the primary objective of project managers using CPM is to make certain all tasks on the critical path start and finish on time.

Planning the Project

When project planners and project managers use CPM, most will exhibit a tendency to estimate task duration with high probability time estimates, meaning they add extra time to each task for all of those things that can and do go wrong. Experience has taught them well. Because they don't know for certain which task will cause them the most problems, they add additional time to each task. The scheduled work within any given task never seems to go exactly as planned, and they anticipate that some tasks will finish late. To compensate for this recurring late finish syndrome, project managers (or task planners) are inclined to add extra time to tasks durations ; in effect, they create a mini-insurance policy for each task—just in case. The planners and project managers want to craft a way to protect themselves (and their projects) against the negative variation of the *late finish* syndrome.

The problem with this type of *task-time protection model* is revealed in what happens next—the task *finish dates* become the task *due dates*. Few tasks, if any, are completed early, even though extra time has been added for the purpose of *late finish* protection. In the early stages of a project, most project managers, most of the time, will report the tasks in their project as "on schedule." Here's the problem—if the task estimates *all* have additional time for protection, then most of the tasks, most of the time, should be well ahead of schedule!

In general, there are several negative effects for projects that can branch from this type of behavior. First, because of this unnecessary time protection practice, projects will incorrectly extend the total project duration, sometimes by as much as 50 percent. What CPM fails to recognize is that tasks are not absolute with start and finish dates. In any given project there is the constant presence of variation, so some tasks will usually be late or early, relative to any single point in time estimate. Using just the *start* and *finish* dates in a project does not encourage capitalizing on the possible benefits gained for completing any task early. There is no motivation to complete early because the next resource in the sequence of tasks does not want to receive the work until the "scheduled" start date. Consequently, any project benefit gained from an early task completion is lost. Because CPM does not have a system technique to help manage early completion, projects using CPM tend to have scheduling variance early on.

At the time of its introduction, CPM seemed like the best way to manage projects. The concepts and methods were considered state-of-the-art (SOTA). However, CPM is a methodology and system that has, through time, generated less than favorable results. Most projects managed with CPM suffer from late product delivery, budget overruns and missed technical objectives. Why? Perhaps defining, measuring and monitoring the critical path *is not* the most important measure to determine project success, especially if this measure continues to demonstrate unsatisfactory results. There are other methods that have been proposed to help manage task variation. One of them is PERT analysis, which uses three task estimates. Another is the Monte Carlo analysis, which represents tasks based on the distribution of task durations. The PERT and Monte Carlo analysis methods are little used because they have shown little benefit and only serve to increase complexity. But if CPM is not the right answer, what is?

Critical Chain Project Management— The CCPM Concept

In the mid-1990s Dr. Eliyahu Goldratt—educator, author and principle guiding force behind the Theory of Constraints (TOC) concepts—began thinking about the unsatisfactory areas associated with project management. He soon realized that project managers tended to suffer from the same type of project issues over and over again. As it turns out, these issues seemed to be related to the same types of issues Dr. Goldratt had already observed and studied.

In his book *The Goal,* Dr. Goldratt defined some of the modern-day issues involved with production processes and pointed out why they happen. One of Dr. Goldratt's breakthrough ideas is a concept known as Drum-Buffer-Rope, or DBR. The design and application of the DBR concept is really quite simple. It states that throughput through a system is constrained by the slowest operation in the chain of events. In other words, the output of a system is equal to the maximum capacity of the slowest operation. If you think in terms of a chain, then it makes sense that a chain is only as strong as the weakest link. Or you can think in terms of a water piping system with varying pipe diameters. Either example drives you to the same conclusion—the system can only produce at a rate equal to, or less than, the slowest operation/process—the one with the least capacity. These same DBR concepts also apply to organizations. As an example, consider the links of the chain as independent organizations—engineering, finance, procurement, production, shipping, and so on. Somewhere in this chain there exists an organization or process that is slower than everything else. Because this operation is the slowest, it determines the "drumbeat" for how fast the entire system can produce products or services. When the slowest operation is identified, then it must be determined how best to manage it.

In the past, production systems have traditionally been managed using many "golden" rules. Most of the rules are applied to the system without any real understanding of the long-term consequences. When viewed in isolation, these rules seem to be doing the right thing. As it turns out, however, many of these production rules are obsolete and in fact cause excessive chaos in a system. The incorporation of these rules creates many devastating negative effects on the system. One of the most popular golden rules is to "keep everybody busy all the time"—in others words, practice high efficiency. Make sure that *all* processes and operations are working at the highest possible efficiency. Globally enforcing this rule will stimulate its own breed of chaos in any system, which causes late order delivery, increased work-in-process, and substantially longer production lead times. However, the efficiency rule is not all bad. But, to be effective, this rule can *only* be enforced at the constraint operation, and the nonconstraint operations need a new rule: *subordination*. In effect, subordination means that all other processes in the system *must* subordinate their activity to the same level (drumbeat) of the constraint. In other words, nonconstraint operations should produce no faster then the constraint operation can produce.

This process of following the drumbeat and subordinating nonconstraints to the drumbeat is known as *synchronized manufacturing*, or *synchronized flow*. The implementation of synchronized flow throughout the system will permit better on-time delivery, reduced work-in-process, and reduced lead times, and these concepts can be applied to any system. An important point to remember: *any time lost at the constraint is time that is lost forever*. Protecting the constraint and keeping it busy is paramount. To keep the constraint busy, it must have something to work on at all times. In order to have something to work on at all times, it must have sufficient work in queue ready to be worked. The work in queue in front of the constraint is known as the *buffer*.

Finally, the "rope" suggests that an imaginary rope, or signal, is positioned from the constraint operation to the front of the system. When the constraint finishes working on a single unit of work, the imaginary rope is pulled (intervals of time can be used for a rope) to signal the front of the line (the first process) to release one more unit of work into the system. These three concepts working in unison are known as Drum-Buffer-Rope. Implementing the concepts of DBR allows the system to work under the rules of synchronized flow.

As it turns out, these simple but powerful concepts, associated with DBR that work so well in the production environment also provide the missing link to better understanding the recurring challenges of project management. Let's discover how.

Critical Path Method —Defining the Issues

In CPM project management there are a minimum of three phenomena that interact with each other during the life cycle of a project. These phenomena work either in tandem or isolation, and each phenomenon contributes to the recurring issues that plague projects. Let's examine each of these phenomena and define their negative effects.

Multitasking: The Negative Effect

Usually in a project management system there is more than one project being worked at a single point in time. In the past it has been deemed acceptable, if not required, to be able to work on several projects at once—in other words, dividing one's time in a day to work on as many projects as possible. It seems like a prudent and necessary thing to do. Spend a little time on every project and show some progress on each one. However, at the end of the day it's easy to realize that the resources appear to be very busy, but the projects are not completing. How come? Some work has been completed on many tasks, but rarely is a single project completed. This scenario unknowingly allows projects to become a victim of the multitasking myth.

At some point in time most, if not all, projects require access to the same limited resources, especially if many projects are simultaneously being worked in a single system. Not properly accounting for the existence of limited resource capacity and availability is a problem that begins during the project-planning phase. Most new projects are planned in isolation of all other active projects, and when planned in isolation, they appear to be very doable.

One of the most erroneous assumptions implied during the planning phase is that resources are "unlimited." The assumption is expressed thusly: "If I schedule a particular resource to do work on my task, then that resource will be available to do my work during the scheduled time." When project planners or project managers prepare the project schedule, the task durations are defined, the tasks are linked in sequence, resources are defined, milestones are noted and an end date is defined. Then the project is scheduled backwards from the end date to create a start date (backwards scheduling). Again, in isolation this single project looks very doable. However, the real problems begin to surface when the project is released and "mixed" with other projects already in the system. As an example, let's assume there are three projects that follow similar scheduled dates and have a requirement to use the same limited resources. Figure 1 defines such a scenario.

Project -1	T-1 5 d Res-A	T-2 4 d Res-B	T-3 4 d Res-C	T-4 3 d Res-D
Project -2	T-1 5 d Res-A	T-2 4 d Res-B	T-3 4 d Res-C	T-4 3 d Res-D
Project -3	T-1 5 d Res-A	T-2 4 d Res-B	T-3 4 d Res-C	T-4 3 d Res-D

Figure 1. Three Sample Projects.

All three projects, when developed in isolation of each other, are all scheduled to start on the same day. Each project is scheduled to complete in a total of sixteen days. Each project manager will want to show some progress on his project as quickly as possible. With limited resources available, in this case Resource "A", and an informal need to show some progress on each of these projects, the Resource "A" *must* employ multitasking. Figure 2 displays the results of multitasking just on Task-1.

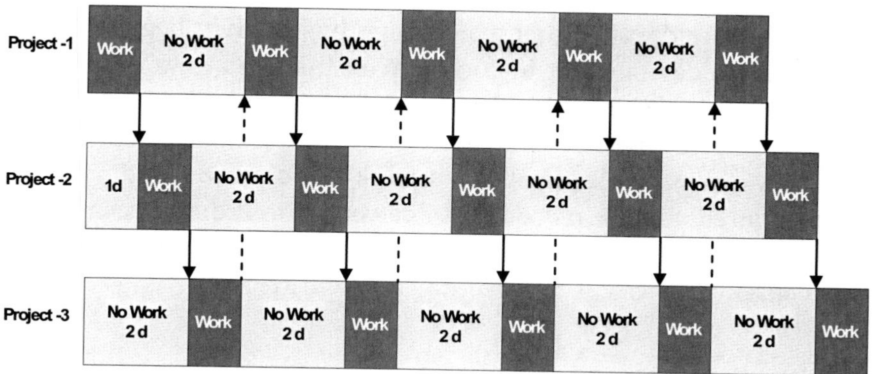

Figure 2: The Effects of Multitasking

Look at Figure 2 and notice what has happened to the very precise schedule you have put together. On the very first task your project is now in total chaos and will probably be delivered late. This simple diagram illustrates the negative effects from invoking multitasking on your projects. The task was originally scheduled to complete in five days. The soonest Project 1/Task-1 can complete now is thirteen days, and Project 3/Task-1 can complete no sooner than sixteen days. For Project 3, completing Task-1 is now equal to the total duration of the entire project. Is it any wonder that projects are late when you try to multitask? What seemed like a good schedule at the beginning of the project quickly begins to erode and could require several iterations of rescheduling in hopes of recovering the lost time.

With multitasking in place, the total project duration for Project 1 is now forty days—twenty-four days longer than originally planned. The more projects you have in the system at the same time, then the worse the negative effects will become.

The Student Syndrome: The Accepted Way to Do It

The Student Syndrome supports the learned behavior of procrastination and is directly related to the start and end dates associated with a task. For example, suppose on a specific task there is an estimated duration of ten days. You, as the resource that must complete this task, know that you can complete the work in five days. What do you do? The Student Syndrome suggests that you ask for as much time as possible and then begin the work as late as possible. In this case, you would let the first five days go by and then begin the work on the sixth day in order to complete on the tenth day. You pass the work to the next resource and are completely guilt-free of any responsibility for any schedule delays. If your task was on the critical path, then any delays involved with your work could cause schedule delays. Even though you are not guilty of causing a task delay, because you completed the task according to the schedule, this type of thinking has caused an unnecessary five-day project extension.

Parkinson's Law: It's What We Do

Parkinson's Law states: "Work expands to fill the available time." The translation is—If there are ten days on the schedule to do the work, then you will use *all* ten days to complete the work." Again, you don't want to be the person (or group) causing any schedule delays. If you complete the required work and send it forward to the next process on the tenth day, then you are not the problem. But what if you actually finished the work in five days and then held the work (because the schedule said you could) or reworked the task again—not because you needed too, but because you could. What if you did finish the work in five days and passed it on to the next work center? Would they be ready to start the work? Or would they hold the work until the scheduled start date? Chances are pretty good they would delay starting the work until the scheduled time. They might even be busy finishing another task and not have time to work the new task yet. Either way, the new task waits and the cumulative lead time increases more and more.

The Unavoidable Consequences

These phenomena, working in isolation and in tandem, can cause many hardships for a project. Any delays created by completing tasks late are passed through the project as a cumulative total for delay. When project delays do occur, then one of three things must happen. First, the end date must be moved to the right, and the projects slips. Second, the project must be replanned with new task estimates. Third, the last few tasks must make up the time difference by reducing their task durations to equal the project time delays. Which one is better?

Moving the end date to the right will only ensure you will be late with delivery. Replanning takes a large effort by many people with still no guarantee of success. Sometimes when the delays are so severe that there is no hope of getting back on track, the program is replanned, or maybe even cancelled. In the replanning effort, all of the remaining work is rescheduled with new task durations; new project timelines are developed and a new schedule put in place. You might even need to replan a second or third time if things do not work out. Reducing the task duration on the last tasks in order to recover the schedule is not always possible or practical. Even with these options, the same devastating phenomena exist and the same problems will reoccur if some kind of action isn't taken to reduce the negative effects of multitasking, the Student Syndrome, and Parkinson's Law. So, what can we do?

The Influence of Critical Chain Project Management (CCPM)—The New Reality

Critical Chain Project Management (CCPM), as a tool shifts the total project focus from *task* completion to *project* completion. In the traditional CPM, each task is estimated (usually hours or days) for task duration. These task durations are usually provided by the estimator or manager doing the work and consist of an estimate based on the work to be completed, historic estimates for the same type of work and the experience of the estimating manager. The task estimates usually allow for additional time to manage the variation of a task, taking into account Murphy's Law. Task durations estimated this way could be twice as long as estimates with only a 50 percent chance of being completed on-time. For example, if the work required in a task could be completed in five days, but the estimate is actually for ten days, then the estimate includes a five-day allowance for variation, better known as "slack" time. In other words, the estimator is adding extra time to help compensate for any variation (risk) that might happen when working the task. The estimator wants to make sure that any variation does not make the task late.

So, how does CCPM address this variation factor? To help compensate for and manage the variation of tasks, CCPM creates three separate buffers. These buffers are always measured in terms of time and have three different locations. They include the following:

Project Buffer

The *project buffer* is located at the end of the project. It acts like a shock absorber to compensate for the effects of tasks that are late. It also acts a repository to accumulate additional time when tasks happen to finish early. It's a project "time" account from which to make time withdrawals and/or deposits.

The project buffer is created based on a series of calculations to determine the proper size. As an example, refresh yourself with Figure 1. You have four different tasks and each task is estimated based on time durations, and the tasks all run in sequence. In other words, I must complete Task-1 before I can begin Task-2 and so on. The rules for CCPM task estimating state that half of the estimated task time will remain as the task estimate, but the other half of the time will be transferred to the project buffer. This rule is applied to all project tasks until all tasks have been reviewed and reduced to roughly 50 percent (or a reasonable level) of their original estimate. This time estimate is based on the assumption that the project estimator and/or project managers are adding slack time to tasks. When the time reduction effort is complete, you then need to "size" the project buffer. In our example we have four tasks. Task-1 is five days, Task-2 is four days, Task-3 is four days and Task-4 is three days, for a total of sixteen days. Of the sixteen days available to complete the work, eight of those days now reside in the project buffer. To properly size the project buffer, the eight days remaining in the buffer will also be cut in half. So your project buffer is now four days. Originally we had a project scheduled to take sixteen days. Figure 3 shows the scheduling results when the actions are taken.

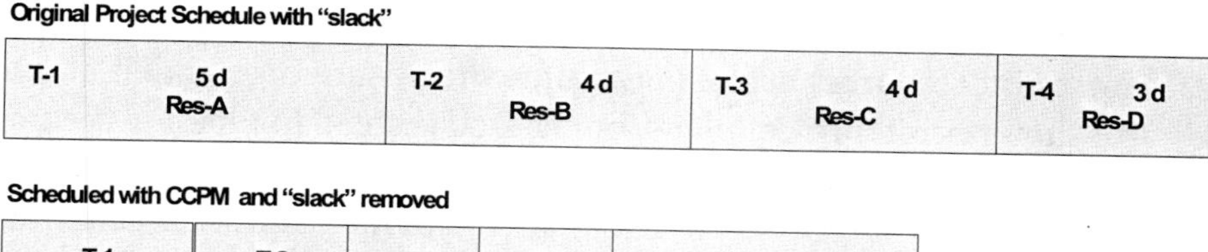

Figure 3: Removing Slack and Adding Project Buffer

Now we have a project scheduled to be complete in twelve days or less.

.Figure 4 provides an example of how the three sample projects might be scheduled using the CCPM concept after the buffers have been added and the project is scheduled factoring in resource contention. Even though two of the projects seem to start later, the end result is that the project finishes earlier than when using multitasking.

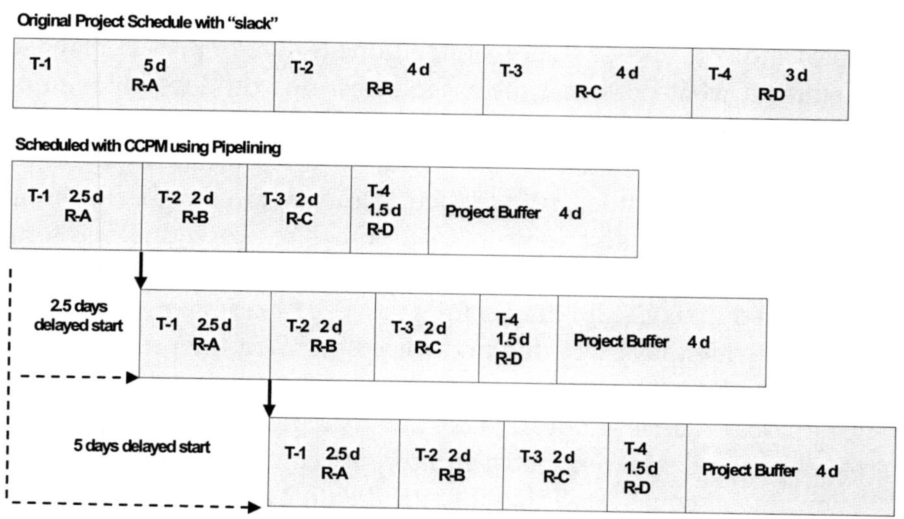

Figure 4. The CCPM Schedule

Capacity Buffer

The *capacity buffer* ensures that the most loaded resource (the constraint resource) *across the organization* is not overloaded. It does not show within project plans, but is used instead to pipeline the project start times (dates) so as to not overload the constraint resource. Since all other resources are less loaded and have more capacity than the constraint, it also serves to ensure that no resource is overloaded overall. It is possible there may be temporary overloads for any particular resource, but when that happens, the prioritized task list is used to help control the resources.

Feeding Buffer

The *feeding buffer* is located at the end of any task that is feeding into the critical chain. This buffer is in place to ensure that any task feeding to the critical chain is complete and ready when it is needed by a critical chain resource.

Linking DBR and CCPM

As discussed earlier, the Critical Chain Project Management (CCPM) concept consists of nothing more than applying the principles and concepts of Drum-Buffer-Rope (DBR) to project management. But what does that mean, and how do you do it? It's simple. First, you define the constraint of the project, which will normally be the most limited shared resource over all the projects. This limited resource becomes the drum. When resources are assigned to more than one project, and some projects must be worked at the same time, a decision must be made about which project and tasks should be worked first. CCPM allows for a resource-loading analysis to determine which tasks are due first, based on all of the projects in the system to determine which one should be worked first, based on the project due date and not the task due date. It's important to be able to make the distinction between *task due date and project due date.* They *are not* equal. Traditional Critical Path Method (CPM) focuses on completing the task on time. Critical Chain Project Management (CCPM) focuses on completing the project on time. If resources contention exists, the system will let you know that a decision must made.

The Concept of Pipelining

CCPM software can offer another valuable analysis tool. When new projects are loaded into the CCPM system, and the new projects have been resource-loaded, the system has the ability to scan all tasks within a project and all projects within the system and develop what is known as the *pipeline*. Pipelining is a process of reviewing all tasks in all of the projects and establishing the intrinsic sequence throughout all of the projects to determine which tasks need to be worked first across multiple projects. Any task manager who could be working on more than one task or project would have available to him a prioritized list of which tasks on which projects need to be worked and what order to work them to meet the project due date. The project task manager knows which tasks to work first and then move on to the next task listed, and then the next. The task priority is already established. No guessing, no phone calls, no priority changes—just work the list.

Overcoming the Obstacles with CCPM

Multitasking

CCPM can overcome the negative effects of multitasking by providing the necessary focus to complete one task at a time. The rules for CCPM are simple:

1. Start work on a single task.
2. Continue working that task until the work is complete.
3. Move the work to the next step.
4. Start work on the next task listed.

With CCPM, multitasking is highly and constantly discouraged. When multitasking is discouraged, it can be difficult to accept, especially if you are a program or project manager. It seems contrary to your popular thought that your project must stop or wait for another project to go first. However, when it is your turn, your project tasks will be worked until they are complete. It is possible that by going slower (waiting) your project could actually finish earlier.
Student Syndrome

CCPM reduces the effects of the Student Syndrome by not associating a start and stop date with each task. Instead, the task is tracked by answering the question "How many more days do you need to complete the task?" The question also assumes that this task is the only task you are working—you aren't multitasking. There is no scheduled finish date, nor is there an absolute start date for the next resource in line. The focus is how many total days are required to finish the current task. The concept is to start the task as quickly as you get it, work on it continuously until it is complete and move it on to the next resource in line. The entire process now becomes event-driven rather than date-driven. This simple concept produces powerful results.

Parkinson's Law

As stated previously, Parkinson's Law is the idea that work expands to fill the available time. In other words, the time given is the time taken, even if I could finish earlier. CCPM is trying to take advantage of the fact that a task could, and sometimes does, finish early. In practice, CCPM allows for each task to take as many days as required to complete, but also encourages completion as quickly as possible. These hurry-up behaviors are not based on start date and end date, but rather on working on the task-dedicated resources. If the required days to finish do take longer, then days are subtracted from the project buffer. If the task is completed earlier, then days are added to the project buffer to be used at another point in time, if required. A single project buffer is usually sufficient to manage all of the project risks (uncertainty) that seemed to get the best of us in the past.

The fever chart is the metric of choice to monitor status of projects using CCPM. Figure 5 shows a project fever chart. Any project that is in the green or yellow zones will have a high probability of finishing early with project-buffer time remaining. It is possible for a project to finish in the red zone and still be completed on-time as long as the percentage of work complete equals the percentage of buffer consumed.

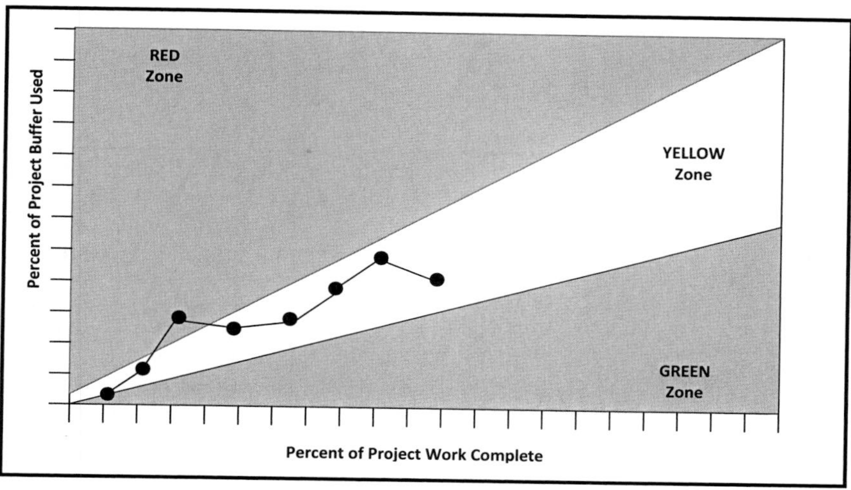

Figure 5. Fever Chart

Any project that is in the red zone early in the project will require immediate attention to move the project back to the yellow or green zone. If a project is already in the green zone, then no immediate attention is required. If the project is in the yellow zone, then it provides an early warning that some attention might be required to get it back on track before it enters the red zone.

Table 1
CPM and CCPM—Side by Side

	Critical Path Method	Critical Chain Project	Projected Benefits of CCPM
1	Estimates and schedules worst-case task durations. Usually P/90 or above	Estimates and schedules tasks-based on "most likely" P/50 durations.	• Task estimates will not collect additional time at the task level. • The project completion risk is shared equally across all tasks & resources. • Resources are neither praised nor scolded for missing an estimate.

	Critical Path Method	Critical Chain Project	Projected Benefits of CCPM
2	Protects individual tasks with added safety time (Slack).	Protects the overall project with strategically placed "buffers."	• Any additional time is not consumed by each task; instead, the system collects the time in the "project buffer." • The "buffers" are used to protect all tasks throughout the duration of the project. Project delivery is focused on the completing the project. On-tie
3	Starts and finishes based on "start" and "finish"	Start task as soon as it is ready. Emphasis to finish the tasks as quickly as possible.	• Project is managed based on "completion events" and not "scheduled dates." • Tasks (events) can begin work as quickly as possible and not wait for a specific "start" date. • Tasks are managed based on "Days Remaining" to complete and not a "finish" date.
4	Always emphasizes progress towards completing the task.	Always emphasizes progress towards completing the project.	• Allows for project monitoring rather then task monitoring. • It's not important to complete the task on time, but it is important to complete the project on time.
5	Resource contention is project management "way of life"	Allows any resource issues to be managed completely.	• If resources are level loaded, then CCPM can identify which resource is the bottleneck and for what length of time. • Project managers focus strictly on the critical resource and focus on preventing project issues.

6	Multitasking over several tasks is acceptable.	Multitasking is discouraged by defining the correct priorities.	• Multitasking is a totally "ineffective" way to manage and complete projects. Multitasking extends the cycle-time of any project. • CCPM discourages Multitasking by defining exactly which tasks should be worked, who should work them, and what order they should be worked in. No more guessing.
7	Uncertainty (Risk) is managed by changing priorities, re-planning, expediting, and creating "new" schedules.	Uncertainty (Risk) is managed by monitoring the percent of "Project Buffer" penetration	• There is minimal, if any, need to conduct re-planning, adjust priorities, invoke expediting, or create new schedules. • The health of the project can be monitored by watching the percent of "Project Buffer" (Fever Chart) penetration compared to the percent of work complete.

Table 1 compares Critical Path Method (CPM) and Critical Chain Project Management (CCPM) and provides an overview and side-by-side comparison of the common strategies of CPM and CCPM.

Conclusion

The ability to manage more and more projects with the same number of resources is proving to be an enormous competitive advantage. Those companies who can do more projects with the same resources, and do it well, will consistently find themselves in the winner's circle. The new reality of project management requires new thinking and new tools. Using the same thinking and the same tools will only continue to generate the same negative results.

The real impact of the CCPM "breakthrough technology" is not associated with software improvements. Granted, there is new software to support CCPM, but that is not the real breakthrough. The biggest improvement comes from the way we think about managing projects that generates the real change. This new thinking and paradigm shift from CPM to CCPM includes the following:

CPM	CCPM
Finishing tasks on time.	Finishing projects on time.
Measuring sequential task durations.	Resource availability and planning.
Start to finish date-driven	Event-driven (task completion)

The end result is that with CCPM projects are now usually completed in half the time, which allows you to do twice as many projects in the same amount of time. Not a bad return when you think about it.

Appendix 8
Supplemental System Tools—Plant Types, Control Point

Theory and Volts Concepts

Supplemental Section

This supplemental section contains guidelines and tools that provide additional understanding for managing a system. Understanding these concepts can greatly improve your ability to manage your system.

Types of Plant Configurations

When considering implementing DBR into your system, it is imperative to consider the type of plant configuration you might be dealing with. Basically there are four types of plant configurations that can exist. These are commonly referred to as "A," "V," "T" and "I." Each configuration offers its own type of challenges, and when your plant includes a combination of configurations, it can pose an even greater challenge. Being familiar with the plant configuration characteristics and consequences will benefit any type of analysis you might undertake.

The "A" Plant

The "A" plant commonly refers to the situation where there are many parts and/or subassemblies coming together to make a single end product. The end product is achieved at the apex of the plant, or the top of the "A." A common example for an "A" plant could be the assembly of the many components required to make a computer. It could also be exemplified in the subassemblies of a computer, such as the manufacture of circuit cards or other assemblies.

"A" plants have certain defined and predictable characteristics and consequences. Figure 1 provides the concept behind an A plant—starting with many raw materials you finally end up with a finished product.

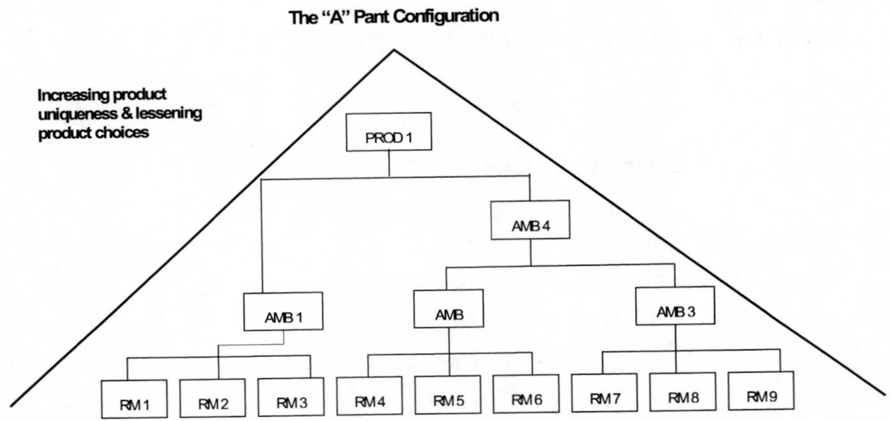

Figure 1: The Configuration of the "A" Plant

"A" Plant Characteristics:

1. Many raw materials (could be hundreds).
2. Unique to end item(s).
3. Few end item(s) relative to raw materials.
4. Many different routings.
5. Generic equipment.

"A" Plant Consequences:

1. Misallocation of capacity (starting work too early).
2. Frequent part shortages.
3. Large batch sizes.
4. Long lead times.
5. High work-in-progres (WIP).

The "V" Plant

In the "V" plant configuration, you start with a single raw material and then make several different products. The base of the "V" starts the distribution of the single raw material out to multiple products. Figure 2 displays an example of starting with a single raw material of steel and following up the lines to the many varied products that can be produced. The "V" plant also has characteristic and consequences

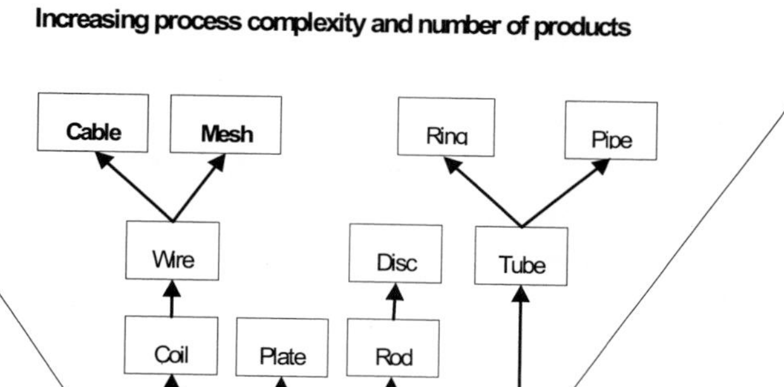

Figure 2: The Configuration of a "V" Plant

Another example of a "V" plant would be a saw mill. The starting raw material is a log that is cut into 2X4s, 2X6s or 2X8s or whatever size is need. Once you commit to making 2X4s you can't go back and change to making 2X8s. The raw material is already committed to make a certain product and cannot be changed.

"V" Plant Characteristics

1. Number of end items is large (relative to number of raw ma terials).
2. All end items are produced essentially the same way.

3. Equipment to produce end items can be capital-intensive. Many different machines to produce many different products.

"V" Plant Standard (Predicted) Consequences

1. Misallocation of material. You commit raw materials in the pro cess too soon.
2. Poor customer service—can't seem to get orders out on time.
3. Priorities seem to changes constantly. (Multitasking)
4. Constant complaint that Manufacturing/Production is being unresponsive to customer needs.

The "T" Plant

In essence, the general flow of a "T" plant is similar to an "I" Plant, except when it reaches the end of the "I" line. At that point it branches and becomes a different product or model or number. An example is the different options you might get with automobiles. Automobiles follow a single assembly process, but near the end they might be outfitted with different option packages, such as leather seats versus cloth seats, or a premium stereo system versus a lesser stereo system. In essence, it's the same car, but with different options at the end. The "T" plant concept could also apply to software when you get versions of the same computer with different languages.

The consequences for a "T" plant are similar to an "A" plant, especially in terms of part shortages, which will have major impact on process synchronization. Figure 3 shows the "T" plant configuration. "T" plants also suffer from the misallocation of parts that is common to the "V" plant. Some parts can be robbed along the way to makes other products. Figure 3 provides a structure of the "T" plant configuration.

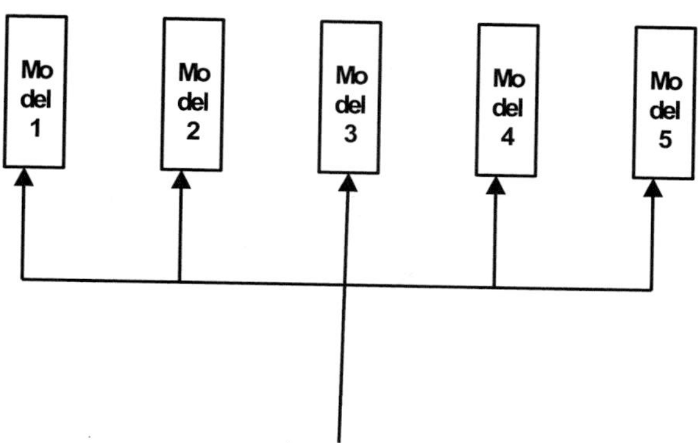

Figure 3: The "T" Plant Configuration.

The "I" Plant

The "I" plant is strictly a sequence of processes all in a straight line. Usually what you start with in the "I" line is similar to what you end up with. "I" lines offer the simplest analysis possible, in that you need only discover the slowest operation in the line to isolate the constraint.

Combined Plant Types

Most systems will contain some type of a combination when it comes to plant configurations. It is possible that your system could start with an "I" line, move into a "V" line, then back to one or more "I" lines, recombine into an "A" line and finish with an "I" Line. Figure 4 provide an example of the combined lines concept.

The Combined Plant Configurations

An "I". "V", "I", "A" and "I" combination.

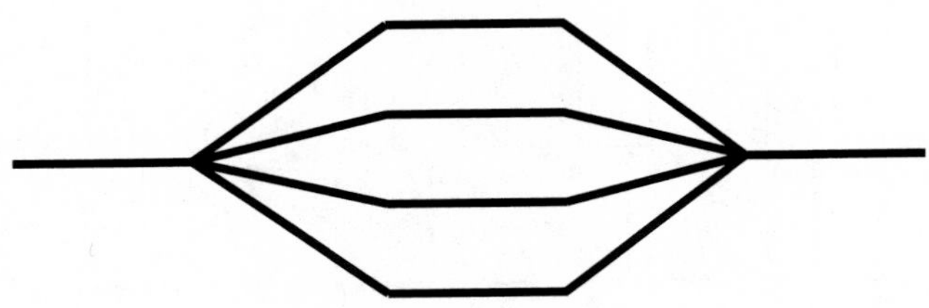

Figure 4. Combined Plant Configurations

Control point theory had its genesis when it was understood that during a DBR implementation the cycle between Step 1 (find the constraint) and Step 2 (exploit the constraint) could happen in very rapid succession. Control point theory argues, in effect, that you can select any location you choose in the system to be the control point. However, there are some recommended guidelines for selecting this location.

First, it should be a process that currently exhibits excess capacity. This allows the control point to keep up with system improvements as capacity demands move upward. In other words, it's a location within the system that won't be hampered by system capacity demands anytime soon, as improvements are completed at other locations in the system.

Second, it should probably be a process located at or near the end of the system sequences. The reason for this is because you want to actively track work that is about to exit the system and not work that has been measured early on, but then gets caught in a rework cycle or worse yet, gets scrapped. With this single point concept, the single process can be used to control the system, monitor the system and create performance metrics for the entire system. This concept becomes especially important when the system is undergoing the flux and change of implementing improvements, especially during a DBR implementation.

As the single point measurement location, the control point can be used to track the productivity measure and financial measures—it's a single pulse point to measure the health and wellness of your system. There is no need to wait until the end of the month or the quarter to figure out how good or bad your system might be doing. With a control point you can and should have information supplied daily to show how your system is performing.

Productivity and Financial Measures

Productivity can be measured in terms of throughput based on the number of units that pass through the control point. The measure remains accurate as long as work that passes through the control point is not somehow recycled back through the system as rework. When the product becomes throughput, then the financial measures can also be calculated. There is a simple and robust method that can be used to measure the financial performance of the system. This simple concept is known as on-the-line charting. Figure 5 gives an example of an on-the-line chart showing a random twenty-day period. ("T" is the shorter line while "OE" is the longer line in the diagram below.)

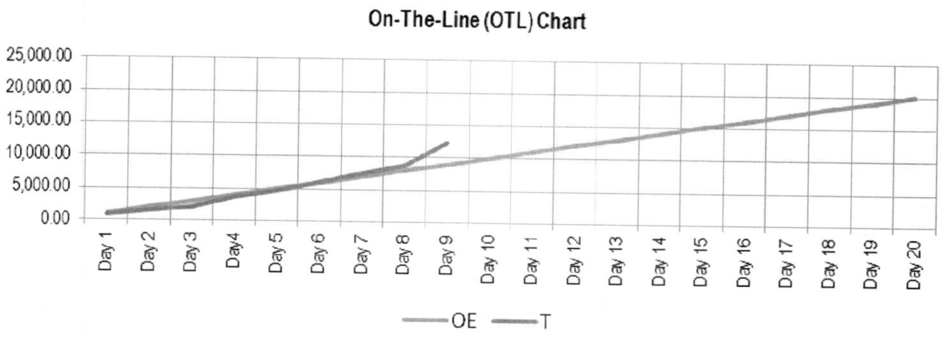

Figure 5: On-the-line Chart for a Period of 20 Days

This chart is constructed using calculations based on the Throughput Accounting (TA) formula for Operating Expenses (OE) and Throughput (T) dollars. In this example you are looking at twenty-day period of time, and each day has an OE of $1,000. The OE becomes cumulative through time to express the OE for each day in a month. The Throughput is derived from the calculation of Selling

Price – Total Variable Costs (TVC). Or T = SP – TVC.

The Net Profit (NP) is derived from the calculation of total throughput dollar value – total operating expenses, or NP = T – OE. If the financial performance of the plant is based on these calcualtions, then when throughput is above the line, the company is making money. In others words, NP = T – OE. If the throughput is below the OE line then the company is not making money, and you are not even making enough to cover the OE costs. As long as the throughput line is above the OE line, then you are making money. The higher throughput is above the OE line, the more money you are making.
A chart of this type could be used on a daily basis by a company owner, operations manager or production manager to determine if there are gaps between T and OE that need attention. It is not required to wait until the end of the month or end of quarter to get a report from accounting to determine if you won or lost the battle for the month. You can have the necessary information daily to make good decisions about adjustments that might be required.

The Concept of VOLTS

With all of this discussion about DBR and setting up system to operate at an optimized level, it's important to have a discussion about VOLTS. VOLTS, in this case, are not defined in terms of electricity, but rather an acronym for Volume, Octane and Lead Time.

Volume

Volume refers to the amount of product and product mix moving through your system and is determined by the constraint. The constraint output is equal to the volume output of the system. Remember, if you find, fix and roll the constraint, it is possible for the volume to go up. Remember also that volume can be limited by market demand and not just production capacity.

Octane

Probably one of the most important and least understood concepts of product pricing is the product octane. Different products will have different product octane ratings. The product octane is calculated based on the overall selling price (SP) minus total variable cost (TVC). The difference between these numbers is the product throughput, or in this case product octane. For reference, think back (or refer to) the discussion in the Cost Accounting and Throughput Accounting appendix. Throughput is determined to be the dollar value after the total variable costs have been subtracted from the selling price of each unit (T = SP - TVC). In this case the octane is equal to the throughput. As an example, suppose you have a product "A" that sells for $10.00 and it has a TVC of $6.00, then the Octane is equal to $4.00 or 40 percent. If you have a second product "B" and it sells for $11.50, and has a TVC of $6.00 (same as Product "A"), then the octane rating is equal to $5.50 or 47.8 percent. If the constraint time is equal for both products, then product "B" will make the most money in the same time period. However, if the there is a constraint utilization time difference, and product "B" takes longer than product "A" to produce, then product "A" will become the best product to push with sales. Cost accounting thinking will point you in the opposite direction. CA would say that product "B" is the better product to produce because it has a higher margin. However, CA does not consider constraint production time and its effect on making money. TA does! This becomes an extremely important number to understand because Net Profit (NP) is determined when the total Operating Expense (OE) is subtracted from the total Throughput (T) value (NP = T – OE). If operating expense is fairly constant through time (and it is), then the amount of net profit will increase if the throughput number goes up. The greater the throughput numbers when operating expenses are subtracted, then the greater the profit.

Many organizations believe and follow the principle and business model that "any work is good work!" They assume this because Cost Accounting implies you should make money on all of the work you do. If capacity is finite (which it is), and you want to use your available capacity to make the most money you can (remember the goal of the company), which products should you spend your time making? When you evaluate products in terms of octane rating, it becomes glaringly obvious which products (product mix) are the most likely contributors towards higher throughput dollars and higher profits.

It is very possible that some of your products may be consume large amounts of constraint time, but yield only minimal throughput in terms of dollars. And there may be other products that zoom through the constraint quickly, but don't seem to offer nearly the margins of other products. If you were looking strictly on the surface and using the CA mentality, then these lower margin products might be the products you would consider avoiding or even getting rid of. However, it is highly recommended that you look again and determine constraint time and product octane values. There is probably considerably more money to be made when you consider the octane value of your products. Some of your "product dogs" might actually turn out to be your real home-run products. Remember: the higher the octane, the higher the profit. The question now becomes, "How much are you leaving on the table?" Some products can be easier to make and generate much higher net profit values than other products do. Look closely at the way you are comparing and rating your products. If you are using strictly CA and margins to make these decisions, then you might be surprised at what you see, if you really stop and look.

Lead Time

In conjunction with volume and octane, consider the lead time through the system. How fast does it move from start to finish? If DBR is in place and subordination is the rule, then is should move quickly through the system. Fast-moving products with higher volumes and an exceptional octane rating can be a gold mine. Don't make these decision based on the traditional cost accounting rules, because it will most likely point you in the wrong direction. Be bold and consider the VOLTS concept.